Cosmic rays at ground level

A volume dedicated to George D Rochester
in the year of his retirement

Cosmic rays at ground level

edited by
A W Wolfendale

The Institute of Physics
London and Bristol

PHYSICS

ISBN 0 85498 025 3

Published by The Institute of Physics, 47 Belgrave Square, London
SWIX 8QX, England, in association with the American Institute of
Physics, 335 East 45th Street, New York, NY 10017, USA

Set in 10/12 pt Monotype Times New Roman, and printed in
Great Britain by Adlard and Son Ltd, Dorking, Surrey

Preface

This volume is offered as a tribute to George Rochester by colleagues in the cosmic ray field who either work in his department or have done so in the past. We have all benefited from his wise counsel in many ways and indeed the bulk of our work in Durham has been possible only through the excellent facilities that he has been instrumental in providing.

We have thought it most appropriate to make our contributions in the form of articles on our main interests: the properties of cosmic rays at ground level, together with a description of a technique that has probably been used more in Durham than in any other laboratory, namely the neon flash-tube. It is intended that the data given should comprise a summary of the energy spectra of the various components of the cosmic radiation—from nucleons to neutrinos—together with some indications as to their interpretation. We consider that not only is the clear presentation of rather precise data in the spirit of George Rochester's work and interest but that there is a contemporary need for such a presentation.

As is well known, there is interest in cosmic rays in all situations—not only at ground level—and at the present time the radiation incident on the top of the earth's atmosphere is of particular interest. In order not to omit entirely this fascinating region a brief review of the primary radiation is given in the introductory chapter.

Returning to our colleague, and friend, we thank him for his services to the study of the cosmic radiation, and indeed to the study of physics as a whole, and wish him a long and happy retirement.

G D Rochester FRS

George Dixon Rochester was born in Wallsend, Northumberland on February 4th, 1908. His early education was at Wallsend Grammar School and in 1926 he went up to his local University—Armstrong College in the University of Durham (now the University of Newcastle) as Earl Grey Memorial Scholar in the Department of Physics. There he studied under the distinguished spectroscopist Professor W E Curtis and took the BSc, MSc and PhD degrees in his department.

Leaving Armstrong College in 1934 he spent a year in Stockholm University as Earl Grey Fellow and two years at Berkeley as a Commonwealth Fellow. Rochester's main researches at this stage were in spectroscopy, in particular an examination of band spectra.

In 1937 he was appointed to an Assistant Lectureship at Manchester University and there followed nearly twenty years of extraordinarily productive work in a new field—the cosmic radiation. In the period 1938–1946, and working largely with Janossy, Rochester made important investigations of the character of the energetic showers of particles produced by cosmic rays in absorbing materials. These investigations used what were at that time very elaborate arrangements of Geiger–Müller counters and called for considerable technical knowledge and expertise at interpretation. An important result was the identification of neutral particles—neutrons—amongst the particles initiating showers and the distinction between the electromagnetic and non-electromagnetic shower components.

Following Blackett's return from wartime service, Rochester and his junior colleague Butler made technical improvements to Blackett's magnet cloud chamber apparatus and used it to continue the studies of the 'penetrating showers' of cosmic rays observed in the earlier work. This led to the most important observation, in 1947, of heavy unstable particles amongst the shower secondaries. These V-particles, the first examples of the 'strange particles', had not been expected and their correct identification from the cloud chamber photographs was a remarkable feat, indicating a complete mastery of the physics of particle behaviour.

The V-particle work was honoured by the award of the C V Boys Prize by The Physical Society in 1956 jointly to Rochester and Butler. Election to Fellowship of the Royal Society came in 1958 and very recently he has been elected to the Council of the Royal Society.

Returning to the Manchester period, Butler continued and extended the strange particle studies and Rochester turned to the nuclear emulsion technique and founded an important group within the research school. Work with emulsions led to applications to accelerator experiments and a continuing interest in 'machine physics'.

In 1955, Rochester was appointed to the Chair of Physics in Durham, the position from which he will shortly retire. There followed the establishment of the cosmic ray group, with its interest in a wide variety of cosmic ray phenomena, and the prosecution of a series of accelerator experiments.

In addition to dedicated service on very many academic and scientific committees, and considerable teaching and administrative commitments, the Durham period has been marked by a close connection with the many experimental projects which have been carried out in his department. The contact has been particularly close with the large extensive air shower project at Haverah Park, of which he was a founder member. In 1964, he took sabbatical leave and used this to start, with Turver, an important series of experiments on the energetic muon component in extensive air showers. It is very fitting that from these experiments has evolved a big programme of work on muons in showers; future measurements in this field hold out the hope of providing some of the answers to the pressing problems of the nature of the primary cosmic rays of highest energy and of the character of ultra high energy interactions.

Durham, March 1973

Contents

Chapter 1

The primary radiation: a brief review

A W Wolfendale

1. Introduction

A small proportion of the energetic primary cosmic rays arriving at the top of the atmosphere have come from the Sun but the majority have come from more distant sources. A simple calculation, based on what is known about the low energy particles emitted by the Sun, shows that other stars in the galaxy which are of similar character cannot be responsible for the bulk of the radiation and one is left with the necessity of finding more energetic objects. Supernovae, pulsars, galactic nuclei—all have been suggested as potential sources and their special merits will be considered later.

Some idea of which particles might be expected to appear in the primary radiation comes from an analysis of the 'universal abundances'—information which comes from studies of stellar spectra, meteorites, etc. The abundances comprise a wide variety of nuclear masses, with hydrogen as the biggest component, and a similar situation arises in the cosmic radiation, at least at energies where mass determinations have been made, with protons being the most common particles. In addition, heavier nuclei, electrons, positrons and γ rays have been detected.

Some of the primary particles will have been present at the site of their original acceleration (the so-called 'primordial' particles) and others will arise as a result of interactions in the intervening interstellar matter. The detected protons are probably mainly in the former category. The problem of distinguishing the primordial and secondary components is one of complexity but also one of importance if the true nature and origin of the radiation is to be understood.

2. Primary protons and nuclei

2.1. The energy spectra

2.1.1. Methods of measurement. The spectra of the primary particles can be expressed in a variety of ways, the choice being usually determined by the method of measurement. Studies at different latitudes, which essentially use the Earth's field as a magnetic analyser, determine the numbers of particles above a given threshold rigidity (pc/Ze) (where p is the momentum, c the velocity and Ze the charge of the particle). Satellite experiments and balloon measurements in which individual nuclei of comparatively low energy are identified enable spectra to be given in terms of the number of nuclei in a given range of energy per nucleus or, more commonly, energy per nucleon. Indirect studies of single muons at low levels in the atmosphere give no information about the mass composition of the primaries but yield the number of primary nucleons with energy per nucleon in a given range. Finally, at the highest energies, where extensive air showers are examined, the information is usually in terms of primary energy per nucleus.

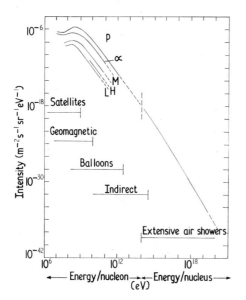

Figure 1. Summary of measurements on the primary spectrum of protons and nuclei in the cosmic radiation, corrected for geomagnetic effects. The sources of the data are given in the text. The groupings of nuclei are as follows. L: $3 \leqslant Z \leqslant 5$; M: $6 \leqslant Z \leqslant 9$ and H: $10 \leqslant Z$.

A survey has been made of the data presently available and the result is given in figure 1. Below 10^{14} eV the ordinate refers to the number of nuclei per unit kinetic energy per nucleon and above it the appropriate unit is energy per nucleus.

2.1.2. Energies below about 10^9 eV/nucleon. The energy regions can be considered in turn, starting with the lowest energies. Here, in view of the fact that satellite measurements are possible, precise measurements can be made, particularly of the comparatively low masses. In the region below about 10^9 eV the interplanetary magnetic field reduces the primary intensity below its value far from the Sun (the 'galactic' intensity). The galactic spectrum is probably more nearly a linear extrapolation to lower energies of the spectrum above 10 GeV, at least for energies down to about 100 MeV/nucleon. The spectra below 10^9 eV in figure 1 come from measurements by J A Simpson *et al* (1968 private communication) and refer to 1965, the period near solar minimum when the intensities were highest. Measurements have been made of the intensities of individual nuclei (as distinct from nuclear groups, $3 < Z < 5$, etc) and figure 2 shows

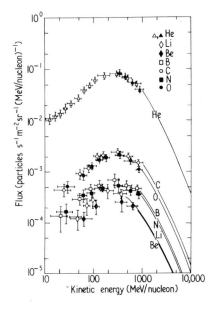

Figure 2. Primary spectrum in the low energy region near sunspot maximum (Garcia-Munoz *et al* 1971).

data from the work of Garcia-Munoz *et al* (1971), who used cosmic ray telescopes aboard the IMP-5 satellite during 1969. For this year the sunspot activity was near maximum and the cosmic ray intensity least. (Below 1 GeV/nucleon the intensities are less than those at sunspot minimum by a factor of approximately 3.)

In addition to the nuclei referred to in figures 1 and 2, charges very much greater than 10 have been recorded, the measurements extending as far as uranium and possibly beyond. The extremely heavy nuclei have been detected by Fowler *et al* (1967, 1970) and Fleischer *et al* (1967) and a summary by Blandford *et al* (1971) gives for their total flux at the top of the atmosphere:

$$J(Z > 96) = (2 \pm 1)\ 10^{-7}\ \mathrm{m}^{-2}\ \mathrm{s}^{-1}\ \mathrm{sr}^{-1}$$

yielding a ratio to the flux of the iron group of about 5×10^{-7}.

The interpretation of the low energy spectra is a matter of much contemporary interest. Concerning the shapes of the spectra and the variation of the intensity with time detailed analyses in terms of the solar wind are being carried out. What concerns us more here is the analysis of the mass composition to try to get back to the origin of the particles. The general method is to try to choose a source composition (the 'primordial composition') which will give the observed primary mass composition (such as that shown in figure 2) after traversal of a thickness of interstellar material in which fragmentation of some of the nuclei occurs. There are uncertainties in the fragmentation probabilities at the energies in question and inevitably the primary mass composition is not known at high Z values as accurately as one would wish; nevertheless, some tentative conclusions have been drawn. Shapiro and associates (Shapiro and Silberberg 1970, Shapiro *et al* 1971) have made analyses as successive improvements in the data have been made and their current conclusions on the primordial composition derived from measurements below about 10^9 eV/nucleon are given in table 1. Associated with this composition is the adoption of a distribution function of path lengths of the form

$$f(x) \propto x \quad \text{for} \quad x < 1 \text{ g cm}^{-2}$$

and

$$f(x) \propto \exp{-(0 \cdot 23x)} \quad \text{for} \quad x > 1 \text{ g cm}^{-2}.$$

The corresponding mean path length is $\bar{x} \simeq 5 \text{ g cm}^{-2}$.

Table 1. Primordial composition of the more abundant cosmic rays, normalized to carbon. The data, which refer to energies below 1 GeV per nucleon, are taken from the work of Shapiro *et al* (1971)

H	5×10^4†	$29 \leqslant Z \leqslant 43$	$\simeq 10^{-2}$
He	$(2 \cdot 7 \pm 0 \cdot 5) \times 10^3$		
C	100	$44 \leqslant Z \leqslant 59$	$\simeq 3 \times 10^{-4}$
N	12 ± 3		
O	102 ± 6	$68 \leqslant Z \leqslant 83$	$\simeq 3 \times 10^{-4}$
Ne	20 ± 3		
Mg	27 ± 4	$90 \leqslant Z \leqslant 96$	$\simeq 2 \times 10^{-4}$
Si	23 ± 4		
Fe	23 ± 5		

† This value applies to source spectra that follow a power law in energy per nucleon.

It is interesting to calculate the lifetime in the galaxy of cosmic rays having this mean path length in interstellar matter. The approximate density in the galactic disc is $1 \cdot 7 \times 10^{-24} \text{ g cm}^{-3}$ (approximately 1 atom/cm³, §5), and the mean distance travelled is $5(1 \cdot 7 \times 10^{-24})^{-1}$ cm. The mean lifetime is thus $5(1 \cdot 7 \times 10^{-24} \times 3 \times 10^{10})^{-1}$ seconds, that is about 3×10^6 years, since the particles are effectively moving with the velocity of light. This lifetime is an important datum when considering possible sources for cosmic rays, although it is necessary to stress that it only applies with certainty to energies below about 10^{10} eV since the mass composition is only known there.

Returning to the primordial composition it is interesting to make a comparison with samples of matter from other sources. A pertinent sample is that of matter in the photosphere of the Sun (approximately that of the 'universal' composition) and a comparison is given in figure 3. It will be noticed that there is a general increase in ratio with increasing atomic number, although particular elements deviate considerably from the average line. What is immediately clear from figure 3 is that the main cosmic ray sources are unlikely to be similar to the Sun, apart from any other problems

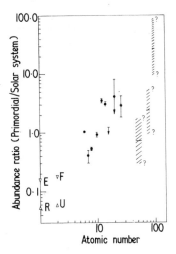

Figure 3. The ratio of primordial cosmic ray abundances to those in the solar system (photosphere) plotted against atomic number, Z. The figure is taken from the work of Shapiro *et al* (1971). Carbon is adopted as the datum. The ratios shown for hydrogen E and R assume that the primordial spectrum follows a power law in energy or rigidity respectively. U denotes the ratio for helium using measurements of solar spectra by Unsold (1969) and F denotes that from measurements by Biswas *et al* (1966) of energetic solar particles. The shaded areas for heavy nuclei are based on the measurements of Fowler *et al* (1970).

that there might be from the energy standpoint, unless, of course, the acceleration mechanisms are very charge dependent. It is interesting to note that supernovae, which are strongly favoured as cosmic ray sources on energy grounds, have a higher abundance of heavy nuclei than the Sun.

2.1.3. Energies between 10^9 and 5×10^{11} eV/nucleon. Moving now to higher energies, there is the region where balloon-borne detectors have been used. The statistical accuracy soon becomes poor for $Z > 2$ and it is customary to group the data into the Z ranges indicated in figure 1. The data for hydrogen and helium given in figure 1 come from the measurements of Schmidt *et al* (1969), Juliusson *et al* (1972), Golden *et al* (1971), Ormes *et al* (1971) and Ryan *et al* (1972). In this region, the slope of the differential spectrum appears to be nearly constant at 2.7 ± 0.1 for protons, with the heavier nuclei having similar, though less precise values.

It should be remarked at this point that there is some evidence from very recent work (by Juliusson *et al* 1972 and others) which suggests that the slopes of the different components are beginning to diverge. In particular there is the likelihood of a reduction of relative intensity of the 'secondary' component with respect to that of primordial origin. The implication is that the higher energy particles have passed through a smaller thickness of interstellar matter.

2.1.4. Energies above 5×10^{11} eV/nucleon. At still higher energies there is virtually no direct information about particles with $Z > 1$ although a few individual nuclei have been detected in balloon-borne nuclear emulsions. Direct measurements on protons extend to about 3×10^{12} eV and above this indirect measurements take over. Brooke *et al* (1964) and a number of more recent authors, for example P V Ramana Murthy (1972 private communication) have worked back from the sea-level muon flux and assumed models for the high energy interaction processes to give the primary nuclear spectrum. If it is assumed that the division of primary nuclei between the Z-ranges is the same above 10^{12} eV as below it then nucleon intensities can be deduced accordingly. The proton spectrum in figure 2 has been derived in this way. If the heavier nuclei cease, in fact, at about 10^{11} eV (a possibility in some origin models) then the proton intensity will need to be a little higher. There is some measure of confidence in the indirect method in so far as it gives a result rather close to the direct measurements in the overlap region and joins on smoothly to the extensive air shower data which start at about 10^{14} eV. However, it should be remarked that there is another body of evidence provided by the PROTON satellite experiments (see Grigorov *et al* 1971 for a summary) which suggests that the slope of the proton spectrum increases rather rapidly at about 10^{12} eV. These measurements appear to indicate that heavier nuclei predominate above this energy. The author's view is that the evidence is not strong but for safety the proton intensity (figure 1) is shown as being uncertain in the range 10^{12}–10^{14} eV.

In view of the later chapters on extensive air showers no mention is needed of the manner of derivation of the spectrum above 10^{14} eV but attention is drawn to the most interesting change in slope which occurs at about 3×10^{15} eV.

In so far as the spectrum follows a power law over a wide range of energy it is of value to quote its form. Writing the energy per nucleus as E, then

$$J(E) = A_1 E^{-\gamma_1} \qquad \text{for} \qquad 10^{11} < E < 3 \times 10^{15} \text{ eV}$$

with

$$A_1 \simeq 3 \cdot 1 \times 10^{18} \text{ m}^{-2}\text{s}^{-1}\text{sr}^{-1}\text{eV}^{-1} \qquad \text{and} \qquad \gamma_1 \simeq 2 \cdot 6,$$

and

$$j(E) = A_2 E^{-\gamma_2} \qquad \text{for} \qquad 3 \times 10^{15} \text{ eV} < E < 10^{20} \text{ eV}$$

with

$$A_2 \simeq 1 \cdot 0 \times 10^{28} \text{ m}^{-2}\text{s}^{-1}\text{sr}^{-1}\text{eV}^{-1} \qquad \text{and} \qquad \gamma_2 \simeq 3 \cdot 2.$$

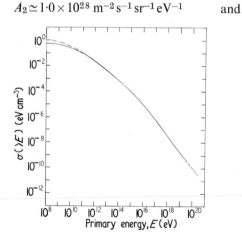

Figure 4. Energy density of primary cosmic rays. The dotted line represents an estimate of the energy density of 'galactic' cosmic rays, that is before modulation of the spectrum by the interplanetary field.

2.2. The energy density of charged particles

The data given in figure 1 can be used to derive the energy density of the primary radiation:

$$\sigma(>E) = \frac{4\pi}{c} \int_E^\infty E j(E) \, dE.$$

The energy density has been calculated, with the result shown in figure 4. As can be seen the total density is about 0.6 eV cm^{-3}, a value which is close to the energy carried by starlight at the Earth (about 0.6 eV cm^{-3}) and that carried by the relict radiation (about 0.25 eV cm^{-3}).

3. Primary electrons and positrons

3.1. The energy spectrum

It has been remarked already that electrons would be expected in the primary beam. Since their first detection, by Earl in 1961, many measurements of the spectrum have been made and figure 5 gives results of a recent summary by Meyer (1971). There is seen to be a large spread of measurements, a fact due to the low flux of particles and difficulties in allowing for the production of electrons by other particles near to the detector (the majority of the measurements are made with balloon-borne detectors).

Magnet spectrometers have also been flown and some information has been derived on the relative numbers of electrons and positrons. The results appear to indicate an e^+/e^- ratio which falls from a value less than unity at about 5×10^8 eV to only some

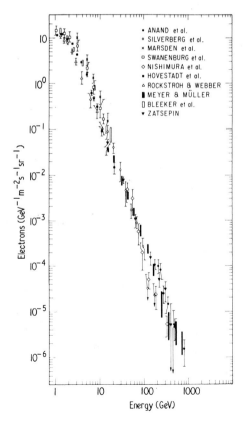

Figure 5. The energy spectrum of primary electrons ($e^+ + e^-$) above 10^9 eV as summarized by Meyer (1971). See the paper by Meyer for references.

B

5% above 10^9 eV. The reduction implies that above 10^9 eV, at least, the electrons are not due to secondary interactions produced in the interstellar matter. This conclusion arises because these interactions would produce π^0 mesons from which γ rays and in turn, e^+e^- pairs would result. Further confirmation comes from the calculated spectrum of secondary electrons for the traversal by protons of 5 g cm^{-2} interstellar matter, as shown in figure 6. In this figure the experimental line is a mean curve drawn through the data of figure 5. The secondary contribution is seen to be significant only at energies in the region of 10^8 eV.

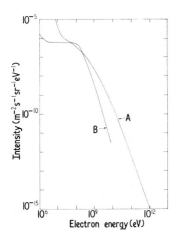

Figure 6. Composite primary electron spectrum for the condition of minimum solar activity. The data for energies below 10^{10} eV come from the summary by Daniel (1968) and refer to the period 1965–6, that is near sunspot minimum. The higher energy line A is the best fit to figure 5 and refers to 1968–70 (approaching sunspot maximum) but at these energies solar modulation will not be important. The expected contribution from the interactions of protons in the galaxy is indicated by line B.

3.2. Relationship to the radio spectrum

From what has been said it is likely that the majority of the primary electron component above several times 10^8 eV is of true primordial origin. These electrons passing through the magnetic fields in the galaxy will undergo magnetic bremsstrahlung (synchrotron radiation) and the radiation produced will be in the radio region. The relationship between the radio spectrum, $I(\nu)$, the electron energy spectrum $N(E) = AE^{-\gamma}$ and the mean magnetic field, H, has been studied in detail by Ginzburg (1956 and later papers). Ginzburg and Syrovatsky (1964) give

$$I_\nu \propto H^\alpha \nu^\beta \qquad \text{with} \qquad \alpha = (\gamma + 1)/2$$

$$\text{and} \qquad \beta = -(\gamma - 1)/2$$

Experimental measurements of the galactic radio emission give $I_\nu \propto \nu^{-0\cdot8}$ for $\nu \geqslant 300$ MHz, so that $\gamma \simeq 2\cdot6$, in good agreement with the experimental slope (figure 5).

There are difficulties in attempting to make predictions of the absolute intensity of electrons from the radio data because of variations of radio intensity with direction, uncertainties in path length for the electrons and the unknown value of H. However, the data are not inconsistent with H in the region of several μG, a value that has relevance to other aspects of cosmic rays as will be seen later.

3.3. Significance of the shape of the energy spectrum

One feature that is not understood at the present time is the continuation of the primary electron spectrum with constant slope to as high an energy as 10^{12} eV (figure 5). The point is that the electrons lose energy through collisions with galactic photons (inverse Compton effect) and the synchrotron radiation already mentioned, and this loss increases as the square of the electron energy. Thus, above some critical energy E_c the volume of space from which electrons are drawn will begin to shrink and the slope of the measured spectrum should increase.

If, for $E \ll E_c$, the electrons have a lifetime in the galaxy of T then it can easily be shown that $T(E_c/mc^2) \simeq (2 \times 10^{19}/W)$ where W is the combined energy density (in eV cm^{-3}) of photons (W_p) and magnetic field (W_B). For starlight near the Earth and the relict radiation (§2.2), $W_p \simeq 0.85$ eV cm^{-3} and for a mean magnetic field of 5 μG, $W_B \simeq 0.6$ eV cm^{-3} so that $W \simeq 1.45$ eV cm^{-3}. If the low energy electrons have the same order of lifetime as the nuclei (§2.1.2) we have $T \simeq 10^{14}$ s and substitution yields $(E_c/mc^2) \simeq 1.4 \times 10^5$, that is $E_c \simeq 7 \times 10^{10}$ eV. The lack of cut-off as far as ten times this value implies that either T is at most one-tenth of the value for nuclei or that W is smaller by a factor of ten. It seems more likely that the former is true.

4. Primary γ rays

4.1. Discovery of the radiation

For a time after the initial discovery of the penetrating radiation from space it was thought that the 'cosmic rays' were very hard γ rays. However, the classic experiments of Skobelzyn (1929) and Bothe and Kolhorster (1929) showed that the majority, at least, were not γ rays but particles. Later studies of the variation of intensity with latitude and angle to the vertical demonstrated that it was certainly charged particles, predominantly positive, rather than γ rays which were responsible for the various effects observed. It was not until 1962, in fact, that even x rays were definitely detected in the primary beam (Giacconi *et al* 1962). Since that time, x ray astronomy has grown rapidly and at present the study of x ray spectra from specific stars is contributing considerably to knowledge of astrophysical processes.

It is conventional to consider only particles and quanta with energies above 1 MeV as coming under the head of 'cosmic rays' and x ray astronomy therefore joins ultraviolet, visible, infrared and radio astronomy as areas not covered in any detail in the present book. An exception can be made in the case of the diffuse background radiation, however, in so far as this probably has relevance to higher energy cosmic rays.

The x rays from discrete sources such as the Crab nebula, or the first source to be discovered, that in the constellation Scorpius (Sco X-1), are superimposed on a diffuse background, which appears to be nearly isotropic (Seward *et al* 1967 and later authors). Figure 7 gives a summary of the measurements of this background, from the work of Ipavich and Lenchek (1970) together with more recent data, as indicated in the caption. Perhaps the most interesting results are those from the γ ray experiment

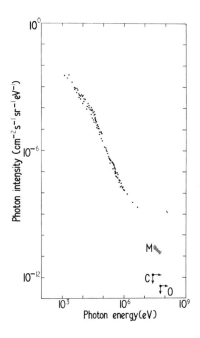

Figure 7. Summary of measurements on the intensity of diffuse x rays and γ rays (after Ipavich and Lenchek 1970 and later measurements).

M: Mayer-Hasselwander *et al* (1972)
C: COSMOS-208 data, Bratolyubova-Tsulukidze *et al* (1970).
O: OSO-III data, Clark *et al* (1971).

of Clark *et al* (1968, 1971) which gave, in fact, the first unambiguous evidence for celestial γ rays with energies of the order of 100 MeV. These experiments showed a variation of γ ray intensity with galactic latitude and longitude, the maximum occurring towards the galactic centre. Perpendicular to the galactic plane there was a significant intensity suggesting an isotropic diffuse component; however, in view of the possibility of spurious effects simulating this isotropic component the measurements have been used simply to give an upper limit in figure 7.

4.2. Interpretation of the diffuse background

The presence of x rays (and perhaps γ rays) having an isotropic distribution suggests an origin outside the galaxy but it is not at present clear whether the quanta are coming from a large number of unresolved galaxies or from the space between these galaxies. Attention has been devoted to a production mechanism involving inverse Compton collisions of high energy electrons with low energy photons—a mechanism that would be effective in both environments (Felten and Morrison 1966 and other authors). Consider first the production in extragalactic space. The ingredients of the calculation are the energy spectrum of the fast electrons and the energy density of the relict radiation. The latter is known (0.25 eV cm^{-3}) but the electron spectrum is doubtful in view of the problem of deciding to what extent fast electrons leak out of their galaxies. Sciama (1971) has shown that an intergalactic electron flux of 10^{-3} of the galactic flux would be sufficient if the whole universe were available for x ray production (a mean line of sight distance of 10^5 times the mean galactic dimension is adopted). Although 10^{-3} would appear at first sight to be a reasonable fraction, in fact it is on the high side in view of the large energy losses that the electrons experience in the actual inverse Compton process. Instead, Sciama favours x ray production by the same process (at least for energies above 10^7 eV) within radio galaxies at red shifts in the range 3 – 5 where the relict radiation will be more intense. It should be remarked that there are other theories, too, which are concerned with the generation of the x ray background, and in fact the whole subject is proving to be a profitable area for astrophysical conjecture.

5. Origin of cosmic rays

5.1. Scope of the discussion

The question of the origin of the energetic cosmic rays is still unsolved despite the considerable efforts that have been made. As mentioned earlier, all that is clear is that the bulk of the particles are not of solar origin. Such is our ignorance that it is not yet certain as to whether the majority of the particles arise from within the galaxy or are of extragalactic origin.

For detailed analysis the reader is referred to articles by Morrison (1961), Ginzburg and Syrovatsky (1964), and Brecher and Burbidge (1972). In the present work attention will be devoted only to a very brief examination of the origin of the energetic primaries, by which is meant primary particles of energy above about 10^{12} eV. The reason for this restriction is that our information on these primaries comes largely from the observations of their secondaries at ground level and this area therefore falls more strictly into the scope of the present book.

5.2. Summary of data about energetic primary cosmic rays $(E > 10^{12}\,eV)$

The main facts about the energetic primary radiation which are relevant to the origin problem can be summarized as follows.

(i) *Energy.* The total energy density is about 1 eV cm^{-3} and that about 10^{12} eV is about 2×10^{-2} eV cm^{-3}. The spectrum extends to at least 10^{20} eV.

(ii) *Energy spectrum.* The slope of the differential spectrum is about $-2 \cdot 6$ from 10^{12} to 3×10^{15} eV and about $-3 \cdot 2$ above 3×10^{15}. The change of slope occurs over a rather small range of energy.

(iii) *Mass composition.* At energies above 10^{12} eV very little is known about the mass composition.

(iv) *Isotropy.* There is a very high degree of isotropy of the primary particles. Away from the energy region affected by the interplanetary magnetic field no significant anisotropy has been detected. The upper limit to the amplitude of the first harmonic of the variation of number with right ascension is about $0 \cdot 5\%$ at 10^{14} eV, about 3% at 3×10^{17} eV and about 15% above 10^{19} eV.

It is useful to examine the extraterrestrial environment in which the cosmic rays originate, are accelerated and are propagated before reaching the Earth's atmosphere. This is done in the next section.

5.3. *The galaxy, the group and the supergalaxy*

Our galaxy appears to be a rather typical spiral galaxy with most of the stars distributed in a disc of radius 15 kpc and thickness very approximately 600 pc. The younger stars are concentrated in roughly formed spiral 'arms' as is the interstellar gas and dust.

Much of the gas is distributed in clouds having density of approximately 10 atoms/cm³ and average size about 10 pc (HI clouds). There are also clouds of ionized gas (HII regions) surrounding hot stars and the whole galaxy is pervaded by dust clouds. Averaging over the galaxy the mean density of matter not in stars is about 1 atom/cm³.

Associated with the spiral arms is a magnetic field of strength several microgauss aligned very roughly along the arms together with many field irregularities presumably associated with the various clouds.

Many of the parameters of the galaxy are not well known, as yet, and the values given are necessarily rather approximate. In particular the important question of the magnitude and distribution of the galactic magnetic field is still the subject of intensive research (recent work relating to cosmic ray trajectories in the galactic field has been carried out by Karakula *et al* 1972).

In addition to the disc-like concentration there is a more nearly spherical system of older stars and star clusters, of lower density—the so-called 'halo'. The strength of the magnetic field and the gas density in this region are virtually unknown.

Galaxies are not distributed uniformly through space. The nearest 15–20 galaxies form the 'local group', dominated by M-31 some 0·6 Mpc away. In turn, there is evidence for a supergalaxy of about 10^4 galaxies dominated by the Virgo group of galaxies about 10 Mpc distant. The strength of the intergalactic field and the density of intergalactic matter are, again, unknown quantities at present.

5.4. *General theories of origin*

The conservative approach to cosmic ray origin is to assume that the particles originate in our own galaxy and that they are largely confined to it by magnetic fields. In this way the comparatively high energy density (1 eV cm⁻³) is restricted to the galaxy and the embarrassment of such a high density over the whole universe disappears.

There appear to be energetic sources within the galaxy capable of providing sufficient energy and the necessary very energetic particles. Supernovae and their subsequent remnants are strong contenders (see the detailed work by Ginzburg and Syrovatsky 1964), not only because of their considerable energy release but because of the identification of heavy elements in their spectra. The identification of a pulsar in the Crab nebula (Cooke *et al* 1969) has provided another possible energy source for cosmic rays coming from supernova remnants and a detailed theory of acceleration has been put forward by Gunn and Ostriker (1969). The galactic nucleus has also been suggested (Kulikov *et al* 1969).

An alternative and rather extreme view is to regard the bulk of the cosmic rays as being of extragalactic origin.

Intermediate between the extremes of 'all galactic' or 'all extragalactic' is the possibility of a mixed origin (eg Morrison 1961). Also in the intermediate class is the idea of confining the particles largely to a restricted region of extragalactic space such as the supergalaxy (Brecher and Burbidge 1972).

In what follows the experimental data on searches for discrete sources, studies of spectral shape and the analysis of anisotropies will be examined in terms of these ideas.

5.5. *Search for specific sources*

Although there have been many searches, there have so far been no observations of energetic cosmic rays coming from specific sources, the reason being the effect of the galactic magnetic field in smearing out the arrival directions. Even at energies as high as 10^{19} eV the angular deflexions are significant; for example, with a reasonable galactic field model the 'aberration' for a 10^{19} eV proton from the Crab is about $10°$. At lower energies the angular deflexions are very large and the trajectories are tortuous. In fact, as the energy considered becomes smaller, irregularities in the galactic magnetic field structure become increasingly important and particle propagation becomes almost one of diffusion; the possibility of identifying specific sources then becomes very bleak.

5.6. *The spectral shape*

A common model of the propagation of the particles is that up to 10^{15} eV they essentially diffuse through the spiral arms, because of the encounters with small scale irregularities in the magnetic field referred to above. If the irregularities are thought of as 'clouds' of field, radius R, field H, then below $(pc)_0 = 300\ HR$ the deflexions are very large and the diffusion mean free path is virtually constant whereas above $(pc)_0$ the deflexions become smaller and the effective mean free path for diffusion lengthens. The result is a reduction in containment time and a corresponding steepening of the spectrum, as required. Unfortunately, there is very little quantitative evidence to support this model. The biggest difficulty arises in explaining the rapid change of slope observed coupled with the magnitude of the change: $\Delta\gamma \simeq 0.6$. In its simple form, with 'clouds' of constant field and size, and with primaries of unique mass, $\Delta\gamma$ should be 2 and not 0.6. By allowing a mass composition at 10^{15} eV similar to that at 10^{10} eV the predicted value of $\Delta\gamma$ can be reduced (Peters 1961) but the transition region is longer than observed. Taking more reasonable models for the field irregularities lengthens the transition still further. If diffusion is the answer then it would appear that a rather special distribution of field irregularities is required; there is no evidence for (or against) such a distribution at present.

An alternative explanation is to regard the change of slope as a consequence of the source, or sources. Since it is unlikely that a number of sources would have very similar characteristics, an origin in mainly one source would appear more likely. The galactic nucleus is a possibility but there is then the problem of an expected anisotropy and furthermore with the present magnetic field models it would appear impossible to keep the mean mass of interstellar matter traversed by low energy particles to 5 g cm^{-2}. An extragalactic origin on the other hand might not suffer from these drawbacks.

5.7. *Relevance of anisotropy measurements and conclusions*

As has been remarked already, the lack of observation of any significant anisotropy in the flux of energetic particles has led many workers to hypothesize that some at least of the particles may originate outside our own galaxy. Osborne *et al* (1972) have recently used all the available experimental data on extensive air shower directions and endeavoured to set limits on the fraction of particles (assumed to be protons)

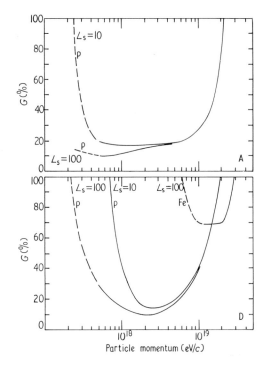

Figure 8. Upper limits (at the 95% confidence level) to the fraction of cosmic rays of galactic origin (G) plotted against particle momentum, from the work of Osborne *et al* (1973). 'p' denotes proton primaries. L_s is the separation of magnetic field scattering centres measured in pc. It is thought that $10 < L_s < 100$ pc. A and D refer to alternative models of the galactic magnetic field.

which can have come from *within* the galaxy, assuming that the sources are distributed uniformly throughout the spiral arms and adopting the most recent information about the structure of the galactic magnetic field. The result is shown in figure 8. It can be seen that, with the assumptions made, there is in fact quite strong evidence for an extragalactic component.

There are two ways to escape this conclusion and allow all the particles to be of galactic origin: to accept the presence of a galactic halo having a rather large magnetic field (several μG) or to postulate that the majority of the nuclei are massive—at least as heavy as iron. (See figure 8, where it is shown that for Fe the region in which the upper limit to G is less than 100% is negligible.) The whole question of the existence of a halo having a sufficient magnetic field to have any relevance to cosmic ray propagation is doubtful, however, particularly with the observation by radio astronomers (eg Lang and Terzian 1969) that normal galaxies do not possess radio halos. It seems most unlikely that the halo field could be big enough to contain particles of energy approaching 10^{20} eV. Explanation in terms of heavy nuclei appears more likely, if only because no mass measurements have yet proved possible at the energies in question, but the postulate seems rather artificial and the more attractive view would be to conclude that the majority of particles above 10^{18} eV are extragalactic.

Even with this conclusion, there is still a problem however. This arises from the presence of the 2·7 K black body radiation (the 'relict radiation'); interactions between the protons and the relict photons will cause an increasing loss of energy of the protons—above the threshold for pion production ($E_p \simeq 5 \times 10^{19}$ eV) the interaction length becomes much shorter than the scale length of the universe and the primary spectrum should fall very rapidly (unless the injection spectrum happens to flatten in this region). As indicated in figure 1, there is no evidence for this steepening experimentally, although it should be pointed out that the number of showers detected above 5×10^{19} eV is rather small (about 10) and energy determinations are not very precise.

It might be thought that by taking the major sources to be in the supergalaxy (in which they would most likely be in the very strong radio sources in the Virgo group) then this problem would be overcome. However, in the absence of an intervening magnetic field, a measurable anisotropy would appear; on the other hand, if a field of sufficient strength to remove the anisotropy were postulated, it appears that the trajectories involved would be so long that a spectral steeping would once again result.

The solution to these problems appears to lie in the amassing of more, precise, experimental data on the arrival directions of very large extensive air showers, the extension of measurements to even higher energies and a renewed attempt to determine the primary mass. The next few years should show significant advances in our knowledge of the origin and behaviour of these most energetic cosmic ray particles.

References

Biswas S, Fichtel C E and Guss D E 1966 *J. Geophys. Rev.* **71** 4071–7

Blandford G E 1971 *Proc. 12th Int. Conf. on Cosmic Rays* (Hobart: University of Tasmania) **1** 269–72

Bothe W and Kolhorster W 1929 *Z. Phys.* **56** 751–77

Bratolyubova-Tsulukidze L I 1970 *Acta Phys. Hung.* **29** suppl 1 123–5

Brecher K and Burbidge G 1972 *Astrophys. J.* **174** 253–91

Brooke G *et al* 1964 *Proc. Phys. Soc.* **83** 853–69

Clark G W, Garmire G P and Kraushaar W L 1968 *Astrophys. J.* **153** L203

—— 1971 *Proc. 12th Int. Conf. on Cosmic Rays* (Hobart: University of Tasmania) **1** 91–6

Cocke W J, Disney M J and Taylor D J 1969 *Nature* **221** 525–7

Daniel R R 1968 *Cosmic Ray Studies in Relation to Recent Developments in Astronomy and Astrophysics* (Bombay: Tata Institute) 181–201

Earl J A 1961 *Phys. Rev. Lett.* **6** 125–8

Felten J E and Morrison P 1966 *Astrophys. J.* **146** 686–708

Fowler P H *et al* 1967 *Proc. R. Soc.* **A301** 39–45

—— 1970 *Proc. R. Soc.* **A318** 1–43

Garcia-Munoz M, Mason G M and Simpson J A 1971 *Proc. 12th Int. Conf. on Cosmic Rays* (Hobart: University of Tasmania) **1** 209–14

Giacconi R *et al* 1962 *Phys. Rev. Lett.* **9** 439–43

Ginzburg V L 1956 *Nuovo Cim.* suppl 3 **N1** 38–48

Ginzburg V L and Syrovatsky S I 1964 *The Origin of Cosmic Rays* (London: Pergamon)

Golden R L *et al* 1971 *Proc. 12th Int. Conf. on Cosmic Rays* (Hobart: University of Tasmania) **1** 203–7

Grigorov N L *et al* 1971 *Proc. 12th Int. Conf. on Cosmic Rays* (Hobart: University of Tasmania) **5** 1752

Gunn J E and Ostriker J P 1969 *Astrophys. J.* **157** 1395–417

Ipavich F M and Lenchek A M 1970 *Phys. Rev.* **D2** 266–70

Juliusson E, Meyer P and Müller D 1972 *Phys. Rev. Lett.* **29** 445–7

Karakula S, Osborne J L, Roberts E and Tkaczyk W 1972 *J. Phys.* A: *Gen. Phys.* **5** 904–15

Kulikov G V, Fomin Yu A and Khristiansen G B 1969 *Zh. Eksp. Teor. Fiz.* **10** 347–59

Lang K R and Terzian Y 1969 *Astrophys. Lett.* **3** 29–33

Mayer-Hasselwander H A *et al* 1972 *Astrophys. J. Lett.* **175** L23

Meyer P 1971 *Proc. 12th Int. Conf. on Cosmic Rays* (Hobart: University of Tasmania) rapporteur paper

Meyer P and Muller D 1971 *Proc. 12th Int. Conf. on Cosmic Rays* (Hobart: University of Tasmania) **1** 117–21

Morrison P 1961 *Handb. Phys.* **46** 1–87

Ormes J F, Balasubrahmanyan V K and Ryan M J 1971 *Proc. 12th Int. Conf. on Cosmic Rays* (Hobart: University of Tasmania) **1** 178–83

Osborne J L, Roberts E and Wolfendale A W 1973 *J. Phys.* A: *Math. Nucl. Phys.* **6** 421–33

Penzias A A and Wilson R W 1965 *Astrophys. J.* **142** 419–21

Peters B 1961 *Nuovo Cim.* **22** 800–19

Ryan M J, Balasubrahmanyan V K and Ormes J R 1972 *Phys. Rev. Lett.* **28** 985–8

Schmidt W K M *et al* 1969 *Phys. Rev.* **184** 1279–82

Sciama D W 1971 *Proc. Int. School of Phys.*, *General Relativity and Cosmology* (New York: Academic Press) 183–236

Seward F *et al* 1967 *Astrophys. J.* **150** 845–50

Shapiro M M and Silberberg R 1970 *Ann. Rev. Nucl. Sci.* **20** 323–92

Shapiro M M, Silberberg R and Tsao C H 1971 *Proc. 12th Int. Conf. on Cosmic Rays* (Hobart: University of Tasmania) **1** 221–7

Skobelzyn D 1929 *Z. Phys.* **54** 686–92

Unsold A O J 1969 *Science* **163** 1015

Chapter 2

Energetic muons

M G Thompson

1. Introduction

The great majority of the particles of the cosmic radiation which are incident on the Earth's surface are not primary particles but are secondaries which owe their origin to high energy, nucleon–nucleus interactions in the atmosphere. The approximate composition of the primary radiation is 87% protons and 13% neutrons, the latter being bound in nuclei (see chapter 1). Such nucleons have an interaction length of approximately 80 g cm^{-2} and the probability of their arriving at the Earth's surface without interacting is less than 10^{-5}. In the interactions of the primary particles in the atmosphere, both charged and uncharged particles, mainly pions and kaons, are produced. The charged pions, if they do not interact, decay to muons as do also some of the kaons (ie $K_{\mu 2}$, $K_{\mu 3}$ decays). The majority of the muons so generated, being weakly interacting particles and having a lifetime of 2·2 × 10^{-6} s, tend to traverse the remaining atmosphere without interacting or suffering decay. The main mechanism by which the muons lose energy is that of ionization and the typical loss for a muon travelling in the near vertical direction is 2 GeV (for $E_\mu \lesssim 100$ GeV).

There is interest in muons at ground level for two main reasons. Firstly, the interactions of the muons can be studied in local detectors with the object of examining the character of the muon itself (ie attempting to distinguish it from a mere 'heavy electron') and of investigating electromagnetic interactions. Secondly, comparison can be made of the energy spectrum of the particles with other cosmic ray observations to give information about various nuclear physical processes. Thus, comparison with underground measurements relates to electromagnetic processes and, by way of neutrinos, to weak interactions. Studies of strong interactions come from comparisons with the primary cosmic ray spectrum, from an analysis of the variation of the muon spectrum with zenith angle and from measurements on the charge ratio, that is, the number of positive muons divided by the number of negative muons in the same momentum interval.

The present article summarizes the present state of knowledge concerning muons at sea level, particular attention being paid to determinations of the momentum spectrum and charge ratio. Indications are also given of the knowledge about nuclear processes that is resulting from the analysis of the experimental data.

2. Experimental techniques

2.1. Indirect methods

Although several methods have been widely used in determining the sea-level muon spectrum up to several TeV, the magnetic deflection method is inherently superior to the others and is described in some detail later. Measurements of the spectrum of bursts produced by muons in lead or iron plates have been made by several groups, and the results interpreted to give the muon spectrum. This method suffers from an inability to determine the sign of the charge of the muon and thus gives no information on the charge ratio. It is further open to criticism because it requires a knowledge of the cross sections for the ionization, bremsstrahlung and direct pair production processes at the highest energies, where they have not been verified experimentally.

The spectrum can also be determined from measurements of the muon intensity underground but interpretation requires an accurate knowledge of the density and of the atomic parameters of the rock above the installation as well as interaction cross sections. Further problems which arise in the interpretation of the data from such experiments are due to the lack of knowledge of the aperture of the experiment, which is usually quite large, and to fluctuation problems.

Yet another method is to use measurements of γ-cascades at various atmospheric depths to give the production spectrum of π^0 mesons and to assume equality of π^0, π^+ and π^-. Hayman *et al* (1963) have used the γ-cascade measurements of Duthie *et al* (1962) to estimate the muon spectrum to 7 TeV. Again the method does not give the muon charge and is only indirectly related to the muon spectrum.

2.2. Magnetic spectrographs

The majority of spectrum determinations have been made by measuring the deflection of the muon in a magnetic field and directly relating the deflection to the particle's momentum. The original spectrographs constructed for this purpose used Geiger counters both as triggering elements and for measuring the particle deflections (see Hyams *et al* 1950, Brooke *et al* 1962).

Subsequently spectrographs were constructed incorporating additional detectors to extend the range of particle momentum which could be measured. For example, Holmes *et al* (1961) added three cloud chambers to the Manchester spectrograph, increasing the maximum detectable momentum (MDM) of the instrument from 21 GeV/c to 240 GeV/c (the MDM, P_m, is defined such that the uncertainty in the momentum ΔP at a momentum P is given by $\Delta P/P = P/P_m$). The spectrograph of

Hayman and Wolfendale (1962a) shown in figure 1 was a modification of the earlier spectrograph described by Brooke *et al* (1962). It will be described briefly because its characteristics and mode of operation were typical of spectrographs in the 1960s. The modified spectrograph contained four trays of neon flash-tubes of internal diameter 5·9 mm near four layers of Geiger counters. Three trays of Geiger counters were incorporated into a momentum selector with which events due to muons of high

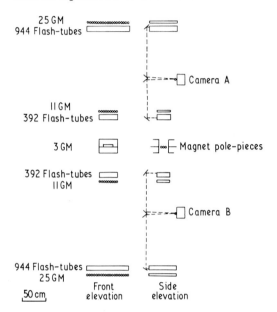

Figure 1. The Durham Air Gap Spectrograph of Hayman and Wolfendale (1962a). GM—Geiger counters.

momenta were selected. The discharged flash-tubes in the high momentum events were recorded photographically. The film was subsequently scanned and the trajectories of the particles traversing the instrument were reconstructed. More recently the spectrographs of Kasha *et al* (1968) and of Asbury *et al* (1970) have used large air-gap magnets with scintillation counters as the triggering elements and spark chambers as the trajectory defining elements. Table 1 includes spectrographs which have been operated since 1950, and contains both air-gap and solid iron types (by 'solid iron' is meant magnets without air gaps where the muons traverse magnetized iron). The solid iron spectrographs generally have a higher MDM than the air-gap types but suffer from enhanced scattering problems.

The latest spectrograph of the Durham group, described by Ayre *et al* (1972a, b) is shown in figure 2. The spectrograph incorporates four large magnet blocks and utilizes 18 trays of neon flash-tubes as trajectory locating devices and large area scintillation counters as triggering elements. In each side of the spectrograph three trays of digitized flash-tubes of internal diameter 1·5 cm are utilized in a momentum selector. Events attributable to muons having momenta in excess of 200 GeV/c are selected and for such energetic events 5 further trays of digitized tubes of internal diameter 0·54 cm are used to locate the particle accurately along its trajectory. The trays of small diameter tubes are connected directly to a computer which analyses the

Table 1. Solid iron and air gap spectrographs which have been operated since 1950, and spectrographs at present under construction

Authors	Location	MDM (GeV/c)	Acceptance (cm^2 sr)	Zenith angle	$\int B\,dl$ (gauss cm)	Detectors
A. *Air gap spectrographs* (post 1950)						
Hyams *et al* (1950)	Manchester, UK	21	0·93	0°	$6\cdot5 \times 10^5$	GM
Holmes *et al* (1961)		240	0·93	0°	$5\cdot97 \times 10^6$	GM and CC
Caro *et al* (1951)	Melbourne, Australia	50	0·69	0°	$6\cdot6 \times 10^5$†	GM
Moroney and Parry (1954)		50	0·69	0°, 30°, 60°	$6\cdot6 \times 10^5$†	GM
Pine *et al* (1959)	Cornell, USA	176	6·9	0°	$1\cdot5 \times 10^6$†	GM and CC
Pak *et al* (1961)		120		0°, 68°	$1\cdot5 \times 10^6$†	GM and FT
Brooke *et al* (1962)	Durham, UK	18	8·0	0°	$6\cdot4 \times 10^5$	GM
Hayman and Wolfendale (1962a)		443	8·0	0°	$6\cdot03 \times 10^5$	GM and FT
Coates and Nash (1962)	Nottingham, UK	29	0·73	0°, 30°, 45°	$1\cdot07 \times 10^5$	GM and FT
Judge and Nash (1965a, b)		28	0·73	30°, 45°, 60° 83°−90°	$1\cdot05 \times 10^5$	GM and FT
Kasha *et al* (1968)	Brookhaven, USA	950	100	75°	$1\cdot64 \times 10^6$	s and OSC
Asbury *et al* (1970)	Argonne, USA	830	500	75°, 80°, 85°	$3\cdot4 \times 10^6$	s and OSC
Flatte *et al* (1971)	Stanford, USA	2000	570	60°−87°	$3\cdot0 \times 10^6$	s and OSC
B. *Solid iron spectrographs*						
Kamiya *et al* (1962)	Nagoya, Japan	100		75°−90°	$4\cdot0 \times 10^6$†	s and FT
Ashton and Wolfendale (1963)	Durham, UK	40		80°	$9\cdot8 \times 10^5$	GM
Ashton *et al* (1966)		198	30	77·5°−90°	$9\cdot82 \times 10^5$	GM and FT
Baber *et al* (1968a, b)	Nottingham, UK	360	18·6	0°	$2\cdot6 \times 10^6$	GM and FT
MacKeown *et al* (1966b)	Durham, UK	1045		82·5°−90°	$1\cdot95 \times 10^6$	GM and FT
Aurela and Wolfendale (1967)		270	13	0°	$8\cdot2 \times 10^5$	GM and FT

Table 1—*Contd.*

Authors	Location	MDM (GeV/c)	Accept- ance (cm² sr)	Zenith angle	$\int B\,dl$ (gauss cm)	Detectors
Alchudjian *et al* (1968)	Mount Aragatz, USSR	3000	105	83°–90°	$3\cdot65 \times 10^6$	GM and WSC
Palmer and Nash (1969)	Nottingham, UK	420		80°	$1\cdot90 \times 10^6$	GM and FT
Flint and Nash (1970)		428		80°	$1\cdot87 \times 10^6$	s and FT
Nandi and Sinha (1970)	Durgapur, India	520	11·7	0°	$3\cdot24 \times 10^6$	GM and FT
Fujii *et al* (1969)	Nagoya, Japan	1280	85	79°–90°	$3\cdot5 \times 10^6$	s and FT
Allkofer *et al* (1970d)	Kiel, W Germany	1000	16	Variable	$3\cdot2 \times 10^6$	s and OSC

C. Spectrographs in course of construction or design

Authors	Location	MDM (GeV/c)	Accept- ance (cm² sr)	Zenith angle	$\int B\,dl$ (gauss cm)	Detectors
R K Adair *et al* (private communication)	Brookhaven, USA	2000	150	Variable	$4\cdot48 \times 10^6$	s and OSC
G E Masek *et al* (private communication)	San Diego, USA	4500	3000	Variable	3×10^6	s and WSC
J Cousins *et al* (1970)	Nottingham, UK	3000	120	0°	$2\cdot7 \times 10^6$	GM and FT (Vidicon camera)
F Reines *et al* (private communication)	Irvine, USA	15 000	2500	90°	$1\cdot8 \times 10^6$	s and WSC
Allkofer *et al* (1971d)	Tel Aviv	7000	1466	85°	$4\cdot8 \times 10^6$	s and WSC
Ayre *et al* (1972a, b)	Durham UK	6000	818	0°	$8\cdot09 \times 10^6$	s and FT

Key:

† Estimated value
FT = Flash-tubes
GM = Geiger counters
OSC = Optical spark chambers
s = Scintillation counters
WSC = Wire spark chambers
CC = Cloud chambers

data automatically. The MDM of the spectrograph is 5850 GeV/c and the instrument differs from most previous spectrographs in that it has multiple magnet-detector layers. A multilayer instrument was chosen because of the need to allow for the increasing probability of burst production by the muon with increasing muon energy. Said (1966) gives the probability for a muon of 1000 GeV leaving a thick steel absorber

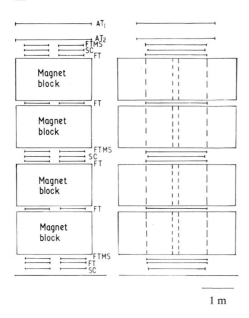

Figure 2. The 300 ton Durham Spectrograph, MARS, of Ayre *et al* (1972a, b). SC—Scintillation counters, FTMS—Flashtube trays of the momentum selector, FT—Trays of small diameter flash-tubes. AT—Azimuthal trays of flash-tubes.

1 m

being accompanied by a large burst as 16%. The four magnet blocks of the spectrograph ensure that most of the muons traversing the instrument will have at least three accurately located points on their trajectories from which their momenta can be found.

The purpose of the instrument is to extend measurement of the muon spectrum and charge ratio to above 5000 GeV/c. In order to do this, and because the vertical muon spectrum falls off steeply, the acceptance of the instrument is quite large (408 cm^2 sr for each side). With such a large acceptance there is a very high flux of low energy muons through the spectrograph; these particles are recorded separately, being analysed automatically with an instrument which calculates the particle deflection and stores the result continually. The rate of recording of all events through one side of the spectrograph is $1\cdot1 \times 10^3$ hr^{-1}.

There are at present several spectrographs of size similar to the Durham instrument under construction and some are listed in table 1. Of interest is the spectrograph of Allkofer *et al* (1971d) shown in figure 3 because it combines the advantages of a multilayer instrument with those of a conventional instrument having two arms. This Kiel–Tel Aviv instrument is to be built in the near horizontal direction, and includes large area spark chambers as trajectory defining elements. The elements outside the magnetic field region contribute greatly to the maximum detectable momentum, which is estimated at 7260 GeV/c, and the acceptance is 1500 cm^2 sr. Data from this spectrograph and further data extending to higher muon momenta from the Durham spectrograph are eagerly awaited.

2.3. Sources of error in spectrum and charge ratio measurements

Before the results of an experiment are evaluated it is necessary to consider any instrumental effects and experimental biases which may be present in the data. To

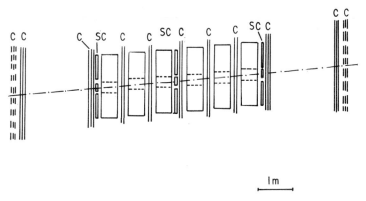

Figure 3. The proposed Kiel–Tel Aviv spectrograph of Allkofer *et al* (1971d). c—Spark chambers, sc—Scintillation counters.

be specific, the acceptance, the Coulomb scattering, the noise, and the MDM of the instrument must all be accurately known. The observed deflection spectrum, $f_{ob}(\Delta)$, can be written as

$$f_{ob}(\Delta) = f'(\Delta)E_f(\Delta)A(\Delta)G(\Delta_0)B(\Delta)$$

where $f'(\Delta)$ is the incident deflection spectrum incorporating an allowance for scattering, $E_f(\Delta)$ is the efficiency of the system, $A(\Delta)$ is the acceptance function of the instrument with respect to the standard acceptance $G(\Delta_0)$, and $B(\Delta)$ is a bias function. $G(\Delta_0)$ is generally taken as the probability of a particle of infinite momentum passing through the spectrograph within the instrument's allowed area and solid angle. The function $B(\Delta)$ allows for the bias which arises from the rejection of events with two or more simultaneous particles at one or more measuring levels. Experimentalists have attempted to correct for $B(\Delta)$ in different ways, and due to the increasing size of spectrographs the accurate determination of this function is becoming increasingly important. Regarding the function $f'(\Delta)$, the most common practice is to take a theoretical muon spectrum, $f(\Delta)$, to estimate the effects of Coulomb scattering in the instrument and finally to incorporate the instrumental noise function to give $f'(\Delta)$.

One of the main difficulties with the interpretation of spectrograph data is the estimation of $E_f(\Delta)$, and indeed few experiments have attempted an absolute determination. As a consequence many groups have normalized their results to a standard point, which until recently has been accepted as being the vertical differential intensity given by Rossi (1948) at 1 GeV/c of $2 \cdot 45 \times 10^{-3} \, \mathrm{cm}^{-2} \, \mathrm{sr}^{-1} \, \mathrm{s}^{-1} \, (\mathrm{GeV}/c)^{-1}$. However, recent work discussed in the next section has shown that this intensity is possibly underestimated by some 10–20%.

As remarked earlier, knowing the MDM of an instrument, P_m, the fractional uncertainty in any momentum measurement is given by P/P_m, P being the estimated momentum. If the data are assumed to follow a normal error distribution it is possible to estimate the muon spectrum to momenta somewhat in excess of the MDM and this has been done by some workers. It is, however, an unsatisfactory procedure since the

c

assumption of a normal error distribution is rarely valid and the practice is to be discouraged. The charge ratio of the muons in the region of an instrument's MDM, according to normal error theory, must approach unity and again whilst a correction for the instrumental effect of the MDM can be made to the charge ratio, little relevance should be placed on ratio measurements at or above the MDM.

3. The absolute intensity of muons at sea level

Due to difficulties concerning uncertain edge effects of particle detectors and in estimating the overall efficiencies of counter systems many experimentalists have normalized their results to a standard intensity point. Until recently this point was that deduced by Rossi (1948) from the data of Greisen (1942). Rossi applied a correction amounting to 4% to the Greisen value to account for the combined effect of showers and scattering in the Greisen apparatus. Allkofer *et al* (1970b), using a scintillation counter telescope which included lead absorber, measured the differential intensity at 1 GeV/c to be $(3 \cdot 09 \pm 0 \cdot 21) \times 10^{-6}$ cm^{-2} sr^{-1} s^{-1} (MeV/c)$^{-1}$, which is approximately 26% higher than the 1 GeV/c Rossi point. This result is supported by Crookes and Rastin (1971a) who measured the intensity at 0·35 GeV/c using a Geiger counter and flash-tube stack. Quantitatively Crookes and Rastin measured an intensity 9% higher than that measured by Greisen.

Measurements of the absolute intensity of muons at higher momenta (above 3·48 GeV/c and 7·12 GeV/c) have been made by Ayre *et al* (1971a) using the Durham spectrograph MARS. Ayre *et al* conclude that at the lower momenta the intensities are $(7 \cdot 7 \pm 1 \cdot 3)\%$ greater than those previously given by Aurela and Wolfendale (1967) which were based on the Rossi normalization. Further measurements by C A Ayre *et al* (1972 private communication) indicate an intensity somewhat greater than that initially reported, being $(10 \cdot 9 \pm 1 \cdot 3)\%$ and $(9 \cdot 5 \pm 1 \cdot 4)\%$ greater than the values of Aurela and Wolfendale (1967) at momenta of 3·48 GeV/c and 7·12 GeV/c respectively. Ashton *et al* (1972) have measured the integral muon intensity above 0·88 GeV/c as $(8 \cdot 22 \pm 0 \cdot 04) \, 10^{-3}$ cm^{-2} s^{-1} sr^{-1}, which is also higher than expected on the basis of the Rossi point.

The measurements of the various workers have been summarized by Allkofer and Jokisch (1972), as shown in figure 4. The latest data from the Durham group at 3·48 GeV/c and 7·12 GeV/c are plotted. Allkofer and Jokisch (1972) have fitted a curve to their data from the Kiel spectrographs as shown in the figure and De *et al* (1972b) have fitted a so-called 'form spectrum' to the data below 10 GeV/c which is of the form

$$N(P)\,\mathrm{d}P = AP^{-\alpha}\,\mathrm{d}P$$

with $\alpha = 0 \cdot 5483 - 0 \cdot 3977 \ln P$, $A = 3 \cdot 09 \times 10^{-3}$ cm^{-2} s^{-1} sr^{-1} (GeV/c)$^{-1}$, P being in GeV/c. From the figure it is apparent that a value of $3 \cdot 0 \times 10^{-3}$ cm^{-2} s^{-1} sr^{-1} (GeV/c)$^{-1}$ for the differential muon vertical intensity at 1 GeV/c is a satisfactory fit to the data and this value is 22% greater than the long standing Rossi point.

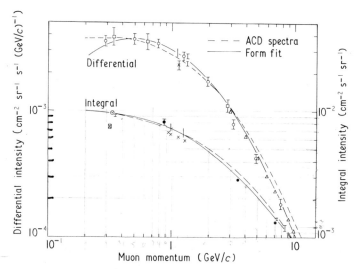

Figure 4. The absolute vertical intensity of Cosmic ray muons—Allkofer and Jokisch (1972).

□   Allkofer *et al* (1970b), Knoblich (1968).
| Allkofer *et al* (1970a, c, 1971a).
○   Allkofer and Clausen (1970).
△   Bateman *et al* (1971).
×   De *et al* (1972a, b).
●   Ayre *et al* (1971a), Ashton *et al* (1972).
⊙   Greisen (1942).
⊠   Bhattachryya (1970).
I   Crookes and Rastin (1971a, b, 1972).

4. The muon momentum spectrum

4.1. Scope of the discussion

Measurements have been made by many groups of the muon momentum spectrum at sea level, at a variety of zenith angles. The various experimental data for the near vertical and near horizontal directions will now be considered separately. Finally the variation of the spectrum with zenith angle and with geomagnetic latitude will be discussed.

4.2. The near vertical muon spectrum

4.2.1. Magnetic spectrograph measurements. The measurements prior to 1948 have been reviewed by Rossi (1948) and combined to give a spectrum to 30 GeV/c, whilst later observations to 1960 have been considered by Fowler and Wolfendale (1961). Briefly, as shown in figure 5, the spectrum deduced by Rossi is in agreement with that of Owen and Wilson (1955) over the range $0.7 < P < 11$ GeV/c, whilst the spectrum of Caro *et al* (1951) shows an excess, amounting to 10 % at 2 GeV/c and 17 % at 1 GeV/c, over the Owen and Wilson spectrum. At higher momenta the Rossi spectrum is in excess of the data of Caro *et al* and this is attributed to an underestimation of the errors due to the turbulence in the cloud chambers used for the experiments contributing to the Rossi spectrum. Data from subsequent work of the Manchester group (Holmes *et al* 1961) confirmed the shape of the Owen and Wilson spectrum and

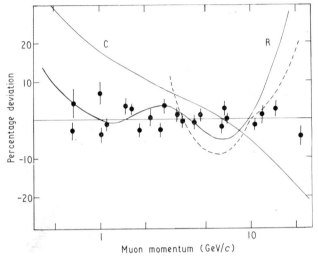

Figure 5. Deviations from the spectrum of Owen and Wilson (1955) of the measurements of Caro *et al* (1951) (C), Rossi (1948) (R), and Glaser *et al* (1950) (broken curve).

extended the measurements to the region of 1000 GeV/c. Similar results were obtained by Pak *et al* (1961) who used a Geiger counter momentum selector in their magnetic spectrograph. Pak *et al* recorded 23 037 particles above 10 GeV/c for their spectrum. Preliminary data of the Durham group (Ashton *et al* 1960), also using a spectrograph incorporating a momentum selector, reinforced the suggestion that the spectrum of Caro *et al* was incorrect. By 1961 four or five consistent experiments had ascertained the shape of the muon spectrum in the range 1–50 GeV/c.

After a more accurate calibration of the momentum selector associated with their spectrograph, and due also to the improved statistical accuracy of their data, Gardener *et al* (1962) and Hayman and Wolfendale (1962a) slightly modified the shape of their preliminary muon spectrum in the region of 1000 GeV/c, this latter spectrum being based upon 191 000 particles above 0·4 GeV/c of which 4520 were above 20 GeV/c. Table 2 gives the best fit differential spectrum obtained by Hayman and Wolfendale (1962a) assuming the muons are all derived from pions. This spectrum has been subsequently modified by Osborne *et al* (1964) to allow in a more accurate manner for the selection bias in the Durham spectrograph, the data for this spectrum (referred to as OWP) also being given in the table. The measurement of Aurela and Wolfendale (1967)—referred to as AW—differs from the OWP spectrum only over the 100–1500 GeV/c range and represents the best estimate at present from the Durham group of the vertical muon spectrum. The OWP spectrum is not purely dependent upon the

Table 2. The absolute spectrum of Allkofer *et al* (1971b) and the three spectra of the Durham group which are normalized to the Rossi 1 GeV/c point

Momentum	Allkofer *et al* (1971b) Integral spectrum intensity	Allkofer *et al* (1971b) γ	Allkofer *et al* (1971b) Differential spectrum intensity	Allkofer *et al* (1971b) γ	Hayman and Wolfendale (1962a) Differential spectrum intensity	Hayman and Wolfendale (1962a) γ	Osborne *et al* (1964) Differential spectrum intensity	Aurela and Wolfendale (1967) Differential spectrum intensity
GeV/c	$\mathrm{cm^{-2}\,s^{-1}\,sr^{-1}}$		$\mathrm{cm^{-2}\,s^{-1}\,sr^{-1}\,(GeV/c)^{-1}}$		$\mathrm{cm^{-2}\,s^{-1}\,sr^{-1}\,(GeV/c)^{-1}}$		$\mathrm{cm^{-2}\,s^{-1}\,sr^{-1}\,(GeV/c)^{-1}}$	$\mathrm{cm^{-2}\,s^{-1}\,sr^{-1}\,(GeV)^{-1}}$
0·2	$9\cdot94\times10^{-3}$	0·05	$3\cdot73\times10^{-3}$	0·06				
0·4	$9\cdot18\times10^{-3}$	0·13	$3\cdot72\times10^{-3}$	0·16	$2\cdot58\times10^{-3}$	−0·44		
0·5					$2\cdot85\times10^{-3}$	−0·16		
0·7					$2\cdot80\times10^{-3}$	0·22		
0·8	$7\cdot81\times10^{-3}$	0·28	$3\cdot10\times10^{-3}$	0·38	$2\cdot45\times10^{-3}$	0·56	$2\cdot45\times10^{-3}$	$2\cdot45\times10^{-3}$
1·0	$7\cdot22\times10^{-3}$	0·35	$2\cdot79\times10^{-3}$	0·49	$1\cdot93\times10^{-3}$	0·90		
1·5	$6\cdot00\times10^{-3}$	0·50	$2\cdot14\times10^{-3}$	0·73	$1\cdot48\times10^{-3}$	1·14	$1\cdot50\times10^{-3}$	$1\cdot50\times10^{-3}$
2·0	$5\cdot05\times10^{-3}$	0·63	$1\cdot67\times10^{-3}$	0·93	$8\cdot73\times10^{-4}$	1·42	$9\cdot01\times10^{-4}$	$9\cdot01\times10^{-4}$
3·0	$3\cdot72\times10^{-3}$	0·82	$1\cdot06\times10^{-3}$	1·24	$3\cdot79\times10^{-4}$	1·76	$3\cdot96\times10^{-4}$	$3\cdot96\times10^{-4}$
5·0	$2\cdot26\times10^{-3}$	1·08	$4\cdot97\times10^{-4}$	1·64	$2\cdot05\times10^{-4}$	1·96	$2\cdot15\times10^{-4}$	$2\cdot15\times10^{-4}$
7·0	$1\cdot52\times10^{-3}$	1·24	$2\cdot73\times10^{-4}$	1·87	$1\cdot02\times10^{-4}$	2·14	$1\cdot09\times10^{-4}$	$1\cdot09\times10^{-4}$
10	$9\cdot42\times10^{-4}$	1·40	$1\cdot33\times10^{-4}$	2·10	$4\cdot16\times10^{-5}$	2·35		
15	$5\cdot13\times10^{-4}$	1·57	$5\cdot40\times10^{-5}$	2·32	$2\cdot04\times10^{-5}$	2·48	$2\cdot20\times10^{-5}$	$2\cdot20\times10^{-5}$
20	$3\cdot21\times10^{-4}$	1·68	$2\cdot70\times10^{-5}$	2·46	$7\cdot20\times10^{-6}$	2·65	$7\cdot85\times10^{-6}$	$7\cdot85\times10^{-6}$
30	$1\cdot57\times10^{-4}$	1·82	$9\cdot59\times10^{-6}$	2·63	$1\cdot77\times10^{-6}$	2·85	$1\cdot94\times10^{-6}$	$1\cdot94\times10^{-6}$
50	$5\cdot93\times10^{-5}$	1·99	$2\cdot36\times10^{-6}$	2·83	$7\cdot20\times10^{-6}$ ... $6\cdot60\times10^{-7}$	2·98	$7\cdot23\times10^{-7}$	$7\cdot36\times10^{-7}$
70	$2\cdot98\times10^{-5}$	2·09	$8\cdot92\times10^{-7}$	2·95	$2\cdot25\times10^{-7}$	3·10	$2\cdot50\times10^{-7}$	$2\cdot61\times10^{-7}$
100	$1\cdot38\times10^{-5}$	2·20	$3\cdot04\times10^{-7}$	3·07	$6\cdot28\times10^{-8}$	3·22		
150	$5\cdot55\times10^{-6}$	2·30	$8\cdot51\times10^{-8}$	3·20	$2\cdot40\times10^{-8}$	3·30	$2\cdot97\times10^{-8}$	$3\cdot35\times10^{-8}$
200	$2\cdot84\times10^{-6}$	2·36	$3\cdot35\times10^{-8}$	3·28	$6\cdot10\times10^{-9}$	3·38	$8\cdot18\times10^{-9}$	$9\cdot60\times10^{-9}$
300	$1\cdot07\times10^{-6}$	2·43	$8\cdot70\times10^{-9}$	3·37	$1\cdot12\times10^{-9}$	3·47	$1\cdot46\times10^{-9}$	$1\cdot73\times10^{-9}$
500	$3\cdot03\times10^{-7}$	2·50	$1\cdot52\times10^{-9}$	3·46	$3\cdot50\times10^{-10}$	3·51	$4\cdot31\times10^{-10}$	$5\cdot30\times10^{-10}$
700	$1\cdot30\times10^{-7}$	2·54	$4\cdot71\times10^{-10}$	3·50	$9\cdot7\times10^{-11}$	3·55	$1\cdot15\times10^{-10}$	$1\cdot42\times10^{-10}$
1000	$5\cdot23\times10^{-8}$	2·56	$1\cdot34\times10^{-10}$	3·54				
2000							$9\cdot38\times10^{-12}$	$9\cdot38\times10^{-12}$
3000							$2\cdot30\times10^{-12}$	$2\cdot30\times10^{-12}$
5000							$3\cdot28\times10^{-13}$	$3\cdot28\times10^{-13}$
7000							$7\cdot43\times10^{-14}$	$7\cdot43\times10^{-14}$

observations made with the Durham spectrograph at sea level, but rather is a spectrum drawn consistent with the spectrograph data to 100 GeV/c and thence consistent with the spectrum of Duthie *et al* (1962) above 1000 GeV/c. Similarly the AW spectrum is derived from the OWP spectrum as a result of considering also the underground intensity measurements of Achar *et al* (1965) and as mentioned above it differs slightly from the OWP spectrum only over a restricted momentum range.

Measurements of the spectrum have been reported by Bull *et al* (1965) in the momentum range 2·34 to 360 GeV/c and these have been extended, initially by Baber *et al* (1968a, b) and subsequently by Appleton *et al* (1971) to cover the range 3–1000 GeV/c. In this study 49 134 muons above 3 GeV/c were recorded of which some 5000 were above 22 GeV/c. The final data of the Nottingham group are included in figure 6, the data having been normalized to the integral intensity at 3 GeV/c of Allkofer *et al* (1971b).

Various measurements of the muon spectrum have been reported over recent years by the Kiel group, this having recently resulted in the production of a precise absolute cosmic ray vertical muon spectrum by Allkofer *et al* (1971a, b). The measurements based upon data obtained from three independent spark chamber spectrographs and one absorbtion spectrograph are presented in table 2. The smallest spectrograph recorded the flux in the region of 0·2 GeV/c, the second in the range 0·2–10 GeV/c and the largest in the range 10–1000 GeV/c. Only data corresponding to a relative acceptance greater than 0·7 and momentum less than the MDM have been included in the final analysis. The absorption spectrograph enabled the absolute intensity to be measured at 1·0 and 1·11 GeV/c. The Kiel spectrum is included in figure 6.

The most recent measurement of the muon spectrum has been made by Nandi and Sinha (1972a) who recorded the traversal of 25 842 single muons through the Durgapur spectrograph. The spectrograph comprised two large solid iron magnets having a total deflecting length of 2 m, and the instrument had an MDM of 985 $\pm$ 25 GeV/c. The experimental results of Nandi and Sinha are shown in figure 6, these data being normalized to the 1 GeV/c point of Allkofer *et al* (1970c).

Figure 6 includes therefore the data from several sources and owing to the recent indicated uncertainty in the absolute muon intensity it is necessary to identify the normalization associated with each set of data. In particular, the spectrum of Allkofer *et al* (1971b) is an absolute spectrum, and the data of Nandi and Sinha are normalized to the integral 1 GeV/c point of Allkofer *et al*. The data of Hayman and Wolfendale, and consequently the OWP and AW spectra given in table 2, are normalized to the 1 GeV/c Rossi intensity. However, in figure 6 the data of Hayman and Wolfendale have been renormalized to the integral intensity at 1 GeV/c of Allkofer *et al*, and the data of Appleton *et al* are normalized to the integral intensity of Allkofer *et al* at 3 GeV/c.

In an attempt to overcome these difficulties, and so that the spectra might be compared more accurately, Nandi and Sinha have renormalized the integral spectra as shown in figure 7. In this figure the best fit spectrum of Nandi and Sinha is compared with the spectra of Aurela and Wolfendale (1967), Baber *et al* (1968a, b) and Appleton *et al* (1971), each spectrum being normalized to the Nandi and Sinha spectrum at 5 GcV/c; and with the spectrum of Allkofer *et al* (1970d) normalized at 20 GeV/c.

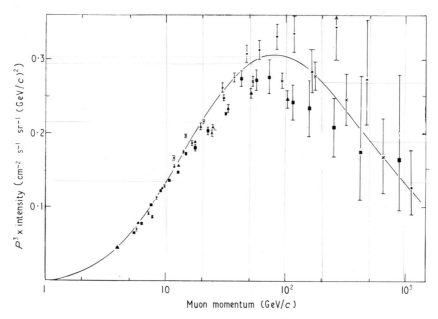

Figure 6. The differential muon spectrum, including the data of Hayman and Wolfendale (1962a) ■, Appleton *et al* (1971) ▲, Allkofer *et al* (1971b) × and Nandi and Sinha (1972a) ● together with the fitted curve of Allkofer *et al* (1971b) (see §4.2.1 for normalization details).

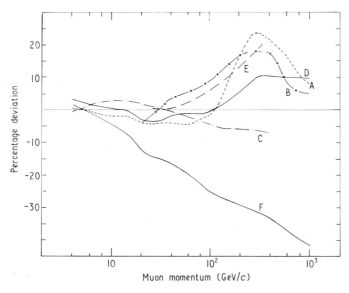

Figure 7. Comparison of the integral intensity of Nandi and Sinha (1972a) with those obtained by other workers. Aurela and Wolfendale (1967)—A, Menon and Ramana Murthy (1967)—B, Baber *et al* (1968a)—C, Allkofer *et al* (1971b)—D, Allkofer *et al* (1970d)—E, Appleton *et al* (1971)—F.

Also included in the figure is the spectrum of Menon and Ramana Murthy (1967), normalized to Nandi and Sinha's results at 20 GeV/c, deduced by these workers from a survey of magnetic spectrograph results and underground intensity measurements. (The Menon and Ramana Murthy spectrum is thus not an independent measurement.)

The figure shows that the spectrum of Baber *et al* (1968a) is in better agreement with the other experiments than are the later data of the Nottingham group (Appleton *et al* 1971). Up to 100 GeV/c the spectra are within the experimental uncertainties of each other; above 100 GeV/c the intensities of Aurela and Wolfendale (1967) and Allkofer *et al* (1970d) are considerably greater than those of Nandi and Sinha, and also greater than the latest results of Allkofer *et al* (1971b). (At least part of the reason for the high intensities of Aurela and Wolfendale is that they arose as a result of the upward normalization at 1 GeV/c whereas above 100 GeV/c the intensities were already near absolute, having been derived from depth intensity data.)

4.2.2. Measurements with other techniques. In addition to the experimental determinations of the vertical spectrum which have been made using magnetic spectrographs several experimentalists have estimated the spectrum by other means. Results obtained using alternative techniques are particularly valuable where magnetic spectrographs become unsatisfactory as is the case at the highest energies where either the rate of muons is extremely low or the MDM limits the accuracy of the data. Consequently attention will only be drawn to experiments which give information on the muon spectrum at the highest energies, that is, in the region of 1 TeV.

Kobayakawa (1968) has used the muon intensities deep underground to estimate the integral muon spectrum in the range 0·4–1 TeV. Taking the experimental data of Bollinger (1951), Barton (1961), Castagnoli *et al* (1965) and Miyake *et al* (1964a, b) and normalizing to the OWP spectrum at 200 GeV/c, Kobayakawa deduces an integral energy spectrum above 400 GeV/c having an exponent of $2·54 \pm 0·19$. Similarly, Chin *et al* (1968) have utilized measurements of the burst spectrum at a depth of 40 mwe from rock, obtained using two large scintillation counters of area 20 m² separated by 2 m, to predict the energy spectrum up to 10 TeV. The spectrum was determined following the method of Christy and Kusaka (1941) in which the expected integral burst size spectrum is given by:

$$n(s) = \bar{\phi} N \int_0^\infty dE \int_0^{\epsilon_m} \frac{d\epsilon}{\epsilon} \int A(\theta, \phi), \, F(E/\epsilon, \theta), \, \sigma(E/\epsilon, \epsilon) \, P(E, s) \, d\Omega$$

where s is a burst size produced by a muon, $\bar{\phi}$ is a unit of cross section $(e^2/\mu c^2)^2 \alpha Z^2$ in which μ is the muon mass, N is Avogadro's number, E is the energy of the secondaries, that is, the burst energy, ϵ is the fractional energy transfer, and $F(E/\epsilon, \theta)$ is the number of muons of energy (E/ϵ) at 40 mwe per unit solid angle per unit energy per cm² per second at an angle θ with the vertical. $A(\theta, \phi)$ is the acceptance function of the apparatus, $\sigma(E/\epsilon, \epsilon)$ is the cross section measured in units of $\bar{\phi}$ for the creation of a secondary of energy E by a primary of energy E/ϵ in the absorber, and $P(E, s)$ is the probability of getting a burst size larger than s from an initial particle of energy E taking account of fluctuation effects. Chin *et al* deduced that their data are consistent with a differential muon spectrum of slope 3·3 to an energy of 6–7 TeV and that above this energy the slope increases slightly.

At the other end of the energy scale Das (1969) has used a multiplate cloud chamber to study the frequency of muons producing knock-on electrons in various absorbers. From this observation he has obtained the muon spectrum by taking into account the variation of the knock-on cross section with muon energy and integrating this cross section over the electron energy intervals of his experiment. The mean spectrum obtained by Das is necessarily not too precise, and in addition is normalized to the HW spectrum. Nevertheless over the range 1–10 GeV/c the spectral shape of Das is consistent with the HW spectrum being possibly slightly steeper at 10 GeV than the latter spectrum.

Of rare application to cosmic radiation studies is the heavy liquid bubble chamber. Kim and Voyvodic (1970) have analysed the tracks of cosmic ray muons in such a device, such tracks occurring as background events to the interactions being studied. The technique necessarily requires that their data be normalized and these workers chose a normalization point of 21 GeV/c. The chamber effectively integrated the muon flux over a zenith angle of $\pm 30°$ and it was necessary in the analysis of the experimental observations to allow for this great angular acceptance. The results of Kim and Voyvodic give a spectrum which is slightly flatter than that measured by conventional spectrographs in the range 50–100 GeV/c. (After normalization of the integral intensity at 21 GeV/c, the integral intensity at 100 GeV/c is 20 % greater than the OWP spectrum.) Considering all the experimental uncertainties and difficulties which are present in the bubble chamber method, such as scanning efficiency and the effect of the magnetic shielding of the chamber, this experiment should not be regarded as conflicting with the spectrograph results.

4.2.3. The best vertical muon spectrum. Figure 6 shows the normalized data from three recent experiments together with those from the older but nevertheless accurate experiment of Hayman and Wolfendale (1962a). The spectrum deduced by Allkofer *et al* (1971a, b) as a fit to their data is also shown in the figure. This spectrum is a satisfactory fit to all the experimental data below 10 GeV/c, but in the range 10–100 GeV/c it is likely that the spectrum is slightly steeper than proposed. From 200 to 1000 GeV/c the uncertainties in the data are large and the data do not disagree with the Allkofer *et al* spectrum. Above 1 TeV/c the measurements reported in §4.2.2. indicate the integral muon spectrum continues with a slope of approximately 2·4 to the highest momenta measured in the region of 7 TeV/c.

4.3. The interpretation of the vertical muon spectrum

4.3.1. Relationship between the pion production spectrum and the muon spectrum. The sea-level muon spectrum is related to the primary spectrum of cosmic radiation via the interactions which occur during the propagation of the particles through the atmosphere. The muons are produced as a result of the decay of pions, kaons and possibly from other sources. The most general starting point for the study of muon phenomena are the diffusion equations governing the pion and muon spectra, and various mathematical techniques have been used by many workers to solve the equations under various assumptions and approximations (for a complete review of the general method of solution see Fowler and Wolfendale (1961)).

A relatively simple treatment has been given by Barrett *et al* (1952) and this has been followed by many workers, for example Bull *et al* (1965), to predict the vertical spectrum. The method requires the assumption of a production spectrum for pions and it is conventional to start with the simple power law form characterized by two constants A_π and γ. The diffusion equation for the pions is then

$$\frac{dN_\pi}{dy} = \frac{A_\pi E_\pi^{-\gamma}}{\lambda_p} \exp\left(-y/\lambda_p\right) - \frac{N_\pi}{\lambda_\pi} - \frac{M_\pi c N_\pi}{\rho(y)\tau_0 E_\pi},$$

where $N_\pi(E_\pi, y)\, dE_\pi\, d\omega$ is the number of pions $cm^{-2} s^{-1}$ having a kinetic energy between E_π and $E_\pi + dE_\pi$, at a vertical depth y $g\,cm^{-2}$ travelling within the solid angle $d\omega$ in the vertical direction. γ is the exponent of the primary spectrum, λ_p and λ_π are the absorption lengths for protons and pions respectively, m_π is the pion mass, $\rho(y)$ is the air density at the depth y, τ_0 is the pion lifetime at rest, and c is the velocity of light. Smith and Duller (1959) have considered the scale height of the atmosphere and following their definition of b as

$$b = \frac{\rho(0)}{y_0} \frac{RT_e}{Mg},$$

the air density can be written $(\rho(y) = \rho(0)\, y/by_0)$ where M is the average molecular weight of air and T_e is the effective mean temperature of the atmosphere.

Hence we can write

$$\frac{dN_\pi}{dy} + N_\pi \left(\frac{1}{\lambda_\pi} + \frac{M_\pi c y_0 b}{\rho(0)\tau_0 E_\pi y}\right) = \frac{A_\pi E_\pi^{-\gamma}}{\lambda_p} \exp\left(\frac{-y}{\lambda_p}\right),$$

which on integration and substitution for $1/\lambda = 1/\lambda_\pi - 1/\lambda_p$ gives

$$N_\pi = \frac{A_\pi E_\pi^{-\gamma}}{\lambda_p} y \exp\left(-y/\lambda_\pi\right) \sum_{n=0}^{\infty} \left(\frac{y}{\lambda}\right)^n \left\{n!\left(1+n+\frac{m_\pi y_0 bc}{\tau_0 \rho(0) E_\pi}\right)\right\}^{-1}.$$

If the survival probability of a muon from a depth y is written as $P_\mu(E_\pi, y)$ where E_π is the energy of the parent pion, the differential muon spectrum at sea level due purely to the decay of pions is

$$D(E_\mu) = \int_0^{y_0} P_\mu(E_\pi, y)\, N_\pi(E_\pi, y)\, \frac{dt}{dy}\, \frac{dy}{\tau}$$

where τ is the dilated mean lifetime of the pion.

The survival probability taken by Bull *et al* (1965) is that given by Rossi (1952):

$$P_\mu(E_\pi, y) = \left(\frac{y}{y_0} \frac{E(y_0)}{E(y)}\right)^\alpha.$$

where $\alpha = by_0 m_\mu c/(\rho(0)\tau_\mu(E(y_0) + \epsilon y))$.

In the equation m_μ is the muon rest mass, τ_μ the muon lifetime, $E(y_0)$ is the energy of the muon at sea-level, $E(y)$ the muon energy at the depth y, and ϵ is the mean rate of energy loss of the muon. The factor b appears in an attempt to improve the approximation involved in assuming an isothermal atmosphere. Taking $r = m_\mu/m_\pi$, it is further assumed that a pion of energy E_π decays to a muon of energy $E_\mu = rE_\pi$.

Whence, a muon at sea level having an energy E_μ will originate from a pion of energy E_π having

$$E_\pi = \frac{1}{r}\{(E_\mu + \epsilon(y_0 - y))\}$$

and therefore the survival probability can be written

$$P_\mu(E_\pi, y) = \left\{\frac{y}{y_0}\left(1 - \frac{\epsilon(y_0 - y)}{rE_\pi}\right)\right\}^{by_0 m_\mu c/\{\rho(0)\tau_0(rE_\mu + \epsilon)y\}}.$$

Thus

$$D(E_\mu) = A_\pi P_\mu \int_0^\infty \frac{E_\pi^{-\gamma}y}{\lambda_p} \exp(-y/\lambda_\pi) \sum_{n=0}^\infty \left(\frac{y}{\lambda}\right)^n \left\{n!\left(n+1+\frac{bm_\pi cy_0}{\rho(0)E_\pi\tau_0}\right)\right\}^{-1} \frac{dt}{dy}\frac{dy}{\tau}$$

where negligible error is introduced in performing the integration to infinity as opposed to y_0.

Since $\qquad dt = \dfrac{dy}{\rho(y)c}$

and $\qquad \tau = \dfrac{E_\pi}{m_\pi c^2}\tau_0$

then

$$D(E_\mu) = \frac{A_\pi P_\mu E_\pi^{-(\gamma+1)}}{\lambda_p} bj_\pi \int_0^\infty \exp(-y/\lambda) \sum_{n=0}^\infty \left(\frac{y}{\lambda}\right)^n \left\{n!\left(n+1+\frac{bj_\pi}{E_\pi}\right)\right\}^{-1} dy$$

where $\qquad j_\pi \equiv \dfrac{(m_\pi cy_0)}{(\tau_0\rho(0))}$

and finally

$$D(E_\mu) = \frac{A_\pi P_\mu E_\pi^{-(\gamma+1)} bj_\pi}{\lambda_p} \lambda_\pi \sum_{n=0}^\infty \left(\frac{\lambda_p - \lambda_\pi}{\lambda_p}\right)^n \left(\frac{1}{n+1+bj_\pi/E_\pi}\right).$$

Following Bull *et al* (1965), we take $\lambda_p = \lambda_\pi = 120 \text{ g cm}^{-2}$ and $y = 100 \text{ g cm}^{-2}$, in which case

$$D(E_\mu) = A_\pi P_\mu E_\pi^{-(\gamma+1)} \frac{bj_\pi}{1 + bj_\pi/E_\pi}.$$

4.3.2. Analysis of experimental data to determine γ and A_π. This simple expression has been used extensively in analyses of the muon spectrum.

In practice when examining experimental data it is more convenient to work with the deflection spectrum as opposed to the momentum spectrum and it is further convenient to allow for instrumental effects by modification of the deflection spectrum.

As has already been remarked, allowance has to be made for:

(i) magnetic deflection and Coulomb scattering in and out of the acceptance solid angle of the instrument.

(ii) multiple scattering in the instrument, which affects the estimates of the angular deflection of the particles.

(iii) errors of location of the trajectory of the particle.

In comparing the experimental observations with theory the usual method is to utilize a χ^2 technique or similar method to fit the expected deflection spectrum to the data, thus determining the parameters γ and A_π of the pion production spectrum.

Returning to the derivation of the trial spectrum, the precise technicalities of the theoretical considerations differ from one group to another, but the principles of the calculations are very similar. All calculations involve a pion production spectrum, the estimation of the muon survival probabilities and considerations of both the atmosphere and the mean free paths for proton and pion interactions.

The results of comparisons made by various groups between their observations and the theoretical spectrum are given in table 3 where values of γ and A_π are tabulated for the best fit spectra to the experimental observations. The value of γ the slope of the primary spectrum in the energy range being studied is shown to be sensibly constant at 2·6.

Table 3. The constants of the pion production spectrum, $A_\pi E^{-\gamma}$ obtained by various workers as a best fit to their measured muon spectra

	P (GeV/c)	γ	A_π (cm^{-2} s^{-1} sr^{-1} GeV^{-1})
Pine *et al* (1959)	2–175	2·64	0·156
Allen and Apostolakis (1961)†	6–1000	2·55	0·15
Gardener and Wolfendale (1962)	5–10	2·65	—
	25–35	2·05	
	1·0–1·5	1·95	
Hayman and Wolfendale (1962a)	70–700	2·67 ± 0·10	
	10–333	2·64 ± 0·05	
Ashton and Wolfendale (1963)†		2·64	0·20
Bull *et al* (1965)	3–360	2·67	0·22
Baber *et al* (1968a)	3–1000	2·65	0·24
Appleton *et al* (1971)	3–1000	2·73 ± 0·02	0·24
Allkofer *et al* (1971b)	0·2–1000	2·63	0·199
Nandi and Sinha (1972a)	5–1200	2·61	0·25

† Measurements at large zenith angles.

The best estimate of γ and A_π has been obtained from the data of table 3 by considering only the three most recent experiments. After normalization of the data of Appleton *et al* (1971) to the 1 GeV/c intensity of Allkofer *et al* (1970c), $\gamma = 2·67 \pm 0·02$ and $A_\pi = 0·25 \pm 0·035$.

4.4. The muon momentum spectrum at large zenith angles

The interest in the muon spectrum at large zenith angles was initiated by Jakeman (1956), Smith and Duller (1959) and others. These workers pointed out that although the integral muon intensity is very much reduced by the increased depth of the Earth's atmosphere, an increase in the intensity of high energy particles above about 100 GeV is to be expected. Hence the median energy of muons at sea level increases with increasing zenith angle and so far as flux is concerned an investigation of high energy particles is more profitably carried out at large zenith angles.

Jakeman (1956), Wilson (1959) and Sheldon and Duller (1962) have measured the overall intensity of near horizontal muons. The initial determinations of the muon momentum spectrum were made by Moroney and Parry (1954), Pak *et al* (1961) and Allen and Apostolakis (1961). The results of these latter workers were obtained using an emulsion spectrograph, containing 8 layers of emulsion separated by 2·54 cm, by which the muon trajectory could be traced. The spectra based upon 1047 particles with momenta greater than 1 GeV/*c* in the zenith angular range 65·3°–85·0° were compared with calculated spectra based upon a differential pion production spectrum of the form $A_\pi E^{-\gamma}$, and the best fit to the data gave $A_\pi = 0\cdot425 - 0\cdot125 \lg E \, \mathrm{cm}^{-2}$ $\mathrm{s}^{-1} \mathrm{sr} \, (\mathrm{GeV})^{-1}$ with E in GeV and $\gamma = 3\cdot92 - 0\cdot94 \, (1 - 0\cdot125 \lg E)^{-1}$ ($A_\pi \simeq 0\cdot15$ and $\gamma \simeq 2\cdot55$).

Following the work of Allen and Apostolakis, Ashton and Wolfendale (1963) using a solid iron spectrograph incorporating Geiger counters studied the zenith range 78° 28′–80° 48′. These workers considered the possibility that at high energies the muons do not all come from pion decay, but may also come from kaon decay. The method of the calculation is worthy of mention in that it illustrates the inter-relation of vertical and near horizontal spectra. From the measured vertical muon spectrum Ashton and Wolfendale (1963) derived the parent pion production spectrum, which in turn was used to predict the muon production spectrum at large zenith angles and hence finally the muon spectrum at sea level in inclined directions. These workers assumed that the absorption length of the primary protons and of the secondaries of the interaction in the atmosphere were the same, being 120 g cm^{-2}, and further they neglected the spread in energy of the muons from the decay of pions of a unique energy. In particular, they assumed, following Barrett *et al* (1952), that the muon production spectrum $M_x(E)$ and the production spectrum of the muon's parents $F_x(E/r_x)$ are related by

$$M_x(E) = \frac{F_x(E/r_x)}{r_x} \frac{1}{1 + E/B_x}$$

where $B_x = M_x c^2 r_x H / c T_x$, T_x is the mean lifetime of the parent particle of mass M_x, H is the weighted scale height of the atmosphere and E/r_x is the effective energy of the parent particles which give rise to muons of energy E. For pions, r_π was taken as 0·76 and B_π as 90 GeV, whilst for kaons $r_k = 0\cdot59$ and $B_k = 517$ GeV.

En route to the muon spectrum Ashton and Wolfendale deduced alternative parent spectra having the following forms; for pions with $10 < E < 1000$ GeV, $F_\pi(E) \propto E^{-2\cdot7}$ and for kaons $20 < E < 500$ GeV, $F_k(E) \propto E^{-2\cdot95}$. The muon production spectrum was derived making allowance for the variation of B_x with zenith angle. The ratio of the muon production spectrum for the case of all muons coming from kaons via the $K_{\mu2}$ mode, to the spectrum for the case of all pion parents is

$$\frac{M_k(E,\theta)}{M_\pi(E,\theta)} = \frac{F_k(E/r_k)\ r_\pi(1+E/B_\pi(\theta))}{F_\pi(E/r)\ r_k(1+E/B_k(\theta))}$$

and this ratio is shown in figure 8. Because the subsequent history of the muons does not depend upon the character of the muons' parents this is also the ratio of the sea-level muon intensities expected for the two extreme cases.

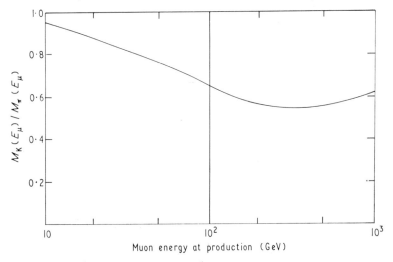

Figure 8. The ratio of the production spectra of muons at a zenith angle of 80° for the cases of all kaon parents and all pion parents—Ashton and Wolfendale (1963).

Ashton and Wolfendale used the data of Allen and Apostolakis (1961) for energy loss and μ–e decay and worked from their muon production spectrum at 80° to the sea-level muon spectrum. Corrections were made to the spectrum to allow for scattering in the atmosphere and geomagnetic effects. Their experimental data are compared with their theoretical spectra in figure 9, and it is seen that the data are consistent with the suggestions that pions are the main parents of the observed muons.

This preliminary work of the Durham group was extended by Ashton *et al* (1966). The momentum range 3–500 GeV/c was studied with an improved spectrograph incorporating neon flash-tubes. In the experiment 10 000 particles above 3·7 GeV/c and a zenith angle of 77·5° were recorded. In deriving the theoretical muon spectrum Ashton *et al* (1966) followed the method of Ashton and Wolfendale (1963) but introduced fewer approximations than the former method and allowed for all possible decay modes of the kaons. The vertical muon spectrum used as the starting point was the OWP spectrum (see §4.2.1.), the muon energy loss in the atmosphere was treated according to Hayman *et al* (1963), an accurate allowance was made for the spread in energy of the muons from the decay of parent particles and finally, a Monte

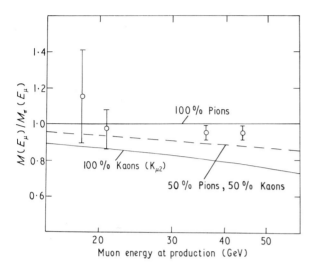

Figure 9. The ratio of the measured muon intensities of Ashton and Wolfendale (1963), translated to energies at production, to the intensities expected for the case of all pions as parents. Also shown are the ratios of the expected intensities for all kaons and 50% kaons as parents to the intensity expected for an all pion parentage.

Carlo technique was adopted for treatment of the scattering problem. Figure 10 shows the experimental data compared with the predicted spectrum assuming the muons parents to be all pions. In an attempt to set an upper limit to the K/π ratio the data of figure 10 are combined in figure 11 and given as the ratio observed/expected rate for various assumptions of muon parentage. Ashton *et al* conclude that the data set an upper limit to the K/π ratio of 0·4.

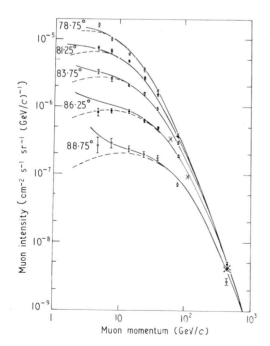

Figure 10. The measured spectra of Ashton *et al* (1966) compared with the expected spectra for an all pion parentage of the muons. Mean values of θ are indicated to the left of the curves.

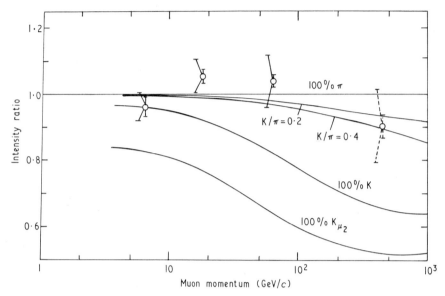

Figure 11. Comparison of the measured intensities of Ashton *et al* (1966) with expectation for various muon parentages.

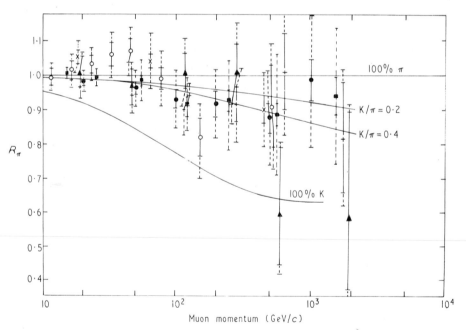

Figure 12. The ratio R_π of the observed intensity to that predicted for various muon parentages, according to various workers. The extended error flags allow for the uncertainty in the vertical muon spectrum. Flint and Nash (1971) ●, Palmer and Nash (1969) ○, Ashton *et al* (1966) ×, Said (1966) +, MacKeown *et al* (1966a) ▲. Mean values ■.

A similar upper limit was set by Judge and Nash (1965b) at about the same time. The theoretical treatment of Judge and Nash followed that of Ashton and Wolfendale (1963) incorporating the energy dependent form of the energy loss similar to that of Barrett *et al* (1952) namely,

$$-\frac{dE}{dx} = 1\cdot88 + 0\cdot174 \ln \frac{E_\mu}{M_\mu c^2} + 2\cdot34 \times 10^{-7} \, E_\mu \ln (E_\mu/100) \; \text{MeV g}^{-1} \text{cm}^2$$

where the muon energy E_μ and the rest mass $M_\mu c^2$ are in MeV. As a starting vertical muon spectrum Judge and Nash used the Nottingham spectrum at 30° reported by Judge and Nash (1965a). Their experimental results show that up to a production momentum of 50 GeV/c the data are close to those expected from a pure pion parentage and it is estimated by Judge and Nash that in the range 40–90 GeV/c and for zenith angles between 83° and 90° the K/π ratio is at the most 0·3.

This result has been subsequently supported by the more recent results of Palmer and Nash (1969) using a solid iron spectrograph incorporating small diameter neon flash-tubes, the MDM of the instrument being 420 ± 14 GeV/c. These observations, together with the latest of the Nottingham group (Flint and Nash 1971) are shown in figure 12.

As was the case with the results of Palmer and Nash, the data of Flint and Nash, based on 25 523 events, are normalized to the intensity of Ashton *et al* (1966) at

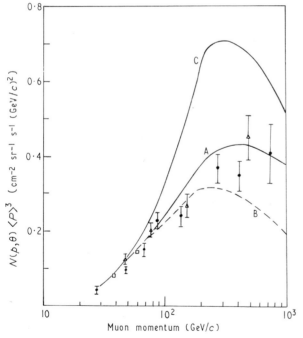

Figure 13. Differential mean intensity at 80° to the zenith according to Asbury *et al* (1970). Theoretical curves: Pure pion parentage—A, Pion parentage plus 20% kaon and 10% of a direct production process—B, Pion parentage and a breakdown of special relativity at distances less than 5×10^{-16} cm—C. Ashton *et al* (1966) □, Palmer and Nash (1969) △, Asbury *et al* (1970) ●.

D

10 GeV/c. For comparison purposes figure 12 includes also the observations of MacKeown *et al* (1966a), Said (1966), Ashton *et al* (1966) and Palmer and Nash (1969). It can be concluded from the mean values of R_π shown in figure 12 that the K/π ratio is reasonably constant over all production energies at approximately 0.3 ± 0.15. It must be remembered that the interpretation relies upon a knowledge of the vertical muon spectrum and in so far as this is uncertain so also is the above conclusion. The errors in the vertical spectrum are certainly such as to not rule out the possibility that the muons have a 100% pion parentage.

The Nagoya group (Kamiya *et al* 1970) have operated a near horizontal solid iron spectrograph incorporating neon flash-tubes having an MDM of 1930 ± 30 GeV/c, making eventual measurements upon 28 149 muon tracks. Kamiya *et al* state that their measured spectrum is fully consistent with the predictions of the pion parentage model of Ashton *et al* (1966).

Measurements have been made of the cosmic ray muon spectra at large zenith angles using a spectrograph incorporating optical spark chambers by Asbury *et al* (1970), the MDM of the system being 830 GeV/c. Absolute values of the energy spectra up to 200 GeV/c were obtained at zenith angles of 75°, 80° and 85°. Some 20 139 events being analysed in the course of the experiment. The differential intensity spectrum at 80° obtained by Asbury *et al* (1970) is shown in figure 13, again compared with theory based upon a pure pion parentage and other *ad hoc* mixtures of parent particles. Clearly the data are not inconsistent with a pure pion parentage for the muons.

4.5. Conclusions on the vertical and horizontal spectrum measurements

The experimental data on the vertical and horizontal spectra have not yet reached sufficient accuracy to enable a precise determination of the K/π ratio to be made, although they do indicate that the present ideas on cosmic ray propagation in the atmosphere are basically correct. At the present time the near horizontal muon spectrum is known to a greater degree of accuracy than is the vertical spectrum and it is evident that more attention should now be paid to vertical measurements.

In so far as the experimental uncertainties allow, a comparison of the spectra in the two directions can be made, with the result that K/$\pi \simeq 0.3 \pm 0.15$ appears to fit most of the data. This value relates to muons in the range 100–1000 GeV, that is, primary proton energies of 1000–10 000 GeV. Comparison can be made with the value of about 0.15 found at ISR energies ($E_p \simeq 1500$ GeV) and it can be concluded that there is no evidence for a rapid increase in the K/π ratio with increasing interaction energy.

It is considered that when data are available from the new spectrographs being brought into service (table 1) some useful conclusions should be possible.

5. The muon intensity at intermediate angles

5.1. The muon spectrum as a function of zenith angle

There is, of course, no difference in the physical processes occurring at the various angles but a tendency has developed whereby very large angle data for high energy muons have been used to study the K/π ratio and data at intermediate angles have been used, largely at low energies, to examine the effect of the Earth's magnetic field.

The Earth's field gives rise to an east–west asymmetry, due principally to the fact that the primary cosmic rays are mostly positively charged, and an east–west effect of the charge ratio as reported by Moroney and Parry (1954). The variation of atmospheric thickness with zenith angle leads to modifications to the muon spectrum in both the low and high energy regions. The preceding sections of the chapter have primarily been concerned with the high energy end of the spectrum, and it has been seen that due to the air density being less at large zenith angles than in the near vertical direction for the regions where most interactions occur, the pions produced by primaries incident at large angles have a greater chance to decay than to undergo nuclear collisions and this gives rise to an enhancement in the intensity at higher energies. At the low energy end of the muon spectrum a considerable reduction in intensity with increasing zenith angle occurs due to the greater absorber thickness and to the greater decay probabilities of the muons themselves.

Allen and Apostolakis (1961) used their emulsion spectrograph to estimate the integral intensity of muons above 1 GeV/c over the range of zenith angle 65°–85° as shown in figure 14. Subsequently Coates and Nash (1962) measured the muon spectrum at angles to the zenith of 30° and 45°; the best fit differential spectrum of the Nottingham workers is given in figure 15. In this figure is shown also the spectrum of Moroney and Parry (1954). It is seen that the spectra of the two groups for a zenith angle of 30° differ in form. The spectrum of Moroney and Parry was obtained using the spectrograph of Caro *et al* (1951) the results of which, in the near vertical direction, are not consistent with those of other workers. It is therefore likely that the spectrum of Moroney and Parry includes the same instrumental uncertainty as that of Caro *et al* (1951), possibly due to errors in the corrections applied for magnetic cut-off and the scattering out of the muons from the instrument.

Observations at 45° to the zenith have also been reported by Allkofer and Andresen

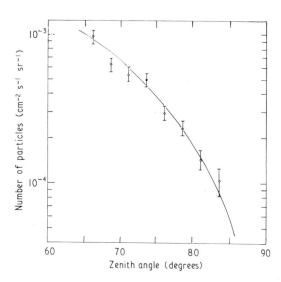

Figure 14. The variation with zenith angle of the integral rate of cosmic rays at sea level above 1 GeV/c according to Allen and Apostolakis (1961).

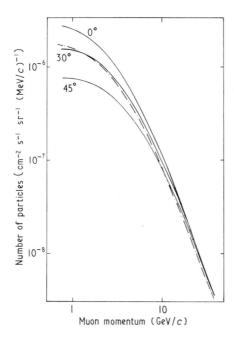

Figure 15. The best fit spectra of Coates and Nash (1962) at 0°, 30° and 45° to the zenith compared with the spectrum of Moroney and Parry (1954)—broken curve, at 30°.

(1967). There is some disagreement between the results of Coates and Nash (1962) and those of Allkofer and Andresen, the disagreement taking the form of an enhancement in the intensity below 2 GeV/c as reported by Allkofer and Andresen for observations from the west. The spectra of Allkofer and Andresen from the east are in satisfactory agreement with the data of Judge and Nash (1965b).

The range of zenith angles 10° to 75° has not been the subject of much work, most workers confining their attention to either the near vertical direction or the near horizontal direction. It has, however, been established by many workers that the intensity of the hard component integrated over all energies can be written in the form $I(\theta) = I_0 \cos^n \theta$, where I_0 is the vertical intensity and n is a constant, approximately 2, over the range of zenith angle 0°–75°. At zenith angles larger than 75° the air density at high altitudes varies rapidly with zenith angle and, as mentioned earlier, this affects the relative probabilities for pion decay and interaction to such an extent that the above simple $\cos^2 \theta$ relation could not be expected to continue.

5.2. The variation of the muon spectrum with geomagnetic latitude

Owing to the magnetic field of the Earth, there is a cut-off rigidity appropriate to each point and direction on the Earth's surface. For particles incident vertically the cut-off rigidity at the geomagnetic latitude, λ, is given by

$$R_0(\lambda) = 14 \cdot 9 \cos^4 \lambda \, (1 + 0 \cdot 018 \sin \lambda)^2 \text{ GV}$$

(Jory 1956) and from this it can be seen that variations of the muon spectrum with λ would be expected for momenta up to several GeV/c.

The differential muon spectra and integral muon intensity have been measured at various latitudes by several groups. Table 4 indicates the integral intensities and figure 16 the differential spectra. The observations of Bhattacharyya (1970) agree with the

Table 4. The measured integral muon intensity in the near vertical direction obtained by various workers at 320 MeV/c

	Geomagnetic latitude (°N)	Vertical cut-off rigidity (GV)	Integral intensity (cm^{-2}s^{-1}sr^{-1}) > 320 MeV/c
Allkofer *et al* (1968)	9	14·1	7·25 ± 0·10
Bhattacharyya (1970)	12	13·7	7·30 ± 0·15
Gokhale (1953)†	19	—	7·30 ± 0·1
Fukui *et al* (1955)	24	12·6	7·35 ± 0·20
Kitamura *et al* (1953)	25	12·5	7·2 ± 0·1
Hayman *et al* (1962a)	57·5	1·8	7·60 ± 0·06
Allkofer (1965)†	55	2·2	8·5 ± 0·2
Allkofer (1965)†	55	2·2	8·4 ± 0·1
Kraushaar (1949)	53	1·6	8·4 ± 0·05
Rossi (1948)	75	1·8	8·3

† See Allkofer *et al* (1968).

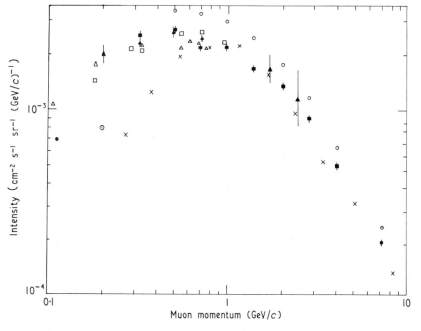

Figure 16. The differential momentum spectrum of muons at sea level at various latitudes. Del Rosario and Davila-Aponte (1952) 29° N, △; Fukui *et al* (1955) 24° N, ×; Fukui *et al* (1957) 24° N, □; Kaneko *et al* (1955) 24° N, ●; Hayman and Wolfendale (1962a) 57·5° N, ○; Subramanian *et al* (1958) 11° N, ⊙; Allkofer *et al* (1968) 9° N, ■; Bhattacharyya (1970) 12° N, ▲. (The intensities of Hayman and Wolfendale (1962a) have been multiplied by 1·26 with respect to the values of table 2 to be consistent with the intensity measurements discussed in §3.)

spectra of Allkofer *et al* (1968) obtained at a similar latitude, and agree also with the calculations of Olbert (1954) for momenta above 1·8 GeV/*c*, but below this momentum the observed spectrum is slightly in excess of the theoretical prediction. The treatment of Olbert has been discussed in the review article of Fowler and Wolfendale (1961). The differential momentum spectra obtained by various workers shown in figure 16 demonstrate the latitude dependence of the low energy end of the muon spectrum.

In conclusion, there is agreement between theory and the experimental data down to momenta in the region of 1·8 GeV/*c*, but below this momentum the observed intensities are slightly underestimated by the theory.

6. The muon charge ratio

The presence of an excess of positive particles in the penetrating component of the cosmic radiation at sea level has been known for some time. The early work of Blackett (1937), Jones (1939) and Hughes (1940) gave for the ratio of the number of positive penetrating particles to negative penetrating particles, hereafter called the charge ratio R, the value $1·225 \pm 0·049$ in the particle momentum range 0·4–20 GeV/*c*. This was supported by Nereson (1948), Conversi (1949), Bassi *et al* (1949) and Brode (1949) who found values typically of 1·25 for particles having momenta in the region of 1 GeV/*c*. Caro *et al* (1951) determined the charge ratio as a function of particle momentum up to 40 GeV/*c* and since this work there have been many measurements of the ratio, the majority of which have been made using magnetic spectrographs· Summaries of the results of various experiments are given in figure 17(*a*, *b* and *c*). Figures 17(*a*) and (*b*) refer to the vertical and horizontal flux of muons at sea level respectively, and figure 17(*c*) refers to the muon momentum at production. The majority of experiments at large zenith angles estimate the muon production momenta but in the case of near vertical studies in order that the data may be included in figure 17(*c*) the values of sea-level momenta given by the various authors have been increased by 2 GeV/*c*. The error incurred in this approximation is negligible.

The results of the underground experiments of Filosofo *et al* (1954) and G K Ashley *et al* (1972 private communication), are also included in the figures. The work of Ashley *et al* is very important as it extends to the highest energies yet investigated. The technique of these workers is to utilize the rock over their equipment, which is situated at a depth of 1850 feet, together with a theoretical range–energy relationship to estimate the ground-level energy of the particles arriving at their apparatus. The apparatus includes a region of magnetic field which is used to define the sign of the particle.

In the determination of the charge ratio systematic errors in the momentum determination may occur, but as it now seems likely that the ratio varies only slowly with momentum this is relatively unimportant when the momentum is well below the MDM. However, the ratio is susceptible to error in the region of the MDM of the instrument, where there is a possibility of assigning the incorrect sign to the charge of the particle and the measured ratio would be expected to approach unity in this momentum region.

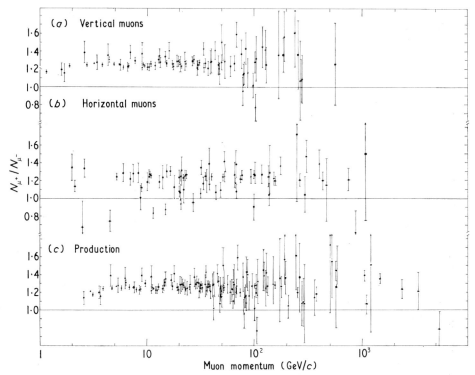

Figure 17. The muon charge ratio as a function of momentum. (*a*) The measured ratio in the near vertical direction. (*b*) The measured ratio in the near horizontal direction. (*c*) The ratio at production as a function of muon production momentum. The data shown come from measurements by: Owen and Wilson (1955), Filosofo *et al* (1954), Moroney and Parry (1954), Pine *et al* (1959), Holmes *et al* (1961), Hayman and Wolfendale (1962a), Ashton and Wolfendale (1963), MacKeown *et al* (1966a), Aurela *et al* (1966), Kawaguchi *et al* (1966), Kasha *et al* (1968), Allkofer *et al* (1970d), Alexander (1970), Allkofer *et al* (1971c), Appleton *et al* (1971), Ayre *et al* (1971b), Flint and Nash (1971), Kamiya *et al* (1971), G K Ashley *et al* (1972 private communication), Nandi and Sinha (1972b).

In view of the rather wide spread in values of the data of figure 17 they have been combined to give figure 18(*a, b* and *c*).

It is useful to examine the degree of consistency of the various measurements, and this has been done by determining the distribution of values of *t* where

$$t = (R_i - \bar{R})/\sigma_{(R_i)},$$

$\bar{R}$ being the overall mean ratio and $\sigma_{(R_i)}$ the standard deviation of an individual ratio R_i. The resulting distributions of *t* are compared with gaussian distributions in figure 19(*a, c*).

An alternative representation of the ratio *R*, is by way of the charge excess $(N_{(\mu+)} - N_{(\mu-)})/(N_{(\mu+)} + N_{(\mu-)}) = \delta(E_\mu)$ say. This latter quantity is preferred when considering the significance of any structure in the ratio, because of the fact that the uncertainty of the ratio is a function of the ratio itself and therefore the points of

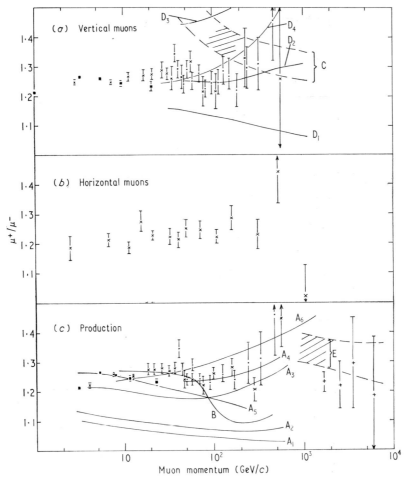

Figure 18. The mean charge ratio as a function of momentum. (*a*) The ratio in the near vertical direction. (*b*) The ratio in the near horizontal direction. (*c*) The ratio at production as a function of muon production momentum.

Experimental data: Filosofo *et al* (1954) ■; C A Ayre *et al* (1972 private communication) ●; G K Ashley *et al* (1972 private communication) +; remaining data of figure 17 ×.

Theoretical curves (MacKeown and Wolfendale 1966):

A_1 Pionization, no fluctuations.

A_2 Pionization plus fluctuations.

A_3 Pionization plus $K/\pi=0.2$, $K^+/K^-=4$.

A_4 Pionization plus $K/\pi=0.5$, $K^+/K^-=4$.

A_5 Pionization plus isobar production having an energy dependent cross section of $\sigma=9.65(\ln E_0)^{-1}$ mb(E_0 in GeV).

A_6 Pionization plus isobar production of 3 mb.

Cohen *et al* (1965)—B, Appleton and Rastin (1971)—C.

Frohlich *et al* (1970)—D_1 $K/\pi=0.3$, $K^+/K^-=1$, $k=0.2$ ⎫

D_2 $K/\pi=0.3$, $K^+/K^-=2$, $k=0.2$ ⎪ (*k* is the inelasticity of the

D_3 $K/\pi=0.3$, $K^+/K^-=4$, $k=0.2$ ⎬   interaction).

D_4 $K/\pi=0.3$, $K^+/K^-=4$, $k=0.35$ ⎭

Frohlich and Leeman (1971)—E.

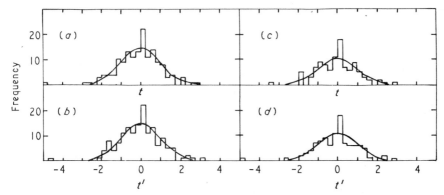

Figure 19. The frequency distributions of the quantities. (a) $(R-\bar{R})/\sigma(R)$ and (b) $(\delta E_\mu - \delta\bar{E}_\mu)/\sigma(\delta E)$ for the data of figure 17(c) and (c) $(R-\bar{R})/\sigma(R)$ and (d) $(\delta E_\mu - \delta\bar{E}_\mu)/\sigma(\delta E_\mu)$ for the data of figure 17(a).

value less than unity appear to be more significant than they really are. On the other hand, the uncertainty in the charge excess is symmetric in $N_{(\mu^+)}$ and $N_{(\mu^-)}$ and ratios above and below unity are then equally significant. Figure 19(b, d) shows the fluctuation of the quantity $(\delta E_\mu - \delta\bar{E}_\mu)/\sigma(\delta E)=t'$, $\sigma(\delta E)$ being the standard deviation of the excess, δE_μ. The closeness of the histograms to the gaussian distributions signifies that there is not much energy dependence of the ratio and that the majority of the experiments were good.

Having said this it should be remarked, however, that there are hazards in combining data because in general different experiments tend to give accurate data in

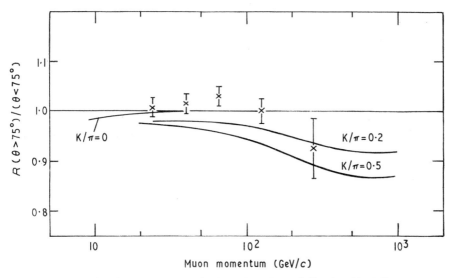

Figure 20. The ratio of the charge ratio in the near horizontal direction ($\theta > 75°$) to that at smaller zenith angles ($\theta < 75°$) as a function of muon momentum at production. Theoretical curves correspond to $R_\mu(80°)/R_\mu(0°)$.

certain relatively narrow ranges of momentum and a systematic error in the data from one experiment could give rise to an apparent variation of the charge ratio with momentum. The data of figure 17 have been combined so that there are effectively four sets of data in figure 18(*a*)—and thus in figure 18(*c*). In particular the data of Filosofo *et al* (1954) have been left as one data set of high precision in the low momentum region, and the latest data of Ashley *et al* have similarly been left alone in the highest momentum range. In the middle momentum range there are effectively two sets of data of equal statistical merit: the latest data from the Durham group (C A Ayre *et al* 1972 private communication), and the combined data from all previous experiments. Consideration of the Durham data alone is not open to the criticism mentioned above and it is seen from these data that the ratio is reasonably constant over the momentum range studied although there is perhaps some slight evidence for a broad minimum in the region of 100 GeV/*c*. Finally, figure 20 shows the charge ratio in the near horizontal direction divided by that in the near vertical direction and this is considered in the next section.

The mean charge ratio of the vertical component above 4 GeV/*c* from the data of figure 17(*a*) (neglecting the experiment of Filosofo *et al* which is sufficiently accurate to be considered separately) is $1 \cdot 2639 \pm 0 \cdot 0061$. Similarly for the near horizontal component the mean ratio is $1 \cdot 2250 \pm 0 \cdot 0081$. Related to momenta at production— the data of figure 17(*c*)—the mean ratio is $1 \cdot 2609 \pm 0 \cdot 0048$.

7. Interpretation of the charge ratio

7.1. General method of approach

The interpretation of the charge ratio involves a knowledge of the properties of the primary radiation and the use of a variety of interaction models together with the standard propagation treatment to yield predicted ratios as a function of muon energy which can then be compared with the experimental data. The early interpretations of the ratio, by Caldirola and Loinger (1950) and Cini and Wataghin (1950), have been discussed by Fowler and Wolfendale (1961). Somewhat later, MacKeown and Wolfendale (1966) reconsidered the theoretical position as improved information on nuclear interactions became available.

Knowledge concerning the particle interactions is not extensive and the solution of the general problem is tedious and as an alternative MacKeown and Wolfendale (1966) have given an approximate but nevertheless satisfactory treatment which brings out the main features of charge ratio calculations. In what follows, a brief account of their treatment will be given.

7.2. The method of MacKeown and Wolfendale (1966)

7.2.1. *The elementary model.* It is assumed that the charge excess $\delta(E_\mu)$ can be represented as $\delta(E_\mu) = \delta_0 D(E_\mu) \delta_i(E_\mu)$ where δ_0 is the charge excess in the primary nucleon beam, $D(E_\mu)$ is a dilution factor relating to the contribution to the flux of muons of energy E_μ from first generation collisions relative to the total flux at this energy, and $\delta_i(E_\mu)$ is the charge excess among muons of energy E_μ produced by a pure proton beam. δ_0 is taken as 0·74 (87% protons and 13% neutrons) in this work and in fact most of the studies to date have taken δ_0 close to this value. The factor $D(E_\mu)$ is a function of energy and zenith angle and varies from about 0·8 at 1000 GeV/c for the near vertical beam to 0·5 at the lowest energies (below 10 GeV), where μ–e decay becomes very important.

In the case of pure pion production the charge excess for a pure proton beam can be written as

$$\delta_i(E_\mu) = \frac{\frac{3}{2}\sum_{n=1}^{\infty} \int_{E_\mu/rE_0}^{1} \int_{E_\mu/r}^{\infty} N(E_0)\, \sigma_n(E_0, k)\, N_\pi\left(\frac{E_\mu}{r}\right) \Delta\left(\frac{E_\mu}{r}, n\right) dE_0\, dk}{\sum_{n=1}^{\infty} \int_{E_\mu/rE_0}^{1} \int_{E_\mu/r}^{\infty} N(E_0)\, \sigma_n(E_0, k)\, N_\pi\left(\frac{E_\mu}{r}\right) dE_0\, dk}$$

where n denotes the total pion multiplicity, k the inelasticity, E_0 the primary energy, $\sigma_n(E_0, k)\, dk$ the cross section for the production of a multiplicity n by a nucleon of energy E_0 with an inelasticity in the range k to $k+dk$, $N(E_\pi)\, dE_\pi$ the energy spectrum of the pions produced in the interactions, $r = m_\mu/m_\pi$ and $\Delta(E, n)$ denotes the charge excess per pion.

Assuming that the charge excess is uniformly distributed over the produced pions and considering a unique elasticity, and a multiplicity variation with primary energy of $\langle n \rangle = 2·7\, E^{1/4}$ (all charges), the curve A_1 of figure 18(c) is obtained. At the highest energies the charge ratio is predicted to vary as $E^{-1/3}$. The poor agreement between the experimental observations and the theory requires alternative models of particle production to be considered.

7.2.2. Improved pionization model. The pionization model cannot be ruled out immediately because of approximations made in the previous treatment. In particular the fluctuation, from one interaction to another, of the pion multiplicity and the primary particle inelasticity needs to be included. Unfortunately little is known of the precise magnitude of the fluctuations and their dependence upon primary energy are not known but some experimental observations (Dodd *et al* 1961, Kim 1964, Fowler and Perkins 1964) are available and these suggest that the multiplicity fluctuations can be represented very approximately by the Polya distribution. This distribution has the form:

$$\sigma_n = \frac{\langle n \rangle^n}{n!}\, (1 + \xi\langle n \rangle)^{-\alpha} \prod_{j=1}^{n-1} (1 + j\xi)$$

where $\alpha = (n+1)/\xi$ and $\xi \equiv \xi(E_0)$ with $\xi(E_0) = 0·4\{1 - \exp(1·8 \times 10^{-4}\, E_0)\}$, E_0 in GeV, and $n\langle \pm \rangle = 1·8\, E_0^{1/4}$.

Concerning fluctuations in elasticity, Brooke *et al* (1964) have given the distribution

$$f(k)\, dk = -(1 + \beta)^2 (1 - k)^\beta \ln(1 - k)\, dk$$

with $\langle k \rangle = 0·31$.

MacKeown and Wolfendale chose a pion spectrum which, when combined with the inelasticity and multiplicity distributions, was consistent with the empirical relation of Cocconi *et al* (1961).

$$N(E_\pi)\, dE_\pi = \frac{n(n-1)(n-2)}{B(kE_0)^{n-1}}\, E_\pi(kE_0 - E_\pi)^{n-3}\, dE_\pi \text{ (valid for } n \geqslant 3).$$

The results of calculations with the above assumptions are given by curve A_2 of figure 18(c). It can be seen that although there is some improvement in shape the discrepancy between theory and experiment is still large.

The next improvement that can be made is to include the effects of kaons.

7.2.3. Inclusion of kaon production. For a given pion or kaon energy, the pions have the longer lifetime. As a result, at high energies the pions produced in an interaction are removed preferentially in subsequent interactions. Consequently the effect of kaons on the charge ratio will be appreciable if their charge excess at production is large.

Calculations have been made assuming that the energy spectra of kaons and pions at production have the same shape, that the ratio K^+/K^- is independent of primary and kaon energy and of the nature of the incident nucleon and that the K^+ and K^- nuclear cross sections tend to equality at high energies, with the results shown in figure 18(c) (the values adopted by MacKeown and Wolfendale were $K^+/K^- = 4$, and $K/\pi = 0.2$ and 0.5). It should be pointed out that there are various combinations of the ratios K^+/K^-, K/π which produce fairly similar curves, for example $K^+/K^- = 4$, $K/\pi = 0.5$ gives a similar energy dependence of the ratio to $K^+/K^- = 8$, $K/\pi = 0.3$.

The fit with experiment is now seen to be better and indeed it looks to be possible to choose appropriate kaon ratios to get a good fit.

7.2.4. Isobar production. Ramana Murthy (1963) suggested that the effect of production of the $N_{1/2}^*(1515)$ and $N_{1/2}^*(1685)$ isobars on the muon charge ratio might be considerable. This is due to the fact that pions from isobar decay take a considerable fraction of the incident energy which, when combined with the steeply falling spectrum, may produce an enhancement of muons at higher energies. MacKeown and Wolfendale have estimated the effects of the isobars for various assumptions about isobar production with the results shown in figure 18(c). This figure indicates that the charge ratio variation is not far from that with an isobar production cross section of 3mb which decreases slowly with increasing energy, together with a small contribution from kaons.

The suggestion by MacKeown and Wolfendale that pure pionization does not account for the observed charge ratio is supported by calculations of Cohen *et al* (1965). The Monte Carlo calculation of these workers utilized the Poisson distribution for the multiplicity and assumed the mean pion multiplicity to vary as $E_p^{1/4}$. A contribution to the production of pions from isobar decay was incorporated based upon the model of Contogouris *et al* (1963), and on this basis the spectrum taken for the pions from isobar decay was

$$\frac{\mathrm{d}N(E_\pi)}{\mathrm{d}E_\pi} = \int_{M_1}^\infty \frac{A}{E_\mathrm{p}{}^3} \frac{\mathrm{d}\sigma}{\mathrm{d}E_\pi} \mathrm{d}E_\mathrm{p} = N_I{}' \qquad \text{say, with} \qquad M_1 = \frac{M^*E_\pi}{2E_\pi^*}$$

where M^* is the isobar mass, E_π and E_π^* the pion energy in the lab system and rest system of the isobar respectively. The charge ratio obtained is then

$$R = \frac{N'^+_\text{pion} + 0.44\, kN_I'^+}{N'^-_\text{pion} + 0.07\, kN_I'^-}$$

where $N'^\pm_\text{pion}$ is the pionization contribution, $N_I'^\pm$ the contribution from isobars of spin $\frac{1}{2}$ and k is a constant adjusted to give the best fit with the experimental data. The curve for $k = 0.03$ is shown in figure 18(c); due to the Monte Carlo errors, k is uncertain to a factor of 2. As is pointed out by Cohen *et al* (1965), this value of k is in agreement as to order of magnitude with that expected for the $\frac{1}{2}$, $\frac{3}{2}^-$ nucleon isobar according to Contogouris *et al* (1963).

7.3. The calculations of Appleton and Rastin (1971)

Monte Carlo calculations have also been carried out by Appleton and Rastin (1971) using the isobar model of Pal and Peters (1964) in which a fraction $(1 - \eta)$ of the incident nucleon energy (E_N) goes into the fireball, ηE_N going to the emergent nucleon, which is possibly an isobar and consequently may decay by kaon emission. The fireball is assumed to generate pions isotropically and monoenergetically in the centre of mass with a multiplicity $\propto E_\mathrm{N}{}^{1/2}$. Similarly, assumptions are made for the probabilities of isobar decay to pions and to a kaon and hyperon, conservation of strangeness limiting the possible kaons and hyperons produced.

The succeeding π–N and K–N interactions are treated by the method of Wayland and Bowen (1967) in which the longitudinal momentum distribution of secondary particles produced in such interactions is taken as

$$N(p)\,\mathrm{d}p = \frac{T}{m^2c^2} \frac{\sum\limits_{k=1}^\infty \{\exp\,(k\mu/T)/k^{3/2}\}(1+k\mu/T)\,\mathrm{d}p}{\sum\limits_{k=1}^\infty \{K_2(kmc^2/T)\}/k}$$

where m is the mass of the incident particle, $\mu^2 = p^2 + m_k{}^2$, m_k being the mass of a secondary particle, p is the longitudinal momentum and T is a characterstic temperature which Appleton and Rastin take as 160 MeV. K_2 is a modified Bessel function of the second type.

The frequency distribution of the multiplicities is taken according to the work of Bozoki *et al* (1969):

$$f(n) = C\left(\frac{n}{\alpha}\right)^{1.26} \exp\,(-n^2/2\alpha^2),$$

where n is the multiplicity and $\alpha = (1.21 \pm 0.03)\,E^{0.34\pm0.02}$, E being the incident particle energy in GeV. Fluctuations in inelasticity and in the average number of kaons are neglected and mean values are taken (0.47 and 0.36 respectively). After folding in the various factors, Appleton and Rastin deduce the curve shown in figure 18(*a*). Although there is some measure of agreement beyond about 100 GeV/*c* the predicted charge ratio rises to very high values at lower momenta and indeed reaches a value of about 3·5 below 8 GeV/*c*. The authors suggest that the lack of agreement is due to an overestimate of the probability of N* production at low energies and they recommend further work using this method.

7.4. *The analysis of Frohlich et al* (1970)

Frohlich *et al* (1970) have used a simple collision model with the solution of the one dimensional diffusion equation and considered interactions of the type.

$$NN \rightarrow \pi + K\overline{K} + Y\overline{Y} + N\overline{N} + NN_0.$$

The mean multiplicity of charged secondaries was taken as proportional to $E^{1/4}$, but multiplicity fluctuations were not considered. The ratio of charged kaons to pions at production was assumed constant, and the mesons were assumed monoenergetic and isotropic in the centre of mass system. By consideration of conservation of strangeness the following assumptions were also made for the multiplicities, n:

$n(K^+) = n(K^\circ),$

$n(K^-) = n(\overline{K}^\circ)$

and

$n(\Lambda) = n(\Sigma^+) = n(\Sigma^\circ) = n(\Sigma^-) = n(\Xi^\circ) = n(\Xi^-)$

(similarly for antihyperons).

Frohlich *et al* give preliminary results of their calculations and these are summarized in figure 18(*a*). As with the results of the calculations of MacKeown and Wolfendale, it appears possible to take a combination of K/π and K^+/K^- which will give a reasonable fit to the experimental data.

It is also convenient to consider in this section the extension of the studies to higher energies by Frohlich and Leeman (1971). This later analysis considers the situation where all the interaction secondaries are relativisitic in the C-system and in consequence the treatment is applicable to muons with laboratory momenta above 100 GeV/*c*. The most important difference from the earlier work is the adoption of a constant kaon charge excess as distinct from a constant kaon charge ratio. Calculations have been made so far for a zenith angle of 80° with the result shown in figure 18(*c*). It can be seen that there is a measure of agreement with the experimental data in the rather restricted energy range to which the analysis refers.

7.5. *Significance of recent results from the intersecting storage ring experiment*

With the commissioning of the intersecting storage rings at the CERN accelerator some data have recently become available on the characteristics of p–p collisions at energies, with respect to a stationary proton, in the region of 1500 GeV. When the experimental data are complete they should enable the expected muon charge ratio to be calculated, for an assumed primary composition, to a little over 100 GeV. So far only preliminary analyses have been made but these can profitably be discussed.

The most important experimental result that has been found is that the predictions of the scaling model (Feynman 1969, Bjorken 1969) appear to be confirmed, at least in so far as the secondary pion component is concerned. Briefly, this means that the number of pions which individually carry off more than about 10% of the energy of the primary particle are constant in number. Now these are the pions largely responsible for the detected muons and, if this feature is reproduced for all primary energies and furthermore if the π^+/π^- ratio is maintained constant for these energetic pions (as seems to be the case below $E_p = 1500$ GeV), then a near constant muon charge ratio will appear. Inclusion of kaons (the ISR data give $K/\pi \simeq 0.15$ and $K^+/K^- \approx 2$–3 for the relevant energy transfers) will give rise to a modest rise in ratio. Implicit in all this is the assumption that the charge composition of the primary particles remains unaltered. It is interesting to note that this interaction model is close to the isobar model (plus some kaon production) considered in §6 and shown there to give a result close to observation. Qualitatively, there seems therefore to be the possibility of explaining the measured charge ratio to about 100 GeV/c using the ISR data. Unfortunately, however, the calculations made so far, by Frazer *et al* (1972) and Garraffo *et al* (1972), give energy-independent ratios somewhat above 1·5 and therefore considerably in excess of the measured values. There appear to be two solutions to this problem; either the neutron to proton ratio in the primary radiation is higher than assumed or the π^+/π^- ratio in proton–air nucleus collisions is considerably less than that in p–p collisions.

It is true that the n/p ratio is not known experimentally at 1000 GeV but it is known moderately well up to about 100 GeV and so there should be agreement between observation and prediction for muons below 10 GeV or so; this agreement is absent.

Turning to the possibility of multiple interactions in air nuclei, Garraffo *et al* (1972) have made an analysis in which the predicted muon charge ratio is reduced from 1·58 to 1·38 after their inclusion. However, the validity of the calculations of the multiple interactions is in doubt, the problem being well known for its difficulty and in fact there is experimental evidence by Eichten *et al* (1972) which shows that the π^+/π^- ratio for energetic secondaries does not change over a wide range of atomic number (it should be noted, however, that no measurements were made for $A = 1$).

The conclusion to be drawn is that there is still considerable experimentation and theoretical analysis to be made. Higher precision is needed in the experimental region above $P_\mu \simeq 100$ GeV/c and measurements at a variety of zenith angles will be useful. The role of muon charge ratio measurements is seen as the following. When a consistent explanation of the ratio for $P_\mu < 100$ GeV/c is available, it will be possible to make conclusions about the primary n/p ratio to $E_p \simeq 2000$ GeV. If it then appears safe to extrapolate n/p to higher primary energies, it should be possible to use the μ^+/μ^- ratios which extend to $P \simeq 3000$ GeV/c to examine the change in character of nuclear interactions (if any) up to about 50 000 GeV.

References

Achar C V *et al* 1965 *Proc. Phys. Soc.* **86** 1305–15
Alchudjian S V *et al* 1968 *Can. J. Phys.* **46** S1169–71
Alexander D 1970 *PhD thesis* Durham
Allen K E and Apostolakis A J 1961 *Proc. R. Soc.* A**265** 117–32
Allkofer O C and Andresen R D 1967 *Nuovo Cim.* **51** 329–40
Allkofer O C, Andresen R D and Dau W D 1968 *Can. J. Phys.* **46** 301–40
Allkofer O C, Carstenson K and Dau W D 1970a *Phys. Lett.* **31B** 606–8
—— 1971a *Phys. Lett.* **36B** 425–8
—— 1971b *Proc. 12th Int. Conf. on Cosmic Rays* (Hobart: University of Tasmania) pp 1314–18
Allkofer O C and Clausen K 1970 *Acta Phys. Hung.* **29** Suppl 2 689–93
Allkofer O C, Dau W D and Jokisch H 1970b *Proc. 6th Interamerican Seminar on Cosmic Rays* (La Paz: Universidad Mayor De San Andres) **6** 930–6
—— 1970c *Proc. 6th Interamerican Seminar on Cosmic Rays* (La Paz: Universidad Mayor De San Andres) **6** 937–48
Allkofer O C *et al* 1970d *Acta. Phys. Hung.* **29** Suppl 4 13–18
Allkofer O C *et al* 1971c *Proc. 12th Int. Conf. on Cosmic Rays* (Hobart: University of Tasmania) 1319–23
Allkofer O C *et al* 1971d *Proc. 12th Int. Conf. on Cosmic Rays* (Hobart: University of Tasmania) vol 4 pp 1596–601
Allkofer O C and Jokisch H 1972 *Nuovo Cim.* to be published
Appleton I C, Hogue M T and Rastin B C 1971 *Nucl. Phys.* B**26** 365–89
Appleton I C and Rastin B C 1971 *Proc. 12th Int. Conf. on Cosmic Rays* (Hobart: University of Tasmania) vol 4 pp 1329–34
Asbury J G *et al* 1970 *Nuovo Cim.* **66** 169–82
Ashton F *et al* 1960 *Nature* **185** 364–65
—— 1966 *Proc. Phys. Soc.* **87** 79–88
Ashton F, Tsuji K and Wolfendale A W 1972 *Nuovo Cim.* **9B** 344–50
Ashton F and Wolfendale A W 1963 *Proc. Phys. Soc.* **81** 593–603
Aurela A M, MacKeown P K and Wolfendale A W 1966 *Proc. Phys. Soc.* **89** 401–8
Aurela A M and Wolfendale A W 1967 *Ann. Acad. Sci. Fenn.* A**6** 226–40
Ayre C A *et al* 1971a *J. Phys.* A: *Gen. Phys.* **4** L89–93
—— 1971b *Proc. 12th Int. Conf. on Cosmic Rays* (Hobart: University of Tasmania) **4** 1364–68
—— 1972a *Nucl. Inst. and Meth.* **102** 19–28
—— 1972b *Nucl. Inst. and Meth.* **102** 29–34
Baber S R, Nash W F and Rastin B C 1968a *Nucl. Phys.* **B4** 539–48
—— 1968b *Nucl. Phys.* **B4** 549–58
Barrett P H *et al* 1952 *Rev. Mod. Phys.* **24** 133–78
Barton J C 1961 *Phil. Mag.* **6** 1271–83
Bassi P, Clemental E, Filosofo I and Puppi G 1949 *Nuovo Cim.* **6** 509–10
Bateman B J *et al* 1971 *Phys. Lett.* **36B** 144–48
Bhattacharyya D P 1970 *Z. Phys.* **234** 17–22
Bjorken J D 1969 *Phys. Rev.* **179** 1547–53
Blackett P M S 1937 *Proc. R. Soc.* A**159** 1–18
Bollinger L 1951 *PhD thesis* Cornell University
Bozoki G, Gombosi E and Posch M 1969 *Nuovo Cim.* **64A** 881–99
Brode R B 1949 *Nuovo Cim.* **6** 465–74
Brooke G *et al* 1962 *Proc. Phys. Soc.* **80** 674–85
Brooke G, Hayman P J, Kamiya Y and Wolfendale A W 1964 *Proc. Phys. Soc.* **83** 853–69
Bull R M, Nash W F and Rastin B C 1965 *Nuovo Cim.* **40** 365–84
Caldiroli P and Loinger A 1950 *Nuovo Cim.* **7** 1–8
Caro D E, Parry J K and Rathgeber H D 1951 *Aust. J. Sci. Res.* A**4** 16–35
Castagnoli C, De Mano A, Longetto A and Penengo P 1965 *Nuovo Cim.* **35** 969–76

Chin S *et al* 1968 *Can. J. Phys.* **46** S297–300
Christy R F and Kusaka S 1941 *Phys. Rev.* **59** 414–21
Cini M and Wataghin G 1950 *Nuovo Cim.* **7** 135–44
Coates D W and Nash W F 1962 *Aust. J. Phys.* **15** 420–31
Cocconi G, Koester L J and Perkins D H 1961 *UCRL High Energy Physics Study Seminars* **28** part 2 (UCID-1444)
Cohen L, Fowler G N and Poulopoulous P 1965 *Nucl. Phys.* **B74** 619–24
Contogouris A P, Frautschi S C and Wong W S 1963 *Phys. Rev.* **129** 974–81
Conversi M 1949 *Phys. Rev.* **76** 311–13
Cousins J *et al* 1970 *Acta Phys. Hung.* **29** Suppl. 4 585–91
Crookes J N and Rastin B C 1971a *Proc. 12th Int. Conf. on Cosmic Rays* (Hobart: University of Tasmania) **4** 1325–28
—— 1971b *Proc. 12th Int. Conf. on Cosmic Rays* (Hobart: University of Tasmania) **4** 1369–73
—— 1972 *Nucl. Phys.* **B39** 493–508
Das A V 1969 *Nuovo Cim.* **61** 234–39
De K E *et al* 1972a *Phys. Rev.* **D5** 1068–72
—— 1972b *J. Phys.* A: *Gen. Phys.* **5** 1236–42
Del Rosario L and Davila-Aponte J 1952 *Phys. Rev.* **88** 998–1002
Dodd P *et al* 1961 *Proc. Int. Conf. on Elementary Particles Aix-en-Provence* vol 1 (Saclay: SEN) 433–47
Duthie J, Fowler P H, Kaddoura A, Perkins D H and Pinkau K 1962 *Nuovo Cim.* **24** 122–38
Eichten T *et al* 1972 *Nucl. Phys.* **B44** 333–43
Feynman R P 1969 *Phys. Rev. Lett.* **23** 1415–17
Filosofo I, Pohl E and Pohl-Ruling J 1954 *Nuovo Cim.* **12** 809–12
Flatte S M *et al* 1971 *Phys. Lett.* **35B** 345–50
Flint R W and Nash W F 1970 *Acta Phys. Hung.* **29** Suppl. 4 99–105
—— 1971 *Proc. 12th Int. Conf. on Cosmic Rays* (Hobart: University of Tasmania) **4** 1346–52
Fowler P H and Perkins D H 1964 *Proc. R. Soc.* **A278** 401–15
Fowler G N and Wolfendale A W 1961 *Handb. Phys.* (Berlin: Springer) **46/1** 272–315
Frazer W R, Poon C H, Silverman D and Yesian H J 1972 *Rev. Mod. Phys.* **44** 214–319
Frohlich A and Leeman S 1971 *Proc. 12th Int. Conf. on Cosmic Rays* (Hobart: University of Tasmania) **6** 2381–6
Frohlich A, Leeman S, Widder M and Yeivin Y 1970 *Proc. 6th Interamerican Seminar on Cosmic Rays* **4** 987–1003
Fukui S, Kitamura T and Murata Y 1955 *J. Phys. Soc. Japan* **10** 735–41
—— 1957 *J. Phys. Soc. Japan* **12** 854–63
Fujii Z *et al* 1969 *Lett. Nuovo Cim.* **1** 845–7
Gardener M, Jones D G, Taylor F E and Wolfendale A W 1962 *Proc. Phys. Soc.* **80** 697–709
Garraffo Z, Pignotti A and Zgrablich G 1972 to be published
Glaser D A, Hammermesh B and Safonov G 1950 *Phys. Rev.* **80** 625–30
Greisen K I 1942 *Phys. Rev.* **61** 212–19
Hayman P J, Palmer N S and Wolfendale A W 1963 *Proc. R. Soc.* A **275** 391–410
Hayman P J and Wolfendale A W 1962a *Proc. Phys. Soc.* **80** 710–28
Hayman P J and Wolfendale A W 1962b *Nature* **195** 166–7
Holmes J E R, Owen B G and Rodgers A L 1961 *Proc. Phys. Soc.* **78** 505–15
Hughes D J 1940 *Phys. Rev.* **57** 592–97
Hyams B D, Mylroi M G, Owen B G and Wilson J G 1950 *Proc. Phys. Soc.* A **63** 1053–74
Jakeman D 1956 *Can. J. Phys.* **34** 432–50
Jones H 1939 *Rev. Mod. Phys.* **11** 235–8
Jory F S 1956 *Phys. Rev.* **102** 1167–73
Judge R J R and Nash W F 1965a *Nuovo Cim.* **35** 999–1024
—— 1965b *Nuovo Cim.* **35** 1025–30
Kamiya Y, Sagisaka S, Ueno H, Kato S and Sekido Y 1962 *J. Phys. Soc. Japan* **17** AIII 315–22
Kamiya Y, Kawaguchi S, Fujii Z, Iida S and Mitsui K 1970 *Acta Phys. Hung.* **29** Suppl. 4 25–31

E

Kamiya Y, Kawaguchi S and Iida S 1971 *Proc. 12th Int. Conf. on Cosmic Rays* (Hobart: University of Tasmania) **4** 1354–58

Kaneko S, Kubozal T and Takahata M 1955 *J. Phys. Soc. Japan* **10** 915–16

Kasha H, Hawkins C J B and Stefanski R J 1968 *Can. J. Phys.* **46** S306–8

Kawaguchi S *et al* 1966 *Proc. 9th Int. Conf. on Cosmic Rays* (London: Institute of Physics) 941–3

Kim C O 1964 *Phys. Rev.* **136** B515–28

Kim Y S and Voyvodic L 1970 *Nuovo Cim.* **66B** 183–92

Kitamura Y and Minakawa O 1953 *Prog. Theor. Phys. Japan* **10** 237–40

Knoblich P 1968 *PhD thesis* University of Kiel

Kobayakawa K 1968 *Can. J. Phys.* **46** S395–98

Kraushaar W L 1949 *Phys. Rev.* **76** 1045–58

MacKeown P K, Said S S, Wdowczyk J and Wolfendale A W 1966a *Proc. 9th Int. Conf. on Cosmic Rays* (London: Institute of Physics) 937–40

—— 1966b *Proc. 9th Int. Conf. on Cosmic Rays* (London: Institute of Physics) 964–6

MacKeown P K and Wolfendale A W 1966 *Proc. Phys. Soc.* **89** 553–65

Menon K G and Ramana Murthy P V 1967 *Prog. in Elem. Part. and Cosmic Ray Physics* **9** 161–243

Miyake S, Narasimham V S and Ramana Murthy P V 1964a *Nuovo Cim.* **32** 1505–23

—— 1964b *Nuovo Cim.* **32** 1524–40

Moroney J R and Parry J K 1954 *Aust. J. Phys.* **7** 423–38

Nandi B and Sinha M S 1969 *Acta Phys. Hung.* **29** Suppl. 4 529–33

—— 1972a *J. Phys.* A: *Gen. Phys.* **5** 1384–93

—— 1972b *Nucl. Phys.* **B40** 201–15

Neresen N 1948 *Phys. Rev.* **73** 565–9

Olbert S 1954 *Phys. Rev.* **96** 1400–7

Osborne J L, Wolfendale A W and Palmer N S 1964 *Proc. Phys. Soc.* **84** 911–13

Owen B G and Wilson J G 1955 *Proc. Phys. Soc.* A**68** 409–18

Pak W, Ozaki S, Roe B P and Greisen K 1961 *Phys. Rev.* **121** 905–7

Pal Y and Peters B 1964 *Math. Fys. Meddr.* **33** No 15

Palmer N S and Nash W F 1969 *Nucl. Phys.* **B9** 315–23

Pine J, Davison R J and Greisen K 1959 *Nuovo Cim.* **14** 1181–204

Ramana Murthy P V 1963 *Nuovo Cim.* **30** 762–71

Rossi B 1948 *Rev. Mod. Phys.* **20** 537–83

—— 1952 *High Energy Particles* (New York: Constable)

Said S S 1966 *PhD thesis* University of Durham

Sheldon W R and Duller N M 1962 *Nuovo Cim.* **23** 63–76

Smith J A and Duller N M 1959 *J. Geophys. Res.* **64** 2297–305

Subramanian A *et al* 1958 *Nuovo Cim.* **7** 110–13

Wayland J R and Bowen T 1967 *Nuovo Cim.* **48** 663–75

Wilson B G 1959 *Can. J. Phys.* **37** 19–29

Chapter 3

Protons and pions

G Brooke

1. Introduction

Although the primary radiation incident on the Earth's atmosphere contains a significant proportion of nuclei other than protons, as discussed in chapter 1, §2, there is a high probability of fragmentation of the compound nuclei in their interactions in the atmosphere. In such interactions, the incident nucleus appears to behave as a group of separate nucleons and usually only one of these takes part in the interaction. The remainder continue with their original energies either independently or as lighter nuclei, so that at a depth in the atmosphere of a few interaction lengths the primary nuclei are completely fragmented into nucleons.

In the interactions of nucleons with air nuclei one of the secondary particles, the 'leading particle', has a much higher energy than have the other secondaries and carries off on average about 50% of the incident energy. This leading particle is a nucleon, normally considered to be the surviving incident nucleon, which may be in an excited state. If this is the case it will quickly decay to the ground state with the emission of one or more pions. Nucleon–antinucleon pairs are produced in the interactions but with very low energies compared to those of the leading particles and because of the steepness of the primary spectrum they give a negligible contribution to the observed spectrum of nucleons. The probability of the leading particle being a neutron when the incident nucleon is a proton, or vice versa, is such that in the lower atmosphere the nucleon spectrum consists almost equally of protons and neutrons, except at low energies where the effect of ionization loss is greater on the proton than on the neutron spectrum.

The number of interactions made by a nucleon in traversing a given thickness of the atmosphere follows a Poisson distribution. When the shape of the primary spectrum is taken into consideration it can be seen that the average number of interactions made by nucleons observed at a given depth and energy is much less than the average for all primary nucleons. For example, in traversing the whole atmosphere a nucleon will make on average twelve interactions but the nucleons observed in any given energy interval at sea level will most probably have made only four or five interactions in the atmosphere. The elasticity, that is the fraction of the incident energy retained by the leading particle, fluctuates in nucleon–air nucleus interactions, so that nucleons observed at a particular depth in the atmosphere correspond in general to those for which there was a downward fluctuation in the number of interactions made before reaching that depth together with some upward fluctuations in the elasticities of those interactions.

The majority of the secondary particles produced in the interactions are pions. The neutral pions decay with a mean lifetime of 9×10^{-17} s into two photons which, if sufficiently energetic, give rise to an electron–photon cascade in the atmosphere. The charged pions either decay into muons with a mean lifetime of $2 \cdot 6 \times 10^{-8}$ s or interact with air nuclei producing more pions. Although the pion spectrum at any depth in the atmosphere is related to the nucleon spectrum at that depth, unpublished calculations by Hillas show that even at sea level equilibrium has not been reached and that the pion to nucleon ratio is still increasing with depth in the atmosphere.

The nuclear interactions of pions appear to resemble those of nucleons except that the leading particle is a pion rather than a nucleon and this pion may be neutral with a probability of approximately 33%. If this is taken to be the case, in a third of pion interactions one neutral pion secondary takes about half the available energy and the remainder is shared between approximately equal numbers of positive, negative and neutral pions; in other words the fraction of the incident energy taken by neutral pion secondaries, K_{π^0}, is two-thirds compared with one-sixth for interactions in which the leading particle is charged. The lifetime of neutral pions is so short that they will always decay rather than interact and K_{π^0} represents the energy removed from the pion flux in the atmosphere. This model of pion interactions is supported by both

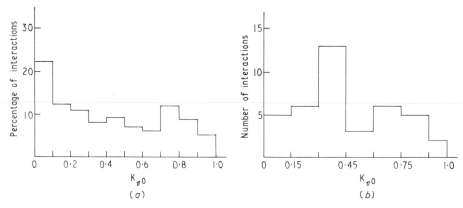

Figure 1. The distribution in K_{π^0} (a) Orlova and Tretyakova (1971) for 60 GeV/c negative pions; (b) Abdullaev *et al* (1971), the difference between charged and neutral incident particles at energies 2×10^{11}–2×10^{12} eV.

accelerator and cosmic ray work. For example, Orlova and Tretyakova (1971), using negative pions with a momentum of 60 GeV/c at the Serpukhov accelerator, observed the distribution in K_{π^0} shown in figure 1(a). They found that for events with no charged leading pion the mean value of K_{π^0} was $0 \cdot 67 \pm 0 \cdot 04$ compared with $0 \cdot 19 \pm 0 \cdot 01$ for events with a charged leading pion. Similarly Abdullaev *et al* (1971), in a high altitude cosmic ray experiment, found the distribution shown in figure 1(b) for the energy interval $2 \times 10^{11} - 2 \times 10^{12}$ eV, this being the difference in behaviour for charged and neutral incident particles.

The behaviour of K_{π^0} in pion interactions is of great importance in the interpretation of the results of 'burst' experiments and this is discussed in §2.4.

2. Measurements of proton and pion intensities near sea-level

It is convenient to discuss the experimental measurements according to the technique used, since each is restricted to a fairly well defined energy range.

2.1. The absorption method

The rate of ionization loss by a singly charged particle in any given medium is a function only of the velocity of the particle. At nonrelativistic energies this loss is inversely proportional to the square of the velocity so that the difference in ionization ranges of protons and the other types of particle present in the cosmic radiation is large. By observing the rates of particles stopped by absorbers of suitable thickness, as a function of energy, the low energy proton spectrum can be derived. Nuclear interactions are an additional source of energy loss for protons passing through an absorber. This gives a probability, decreasing with increasing proton energy, for protons, and the secondary particles from their interactions, being stopped for energies greater than the total energy loss by ionization alone. If, however, the probability of secondary particles emerging from the absorber can be measured as a function of energy, measurements by this method can be made up to energies of about 10^{10} eV.

The spectrum of positive particles which appear to have been stopped by an absorber will include pions and muons which undergo nuclear interactions or which, owing to inefficiency in the detection arrangement, have not been observed to emerge from the absorber; for this reason it is necessary to consider the difference in the spectra of 'stopped' positive and negative particles in order to evaluate the proton spectrum.

There have been many experiments performed using this method. Proton momenta were determined either magnetically or from a comparison of their rates of ionization loss and their ranges. These measurements of the proton intensity are presented in table 1. (The measurements of Brooke and Wolfendale (1964) for momenta above $2 \cdot 5$ GeV/c are not included as these were combined with other measurements as described in §2.2.1.) In some experiments the proton intensity was determined as a percentage of the muon intensity and in these cases the proton intensity has been

Table 1

Number	Observer	Momentum interval (MeV/c)	Vertical proton intensity $\times 10^8$ s^{-1} cm^{-2} sr^{-1} (MeV/c)$^{-1}$
1	Rochester and Bound (1940)†	340–400	15 ± 6
2	Merkle *et al* (1950)	480–880	23 ± 3
3	Goldwasser and Merkle (1951)	780–1100	20 ± 5
4	Mylroi and Wilson (1951)†	530–710	$21 \cdot 8 \pm 5 \cdot 7$
		710–930	$11 \cdot 6 \pm 2 \cdot 1$
		930–1350	$7 \cdot 1 \pm 1 \cdot 2$
		1500	$5 \cdot 6 \pm 1 \cdot 0$
		2000	$2 \cdot 7 \pm 0 \cdot 6$
5	York (1952b)	550–750	28 ± 3
		750–880	$10 \cdot 7 \pm 0 \cdot 8$
6	Ballam and Lichtenstein (1954)	757–842	$13 \cdot 5 \pm 4 \cdot 3$
		842–983	$12 \cdot 4 \pm 2 \cdot 6$
		983–1105	$13 \cdot 3 \pm 3 \cdot 2$
		1105–1217	$10 \cdot 0 \pm 3 \cdot 4$
7	Rozen (1954)	590–770	$9 \cdot 1 \pm 1 \cdot 9$
		770–930	$12 \cdot 1 \pm 2 \cdot 3$
8	Filthuth (1955)	180–210	$2 \cdot 2 \pm 0 \cdot 3$
		210–236	$3 \cdot 7^{+0 \cdot 4}_{-1 \cdot 1}$
		236–260	$3 \cdot 3^{+0 \cdot 4}_{-0 \cdot 8}$
		275–312	$6 \cdot 5 \pm 0 \cdot 5$
		332–358	$8 \cdot 0 \pm 1$
		432–446	$8 \cdot 3 \pm 1$
		456–469	11 ± 1
		615	10 ± 1
		730	$8 \cdot 4 \pm 1$
		887	$4 \cdot 8 \pm 1$
9	Ogilvie (1955)	590–700	14 ± 4
		700–1100	$7 \cdot 8 \pm 1$
		850–1240	$6 \cdot 5 \pm 0 \cdot 5$
		950–1300	$6 \cdot 0 \pm 0 \cdot 7$
		1050–1400	$5 \cdot 5 \pm 0 \cdot 7$
10	McDiarmid (1959)	716–739	24 ± 3
		739–828	13 ± 1
11	Brooke and Wolfendale (1964)†	740	$20 \cdot 3 \pm 3 \cdot 7$
		1030	$10 \cdot 5 \pm 0 \cdot 94$
		1530	$3 \cdot 65 \pm 0 \cdot 38$
		2120	$2 \cdot 37 \pm 0 \cdot 21$
12	G Hook and K E Turver (1972 private communication)	1000	$6 \cdot 0 \pm 0 \cdot 24$
		2000	$2 \cdot 4 \pm 0 \cdot 22$

† Renormalized using the absolute muon intensity given by Ashton *et al* (1972)

recalculated using the absolute muon intensity given by Ashton *et al* (1972), as indicated in the table. The earlier measurements were summarized by York (1952a) who also calculated the proton intensity from the data of several experiments not originally intended to measure this as such and these are included in table 1. The measurements are also shown in figure 2. The curve has been drawn through the measured points taking into account also the measurements described in §2.2. The absolute intensities given by Filthuth (1955) are lower than found by other workers in the region above 500 MeV/c by about 70% and have not been considered there. However, below 500 MeV/c there is virtually no other work and the spectrum has been derived from Filthuth's measurements but with the intensities increased by 70%.

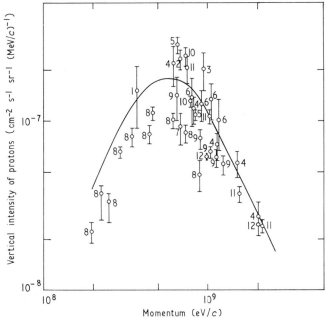

Figure 2. Measurements of the vertical proton intensity for momenta less than 2·5 GeV/c. The numbers against the points refer to the authors given in table 1.

2.2. The nuclear interaction method

For energies greater than about 1 GeV either the pions produced in nuclear interactions or evaporation neutrons from the 'target' nuclei can be detected. In both experiments described here, nuclear-active particles were recognized by their production of evaporation neutrons. As with the absorption method, the proton spectrum has been derived from the difference between the spectra of positively and negatively charged particles which produce nuclear interactions. The spectrum of negative pions has been derived by subtracting the muon contribution from the spectrum of negative interacting particles.

2.2.1. Brooke and Wolfendale (1964). This work consisted of a series of experiments using both the absorption and the nuclear interaction methods. The spectrograph described by Brooke *et al* (1962) was used with a standard IGY neutron monitor and an additional tray of G–M counters operated above the bottom flash-tube array. This arrangement is shown in figure 3. For one of the absorption measurements the neutron monitor was replaced by a single layer of lead absorber, whilst for the other the material of the neutron monitor was used as the absorbing material.

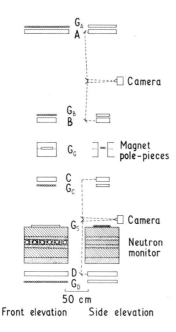

Figure 3. The experimental arrangement of Brooke and Wolfendale (1964). Hatched areas: paraffin wax; stippled areas: lead; A, B, C, D: flash-tube arrays; $G_{A, B, G, C, S, D}$: Geiger–Müller counters.

Two further experiments were performed in which nuclear-active particles were identified by demanding that neutrons be detected by the neutron monitor during a well defined time interval following the passage of a single particle through the spectrograph which gave a five-fold coincidence $G_{A, B, G, C, S}$.

The absolute acceptance of the instrument, that is the product of solid angle and area of acceptance, was found by comparing the observed coincidence rate at $G_{A, B, G, C, S}$ with that calculated from the vertical muon spectra of Gardener *et al* (1962) and of Hayman and Wolfendale (1962). As these muon spectra were normalized to the value of the absolute intensity at 1 GeV/c given by Rossi (1948), the proton spectrum was also in effect normalized to this value. However, recent measurements by Allkofer *et al* (1970) and Ashton *et al* (1972) have shown that the absolute intensity given by Rossi was too low by about 30% and so the proton intensities given by Brooke and Wolfendale have been renormalized to the absolute intensity (of $3 \cdot 18 \times 10^{-3}$ cm^{-2} s^{-1} sr^{-1} (GeV/c)$^{-1}$) at 1 GeV/c given by Ashton *et al*.

The proton intensity at a given momentum calculated from observations with the neutron monitor is inversely proportional to the mean number of neutrons produced in the monitor by protons of that momentum. Hatton (1971) has shown that the numbers of produced neutrons given by Hughes *et al* (1964), which were used in the original calculations, are too low by 10%. The intensities derived from this part of the work have been reduced by the appropriate factor to allow for this. The revised intensities from this work are shown in figure 5, the points shown being the combined results from all four experiments.

2.2.2. Hook and Turver (1972). These workers have recently measured the proton spectrum in the momentum range 1–20 GeV/c using a magnetic spectrograph and a modified neutron monitor in an experimental arrangement very similar to that of Brooke and Wolfendale (see figure 4). The ultimate object of this work is the study

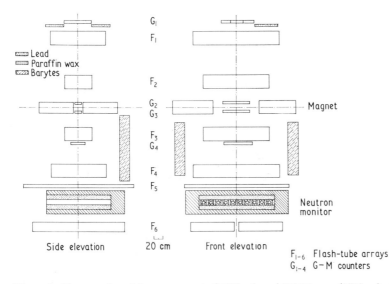

Figure 4. The experimental arrangement of G Hook and K E Turver (1972 private communication).

of nuclear-active particles in extensive air showers; this requires the use of a spectrograph with large acceptance, the value being about twice that of the spectrograph used by Brooke and Wolfendale. However, the integral of the magnetic field along the path of a particle passing through the spectrograph was about half and the diameter of the neon flash-tubes about double the corresponding values for the earlier work, resulting in a significantly lower maximum detectable momentum.

The positions of the proportional counters which detected neutrons were recorded; in this way it was possible to reduce the contributions to the measured spectra from muons in chance coincidence with unassociated neutrons by imposing restrictions on the predicted impact points of particles on the monitor.

The measured proton intensities, shown in figure 5, were normalized using the absolute muon intensity given by Allkofer *et al*. This intensity is consistent with that given by Ashton *et al* and so no further renormalization has been made.

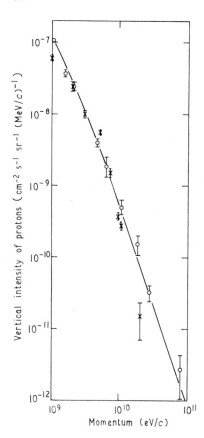

Figure 5. Measurements of the vertical proton intensity by Brooke and Wolfendale (circles) and by Hook and Turver (crosses).

2.2.3. The proton spectrum in the momentum range 1–100 GeV/c. The line shown in figure 5 is the suggested best estimate of the proton spectrum in this momentum range. It has been drawn taking into account not only the points shown but also the other measurements in the region of 1 GeV/c given in table 1 and at much higher momenta the measurements described in §2.3. If the spectrum is taken to be represented by a power law for momenta above 5 GeV/c the exponent of this best estimate spectrum is $-2 \cdot 9$. The measurement of Brooke and Wolfendale alone gives an exponent of $-2 \cdot 6 \pm 0 \cdot 2$ in the same region whilst those of Hook and Turver give a value of $-4 \cdot 0 \pm 0 \cdot 3$. The significance of this best estimate of the proton spectrum is discussed in §3.

2.2.4. The pion spectrum for momenta < 100 GeV/c. The negative pion spectrum at sea level has been derived by Hook and Turver using the data from the experiment described in §2.2.2 and by Brooke *et al* (1964) using the basic data from the two experiments of Brooke and Wolfendale (see §2.2.1) in which hadrons were identified by demanding that neutrons be detected by the neutron monitor during a short time interval following the passage of a particle through the spectrograph. Very similar criteria were used in both cases to select negative pion interactions from the background of negative muons which had either interacted in the monitor or been observed in chance coincidence with a random neutron. Events were identified as negative pion interactions if either:

(i) there was no track observed in the flash-tube array beneath the neutron monitor, the predicted position in that array calculated from the measured positions of the trajectory in the flash-tube arrays above the monitor was greater than a predetermined distance from the edge and the momentum was greater than the highest for which muons would be stopped by ionization loss in the monitor; or

(ii) one or more tracks were observed in the flash-tube array beneath the monitor, and the difference between the predicted position in that array and the nearest observed track was greater than $n\sigma$, where σ is the calculated root-mean-square displacement at that level for muons due to Coulomb scattering in the neutron monitor.

The choice of n is to some extent arbitrary; too large a value would lead to the rejection of a significant proportion of genuine pion interactions, too small to the inclusion of muons. Brooke *et al* used $n=7$, and Hook and Turver, from a study of the distribution of the observed scattering measured in terms of the root-mean-square Coulomb scattering, used $n=8$. The spectra of negative pions were then derived by methods similar to those used for the corresponding proton spectra. In both cases it was found necessary to take the values of the mean numbers of neutrons produced in the monitors to be the same for pion and proton interactions at the same energy because, owing to the small numbers of pion interactions observed, it was not possible to evaluate this for pions alone.

The momentum spectrum of negative pions measured by Hook and Turver is shown in figure 9. The measurements of Brooke *et al* (1964), renormalized using the absolute muon intensity given by Ashton *et al* (1972) and taking into account the increased values for the numbers of neutrons produced given by Hatton (1971), are also shown in that figure. Although there is good agreement on the shape of the spectrum, there appears to be a discrepancy of about a factor of two in the absolute rates. It does not seem possible to resolve this difference at present as no other measurements have been made of the pion intensity near sea level in this momentum range. More weight should perhaps be given to the measurements of Hook and Turver since their requirement that the point of impact on the neutron monitor should be close to the proportional counter which detected the neutrons would lead to a lower muon background.

2.3. The 'ionization calorimeter' method

In this method a target many nuclear interaction lengths in thickness is employed, with the object of absorbing the whole of the energy of incident hadrons (ie nuclear-active particles). A high proportion of this energy goes into the electron–photon cascades which develop from the neutral pions produced either in the interactions of the incident hadrons or in subsequent interactions of secondary charged pions. The numbers of electrons in the cascades are sampled at many depths within the target so that their development is known and the incident energies can be calculated. The effect of fluctuations in the nuclear interaction process is very small. This is because multiple interactions are observed for each incident hadron; random errors in energy determination can be as low as 20% although the absolute energy calibration is difficult and systematic errors may be significant.

Cowan and Matthews (1971) used an ionization calorimeter together with nine cloud chambers principally to study hadron interactions but also to measure the energy spectrum of unaccompanied incident hadrons. The arrangement used is shown in figure 6. The neutral to charged ratio was measured for incident particles which interacted in one of the layers of carbon, the value found being 0.295 ± 0.035 at an average energy of 330 GeV. Within the statistical errors, this ratio was found to be

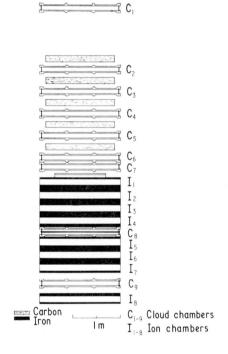

Carbon
Iron $1\,m$ C_{1-9} Cloud chambers
                     I_{1-8} Ion chambers

gure 6. The arrangement of ionization calorimeter and cloud chambers used by Cowan and Matthews (1971).

constant for the energy range studied. The energy spectra of pions and protons have been calculated from the measured spectrum of incident charged hadrons using the measured neutral to charged ratio and, following Cowan and Matthews, taking the neutron to proton ratio to be 0·9, although this would be a lower limit at large atmospheric depths. The effect of taking this ratio to be unity is to increase the calculated pion intensities by only about 5%, with a corresponding decrease for protons. The spectra calculated in this way are shown in figures 8 and 9. However, the measured neutral to charged ratio leads to the conclusion that the incident spectrum of hadrons consists of almost exactly twice as many pions as protons and it is very difficult to understand how such a high intensity of pions could occur, in that it implies that frequently the leading particle from a nucleon interaction is a pion, rather than a nucleon, contrary to other evidence. Cowan and Matthews rejected all events in which there was more than one incident charged particle and it is likely that this would give, for the remaining events, a neutral to charged ratio different from the true ratio for incident hadrons; accompanied charged hadrons would be rejected but incident neutrons accompanied by a single charged particle would be classed as charged hadrons. The pion and proton spectra have therefore been recalculated using a pion to proton ratio of 0·5 as found at lower energies and the effect of this change of the ratio is indicated in figures 8 and 9 by the broken lines drawn above the proton and below the pion intensities.

2.4. The 'burst' method

The electron–photon cascades or 'bursts' which develop from the neutral pions produced in single interactions of incident hadrons can be used to give estimates of their energies. In its simplest form the apparatus used consists of a single layer of a target material, about one nuclear interaction length in thickness, above a detector which is capable of measuring the numbers of electrons in the cascades. Usually the apparatus is surrounded by a layer of lead to absorb the electron–photon component of any accompanying air showers. The energy estimates for individual hadrons obtained in this way are subject to large errors due to variation in the point of inter-action so that cascades vary in development at the detector level and also due to fluctuations in K_{π^0}, because only one interaction of each incident hadron is observed. However, the general features of the incident spectrum may be observed by this method.

The interpretation of the measurements is made more difficult by the different behaviour of K_{π^0} in pion and in nucleon interactions, as discussed in §1, and the rela-tive intensities of pions and nucleons are not known at high energy. If the probability of the fraction of the incident energy given to neutral pions lying between K_{π^0} and $K_{\pi^0} + \mathrm{d}K_{\pi^0}$ is $P(K_{\pi^0})\,\mathrm{d}K_{\pi^0}$, then the effective value, K_{eff}, when single interactions are observed, is given by the expression:

$$K_{\mathrm{eff}}{}^{\gamma} = \int_0^1 P(K_{\pi^0}) K_{\pi^0}{}^{\gamma}\,\mathrm{d}K_{\pi^0}$$

where $-\gamma$ is the exponent of the integral spectrum of incident particles. Assuming that in a third of the interactions of pions an additional 50% of the incident energy is given to neutral pions, then K_{eff} is almost three times larger for pions than for nucleons. This means that the ratio of pions to nucleons producing bursts of a given size is much higher than the ratio for a given incident energy, since pions will have only about one-third of the energy of nucleons to produce the same size burst.

In the experiments described here, very similar experimental arrangements have been used. In each case there was a target of about one nuclear interaction length of carbon, the low atomic number of this giving a large ratio of radiation length to interaction length so that there was little development of the electron–photon cascade in the target; this was followed by a few centimetres of lead in which the cascades developed. The high atomic number of lead gave a low probability of nuclear interactions occurring in that material whilst providing a sufficient number of radiation lengths for the cascades to reach their maximum development. The ionization was measured beneath the layer of lead by means of proportional counters or ionization chambers. In each experiment also, a shielding layer of lead of thickness 5–10 cm was placed above the carbon target. Unfortunately, there is a significant probability that nuclear interactions will occur in such a shielding layer since to be at all effective in reducing the electron–photon component it must be about half a nuclear interaction length in thickness, and cascades resulting from such interactions have not reached a known stage of development at the detector level. It follows that estimates of the energies of incident particles interacting in the shielding lead will be inaccurate and the inclusion of such events will probably distort the shape of the observed energy spectrum. The inclusion of multiple events in which several nuclear-active particles simultaneously interact in the detector will also affect this shape.

The earliest work reported was that of Dmitriev *et al* (1960). In that experiment a single detector layer consisting of four ionization chambers of total area 1 m² was used. It was not possible from the data available to distinguish between interactions occurring in the carbon target and the shielding lead nor to resolve more than a small proportion of the multiple events owing to the large size of the ionization chambers. The layer of lead immediately above the ionization chambers was chosen such that cascades resulting from interactions in the carbon were near maximum development at the ionization chambers; cascades from interactions in the shielding lead would be well past maximum development. The proton and negative pion intensities calculated from these measurements are shown in figures 8 and 9. The points shown correspond to the assumption that the incident charged pion to proton ratio is 0·5, the errors being statistical, and the dashed extensions to the error bars show the effect of taking the pion to proton ratio found by Cowan and Matthews.

The apparatus used by Babecki *et al* (1961) is shown in figure 7(*a*). The ionization chambers used were much smaller than those of Dmitriev *et al* so that it was possible to resolve closer multiple structure. Although the pulses from each of the chambers were individually recorded, no attempt was made to identify interactions in the shielding lead from the stage of development of the cascades at the level of the lower two layers of chambers. Events were recorded if the total ionization exceeded a given threshold value simultaneously in each of any two of the layers of ionization chambers.

The burst size spectrum was derived from the responses of the bottom layer of chambers only, the individual bursts within multiple bursts being included separately. The value found for the exponent of the integral spectrum was $-1·96 \pm 0·03$ and if allowance is made for the variation of burst size with energy this gives a value of $-1·88 \pm 0·03$ for the exponent of the integral energy spectrum of all hadrons.

In the experiment by Baruch *et al* (1973) the experimental arrangement (see figure 7(*b*)) was very similar to that of Babecki *et al*. Proportional counters of diameter 3·5 cm were used to measure the ionization and the pulses from each counter were recorded individually, enabling closely spaced multiple events to be recognized. The

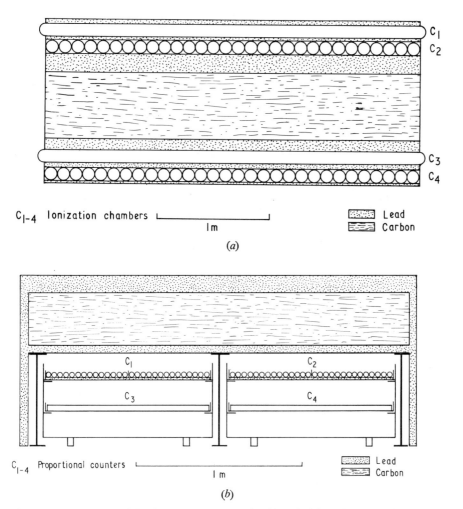

C_{1-4} Ionization chambers

1 m

Lead
Carbon

(*a*)

C_{1-4} Proportional counters

1 m

Lead
Carbon

(*b*)

Figure 7. Apparatus used for burst measurements by (*a*) Babecki *et al* (1961) and (*b*) Baruch *et al* (1973).

recording was triggered by requiring that the total ionization in each of the two layers of counters exceeded a predetermined level. The absolute energy calibration of the apparatus was made by studying its response to artificially accelerated electrons of known energies, the response at other energies being calculated from the cascade curves given by Buja (1963). For the energy range studied, bursts produced from interactions in the carbon were either close to or before their maximum development at the counter levels whereas bursts originating from above the carbon were in general past maximum development. This made it possible to select events where the inter-action took place in the carbon target by imposing limits on the acceptable ratio of the ionization in the two layers of proportional counters. These limits were determined as a function of burst size from cascade theory, both for incident pions and for incident nucleons. Although the limits are different for these two cases, the distribution of ratios observed was such that there was negligible difference, compared with the statistical errors, between the spectra derived for the limiting assumptions that the incident hadrons were either all nucleons or all pions. The intensities shown in figures 8 and 9 were calculated assuming a charged pion to proton ratio of 0·5 and the broken lines show the effect of assuming the ratio found by Cowan and Matthews.

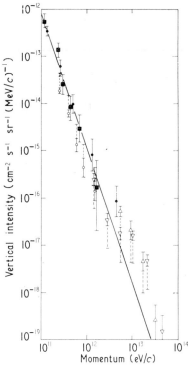

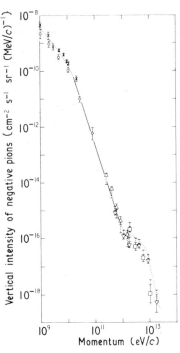

Figure 8. Measurements of the proton intensity for momenta greater than 10^{11} eV/c. The extended errors show the effect of assuming different values for the pion-to-proton ratio, as explained in §2.3 and 2.4. Measurements of the neutron intensity are also shown. ○ Cowan and Matthews (1971); △ Dmitriev *et al* (1960); ▽ Baruch *et al* (1973); ■ Ashton *et al* (1970), neutrons; ● Ashton and Coats (1968), neutrons.

Figure 9. The vertical momentum spectrum of negative pions near sea level. × G Hook and K E Turver (1972 private communication); ○ Brooke *et al* (1964); △ Cowan and Matthews (1971); ▽ Baruch *et al* (1973); □ Dmitriev *et al* (1960).

3. Discussion and conclusions

3.1. The proton spectrum

The best estimate of the sea-level proton spectrum from this survey is shown by the lines drawn in figures 2, 5 and 8. The derivation for low momenta is described in §2.1.

The shape of the spectrum in this region is consistent with that expected for a primary spectrum with constant exponent when ionization loss in the atmosphere is taken into consideration; it is assumed that the protons observed at sea-level have traversed half the atmosphere, on average, as neutrons.

In the range 2–10 GeV/c the spectrograph measurements of Brooke and Wolfendale and of Hook and Turver are in reasonably good agreement although the intensities from either experiment considered separately would give a quite different value for the spectrum exponent. When measurements at higher momenta are considered, it is seen that the intensity given by Hook and Turver at 20 GeV/c is not consistent with a power law form of the spectrum with a constant exponent. It is possible that this point has been overcorrected for the apparent increase in intensity which occurs near the maximum detectable momentum of a spectrograph.

In order to separate the nucleon and pion components above 10^{11} eV/c a pion to proton ratio has to be assumed, as this has not yet been measured. The effects of taking values of 0·5 and 2·05 for this ratio are shown in figures 8 and 9. For any constant value of the ratio, the measurements in the range 2×10^{11}–2×10^{12} eV/c give a proton spectrum with exponent $-2·9 \pm 0·1$, but obviously the absolute intensities cannot be determined without additional information. Because incident neutrons can be unambiguously identified, measurements of neutron intensities provide the best evidence for the behaviour of the nucleon spectrum at high energies. The measurements of Ashton and Coats (1968) and Ashton *et al* (1970) shown in figure 8 have therefore been used to determine the absolute proton intensities in this region. The exponent of the neutron spectrum is in good agreement with that for the proton spectrum derived from observations of all hadrons up to 2×10^{12} eV/c so that normalizing the proton intensities to the neutron intensities corresponds to taking a constant charged pion to proton ratio of 0·33.

For burst sizes corresponding to nucleon momenta above 2×10^{12} eV/c, the change of exponent of the burst size spectrum observed by Baruch *et al* appears to be confirmed by the measurements of Dmitriev *et al* in that there is agreement with the enhanced intensities found for the larger burst sizes. However, it is possible that there is a systematic error in the absolute energy calibration of the apparatus used by Dmitriev *et al* and any conclusions related to the behaviour of the burst spectrum in this region must be tentative until direct measurements are made of the neutral to charged hadron ratio. A possible explanation of the behaviour of the burst spectrum is that it could be due to a change of exponent of either the nucleon or pion spectra. It is very unlikely that the exponents of both could change and give the observed burst spectrum shape since the changes would have to occur at energies differing by a factor very close to 2·5 so that both correspond to the same burst size. The assumption that it is the exponent of the pion spectrum which is unchanged requires such high nucleon intensities as to make this highly improbable. For the calorimeter and burst measurements to be compatible with a simple power law spectrum for protons it must be assumed that the charged pion to proton ratio increases rapidly to a value of about 6 at 5×10^{13} eV/c, decreasing again at higher momenta. The behaviour of the burst spectrum is discussed further in §3.2.

The best estimate of the differential proton spectrum near sea level for momenta

F

greater than 10^{10} eV/c may be expressed in the form: $N(p)\,dp = Ap^{-\gamma}\,dp$ where $A = 5 \cdot 4 \times 10^{-7} \pm 20\%$, $\gamma = 2 \cdot 9 \pm 0 \cdot 1$, p is expressed in GeV/c, and $N(p)$ is in units of cm^{-2} s^{-1} sr^{-1} (MeV/c)$^{-1}$.

It is not possible to deduce from work performed so far whether or not the spectrum continues with the same exponent above 10^{12} eV/c.

3.2. The pion spectrum

At low momenta the measurements of Brooke *et al* (1964) and Hook and Turver disagree by a factor of two in absolute intensity. When compared with the best estimate of the proton spectrum those of Brooke *et al* correspond, above 10^{10} eV/c, to a charged pion to proton ratio of approximately 0·5 and those of Hook and Turver to a ratio close to unity. As explained in §3.1, in order to obtain agreement between the proton and pion intensities in the region of 5×10^{11} eV/c this ratio must be assumed to be about 0·33. Consequently the best estimate of the pion spectrum in the range 10^{10}–10^{12} eV/c would appear to be steeper than the proton spectrum, and if the spectrum is expressed as a power law the exponent is $-3 \cdot 1 \pm 0 \cdot 1$. This conclusion is not consistent with the assumption made when calculating the intensities that the pion to nucleon ratio is constant, but the effect on the calculated intensities of taking exponents differing by 0·2 for the two spectra is negligible when compared with the other uncertainties in this region.

At higher momenta, if the shape of the burst spectrum is assumed to be due to a change of exponent of the pion spectrum only, the pion to proton ratio appears to increase to about 6 at 5×10^{12} eV/c. Such a rapid variation in the ratio could be due to a change in the characteristics of nucleon–air nucleus interactions such that above some well defined threshold momentum, which would be greater than or approximately equal to 10^{13} eV/c, a large fraction of the available energy is given to one of the secondary pions. An alternative explanation is that a similar change occurs in the characteristics of nucleon interactions for momenta above about 10^{12} eV/c so that in a third of those interactions a very energetic neutral pion is produced causing a large increase in K_{eff} and consequently a systematic overestimation of energies when using burst methods. Obviously this explanation would also give rise to a change of exponent for the charged pion spectrum, but not necessarily for the nucleon spectrum as there could be simply a redistribution of energy amongst the secondary pions with the nucleon elasticity remaining constant. No firm conclusions can be reached about the behaviour of the pion and nucleon spectra above 10^{12} eV/c until further work has been performed to measure the charged to neutral hadron ratio and also to confirm the shape of the burst spectrum.

3.3. Comparison of the proton spectrum with high altitude measurements

The measurements of the hadron intensities at various depths in the atmosphere were surveyed by Ellsworth and Yodh (1970). It is clear from this that there are many discrepancies between the measurements both with regard to the exponent of the spectrum and also the rate of attenuation with increasing depth in the atmosphere, probably due to the different effects produced by accompanying particles in the various experiments and to the varying proportion of pions in the hadron spectrum. The present comparison is therefore confined to that of the 'best fit' proton spectrum at sea level with direct measurements of the primary spectrum. The series of PROTON satellites has been used to measure the primary spectrum in the range 10^{10}–10^{15} eV. The PROTON-1, 2, 3 satellites carried apparatus capable of measuring energies in the range 10^{10}–10^{14} eV and in addition of determining the charges carried by the observed particles so that the primary composition could be found. An unexpected feature of these measurements was an abrupt steepening of the primary proton spectrum at an energy of about 10^{12} eV. The PROTON-4 satellite apparatus was used to measure the spectrum of all particles in the range 10^{11}–10^{15} eV. The results obtained have been compared with the data of PROTON-1, 2, 3 by Grigorov *et al* (1971) and agree well with the steepening of the primary proton spectrum found in the PROTON-1, 2, 3 experiments. The primary energy spectrum of nucleons was derived from the PROTON-1, 2, 3 measurements by Grigorov *et al* (1967). The exponent of this spectrum in differential form is -2.75 below 10^{12} eV, changing to -3.05 in the region above 10^{12} eV owing to the rapid change in the exponent of the proton spectrum. The attenuation length for nucleons in the atmosphere derived from the best estimate sea-level proton spectrum and this primary nucleon spectrum varies from 133 g cm^{-2} at an energy of 2×10^{10} eV to 119 g cm^{-2} at 2×10^{12} eV. However, the attenuation length, involving as it does a comparison of intensities at the same energy for different depths, is a poor indication of the behaviour of nucleons in the atmosphere if the primary spectrum exponent is not constant. In traversing the atmosphere, nucleons are losing energy in the interactions which they make and it is more realistic to compare, for example, the energies for which the same intensities are observed for the primary and sea-level spectra. If this is done for the spectra under consideration, the ratio of primary to sea-level energies is found to vary by less than 5% for the energy range 5×10^9 eV to 10^{12} eV at sea level. Although a detailed calculation must be performed, allowing for the effects of fluctuations in nucleon elasticity and in the number of interactions made by nucleons in reaching sea level, the conclusion is that the best estimate proton spectrum at sea level is consistent with the primary spectra measured by the PROTON satellites, with the characteristics of nucleon interactions remaining constant in the energy range 5×10^9 eV to 2×10^{13} eV.

References

Abdullaev A M *et al* 1971 *Proc. 12th Int. Conf. on Cosmic Rays* (Hobart: University of Tasmania) **6** 2273–7
Allkofer O C, Dau W D and Joksich H 1970 *Phys. Lett.* B **31** 606–8
Ashton F and Coats R B 1968 *J. Phys.* A: *Gen. Phys.* **1** 169–70
Ashton F, Smith N I, King J and Mamidzhanian E A 1970 *Acta Phys. Hung.* **29** suppl 3 25–6
Ashton F, Tsuji K and Wolfendale A W 1972 *Nuovo Cim.* **9B** 344–50
Babecki J *et al* 1961 *Sov. Phys.–JETP* **40 (13)** 1089–95
Ballam J and Lichtenstein P G 1954 *Phys. Rev.* **93** 851–7
Baruch J E F, Brooke G and Kellermann E W 1973 *Nature* **242** 6–7

Brooke G *et al* 1962 *Proc. Phys. Soc.* **80** 674–85
Brooke G, Meyer M A and Wolfendale A W 1964 *Proc. Phys. Soc.* **83** 871–7
Brooke G and Wolfendale A W 1964 *Proc. Phys. Soc.* **83** 843–51
Buja Z A 1963 *Acta Phys. Polon.* **24** 381–7
Cowan E W and Matthews K 1971 *Phys. Rev.* D **4** 37–45
Dmitriev V A, Kulikov G V and Khristiansen G B 1960 *Sov. Phys.–JETP* **37 (10)** 637–47
Ellsworth R and Yodh G B 1970 *Acta Phys. Hung.* **29** suppl 3 321–6
Filthuth H 1955 *Z. Naturf.* **10a** 219–29
Gardener M, Jones D G, Taylor F E and Wolfendale A W 1962 *Proc. Phys. Soc.* **80** 697–709
Goldwasser E L and Merkle T C 1951 *Phys. Rev.* **83**, 43–6
Grigorov N L *et al* 1967 *Cosmic Res. (USA)* **5** 342–61
Grigorov N L *et al* 1971 *Proc. 12th Int. Conf. on Cosmic Rays* (Hobart: University of Tasmania) **5** 1752–9
Hatton C J 1971 *Progress in Elementary Particle and Cosmic Ray Physics* (Amsterdam: North Holland) vol 10 pp 3–100
Hayman P J and Wolfendale A W 1962 *Proc. Phys. Soc.* **80** 710–28
Hughes E B *et al* 1964 *Proc. Phys. Soc.* **83** 239–51
McDiarmid I B 1959 *Canad. J. Phys.* **37** 79–81
Merkle T C, Goldwasser E W and Brode R B 1950 *Phys. Rev.* **79** 926–8
Mylroi M G and Wilson J G 1951 *Proc. Phys. Soc.* A **64** 404–17
Ogilvie K W 1955 *Canad. J. Phys.* **33** 746–56
Orlova G I and Tretyakova M I 1971 *Proc. 12th Int. Conf. on Cosmic Rays* (Hobart: University of Tasmania) **6** 2297–306
Rochester G D and Bound M 1940 *Nature, Lond.* **146** 745–6
Rossi B 1948 *Rev. Mod Phys.* **20**, 537–83
Rozen A Z 1954 *Phys. Rev.* **93** 211–4
York C M 1952a *Proc. Phys. Soc.* A **65** 558–9
—— 1952b *Phys. Rev.* **85** 998–1003

Chapter 4

Neutrons

F Ashton

1. Introduction

Apart from its interest as a constant of the cosmic radiation the energy spectrum of neutrons at sea level can be used to determine some average characteristics of high energy nucleon–nucleon collisions when compared with measurements of the primary cosmic ray spectrum. In this chapter measurements of the sea-level neutron spectrum are reviewed and the results compared with the theory of the propagation of nucleons through the atmosphere.

2. Measurements of the neutron spectrum

The existence of a flux of fast neutrons in the cosmic radiation at sea level was first established using penetrating shower detectors by Janossy (1950). Subsequently an estimate of the low energy (<500 MeV) neutron spectrum was made by Hess *et al* (1959) using a variety of different techniques. These included a bismuth fission ioniza-tion chamber, a CH_2-lined proportional counter and a gold foil resonance detector. In the intermediate energy range (300 MeV to a few GeV) Hughes and Marsden (1966) estimated the spectrum from indirect measurements of the multiplicity distribu-tion of neutrons in a neutron monitor. Only comparatively recently has a direct measurement of the spectrum been made in the energy region 0·4–1·2 GeV using the charge exchange reaction $n+p \rightarrow p+n$ (Ashton *et al* 1971). At higher energies (>20 GeV) an estimate of the spectrum has been made from the burst spectrum produced by neutral particles in a thick steel target (Ashton *et al* 1970). Figure 1 shows the best available estimate of the low energy sea-level vertical spectrum (Ashton *et al* 1971) and figure 2 that up to the highest energies so far measured (Ashton *et al*

1970). A measurement of the high energy neutron spectrum has also been made by Cowan and Matthews (1971). In the energy range 150–400 GeV this work is in agreement with the measurements of Ashton *et al* (1970) but for energies greater than

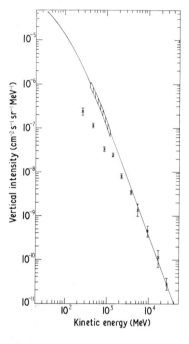

Figure 1. Summary of the low energy sea-level vertical neutron and proton spectra. The full line is the vertical neutron spectrum calculated from the global spectrum of Hughes and Marsden (1966). The crosses are the proton measurements of Brooke and Wolfendale (1964) and the hatched area is the vertical neutron spectrum given by Ashton *et al* (1971).

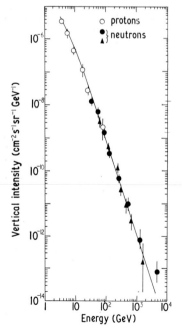

Figure 2. The high energy differential energy spectrum of neutrons at sea level. Over the range 50–1000 GeV the differential spectrum can be represented by $N(E)\,dE = KE^{-\gamma}\,dE$ where $\gamma = 2\cdot95 \pm 0\cdot10$ (Ashton *et al* 1970). The proton measurements are from Brooke and Wolfendale (1964).

400 GeV Cowan and Matthews (1971) find evidence for a sharp decrease in the sea-level neutron intensity.

3. The propagation of primary cosmic ray nucleons in the atmosphere

Measurements using satellites and balloons indicate that the primary cosmic radiation consists predominantly of protons and α particles with a small admixture of all the other elements of the periodic table. Using the data of Fan *et al* (1968) and Pinkau *et al* (1970) it is concluded that for energies above 10^{10} eV/nucleon the differential energy spectrum of primary nucleons can be represented by $N(E_p)\,dE_p = AE_p^{-\gamma}\,dE_p$ where A is a constant and $\gamma = 2{\cdot}75$. At a given energy per nucleon, 87% of primary nucleons are protons and 13% are neutrons bound in nuclei. Given this information it is possible to calculate the expected shape of the nucleon spectrum at a given atmospheric depth and also the fraction of nucleons that are protons or neutrons at that depth.

3.1. The expected shape of the nucleon energy spectrum at a given atmospheric depth

Suppose the mean free path for a nucleon to make an inelastic collision in air is λ and consider the energy spectrum of nucleons at atmospheric depth x. The average number of collisions, z, made by a primary nucleon in this atmospheric thickness is given by $z = x/\lambda$ and the probability that a nucleon makes r collisions if the mean is z is

$$P(r) = \frac{e^{-z}z^r}{r!}.$$

Suppose that in a nucleon–nucleon collision an incident nucleon of energy E emerges on the average with an energy βE of its incident energy, the energy loss $(1-\beta)E$ going into meson production and the kinetic energy of the recoil nucleon. Consider a nucleon of energy E at atmospheric depth x and suppose that it has made r nuclear collisions on the way, then $E = \beta^r E_p$ and $dE = \beta^r\,dE_p$, and the differential energy spectrum of nucleons at depth t is thus given by

$$N(E)\,dE = \sum_{r=0}^{\infty} A\left(\frac{E}{\beta^r}\right)^{-\gamma} \frac{dE}{\beta^r} P(r)$$

$$= AE^{-\gamma}\,dE\,e^{-z} \sum_{r=0}^{\infty} \frac{\beta^{r(\gamma-1)}z^r}{r!}$$

$$= AE^{-\gamma}\,dE\,e^{-z}\left(1 + \frac{\beta^{(\gamma-1)}z}{1} + \frac{\beta^{2(\gamma-1)}z^2}{2} + \ldots\right)$$

$$= AE^{-\gamma}\,dE\,\exp\{-z(1-\beta^{(\gamma-1)})\}$$

$$= A\,\exp\{-(x/\lambda)(1-\beta^{(\gamma-1)})\}\,E^{-\gamma}\,dE$$

$$= A\,\exp -(x/\Lambda)\,E^{-\gamma}\,dE$$

where
$$\Lambda = \frac{\lambda}{1-\beta^{(\gamma-1)}}.$$

Table 1. Steps in the evaluation of the proton excess, $\delta_x = (P_0 - N_0)(1 - 2\omega)^z/(P_0 + N_0)$, at atmospheric depth x where $z = x/\lambda$, ω is the probability that a nucleon, after making an inelastic collision with an air nucleus, emerges from the collision in a different charge state

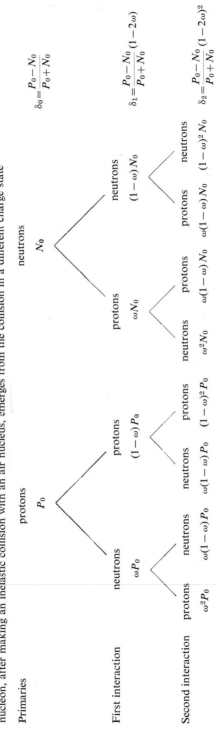

Primaries

protons

P_0

neutrons

N_0

$$\delta_0 = \frac{P_0 - N_0}{P_0 + N_0}$$

First interaction

neutrons ωP_0

protons $(1-\omega) P_0$

protons ωN_0

neutrons $(1-\omega) N_0$

$$\delta_1 = \frac{P_0 - N_0}{P_0 + N_0}(1 - 2\omega)$$

Second interaction

protons $\omega^2 P_0$

neutrons $\omega(1-\omega) P_0$

neutrons $\omega(1-\omega) P_0$

protons $(1-\omega)^2 P_0$

neutrons $\omega^2 N_0$

protons $\omega(1-\omega) N_0$

protons $\omega(1-\omega) N_0$

neutrons $(1-\omega)^2 N_0$

$$\delta_2 = \frac{P_0 - N_0}{P_0 + N_0}(1 - 2\omega)^2$$

Thus the differential energy spectrum of nucleons at depth x has the same form as the primary nucleon spectrum except that the intensity is reduced by a factor $\exp(-x/\Lambda)$.

3.2. The ratio of neutrons to protons at a given atmospheric depth

Let ω represent the probability that a nucleon after making an inelastic collision with an air nucleus emerges from the collision in a different charge state. If the proton excess in the primary cosmic ray beam is

$$\delta_0 = \left(\frac{P_0 - N_0}{P_0 + N_0}\right)$$

then it is required to calculate δ at a given atmospheric depth. From table 1 it can be seen that the proton excess after all primary nucleons have made one inelastic collision is

$$\delta_1 = \left(\frac{P_0 - N_0}{P_0 + N_0}\right)(1 - 2\omega)$$

and after two inelastic collisions is

$$\delta_2 = \left(\frac{P_0 - N_0}{P_0 + N_0}\right)(1 - 2\omega)^2.$$

After z inelastic collisions

$$\delta_z = \left(\frac{P_0 - N_0}{P_0 + N_0}\right)(1 - 2\omega)^z = \delta_0(1 - 2\omega)^z.$$

Table 2. Steps in the evaluation of the proton excess δ_x at atmospheric depth x. The integral energy spectrum of primary nucleons is $N(>E) = BE^{-(\gamma-1)}$

Number of inelastic collisions, r	Primary energy	Probability of making r collisions when the mean number is $z = x/\lambda$	Contribution to proton excess
0	E	e^{-z}	$BE^{-(\gamma-1)}\, e^{-z}\, \delta_0$
1	E/β	$e^{-z}\, z$	$B(E/\beta)^{-(\gamma-1)}\, e^{-z}\, z\, \delta_0(1-2\omega)$
2	E/β^2	$\dfrac{e^{-z}\, z^2}{2!}$	$B(E/\beta^2)^{-(\gamma-1)}\, \dfrac{e^{-z}\, z^2}{2!}\, \delta_0(1-2\omega)^2$
3	E/β^3	$\dfrac{e^{-z}\, z^3}{3!}$	$B(E/\beta^3)^{-(\gamma-1)}\, \dfrac{e^{-z}\, z^3}{3!}\, \delta_0(1-2\omega)^3$
etc	etc	etc	etc

Using table 2 it can be seen that the expected proton excess at atmospheric depth x is given by

$$\delta_x = \frac{BE^{-(\gamma-1)}\, e^{-z}\, \delta_0\{1 + \beta^{(\gamma-1)}z(1-2\omega) + \beta^{2(\gamma-1)}z^2(1-2\omega)^2 + \ldots\}}{B \exp\{-z(1 - \beta^{(\gamma-1)})\}\, E^{-(\gamma-1)}}$$

where $B \exp\{-z(1-\beta^{(\gamma-1)})\} E^{-(\gamma-1)}$ is the integral spectrum of nucleons at depth x. Evaluating gives

$$\delta_x = \delta_0 \exp\left(-\frac{2x}{\lambda}\beta^{(\gamma-1)}\omega\right).$$

Thus if the differential energy spectrum of primary cosmic ray nucleons is of the form $N(E)\,dE = AE^{-\gamma}\,dE$ the differential spectra of protons and neutrons at depth x are of the form

$$N_p(E)\,dE = \frac{1+\delta_x}{2}\exp(-x/\Lambda)\,AE^{-\gamma}\,dE$$

$$N_n(E)\,dE = \frac{1-\delta_x}{2}\exp(-x/\Lambda)\,AE^{-\gamma}\,dE$$

where

$$\Lambda = \frac{\lambda}{1-\beta^{(\gamma-1)}}.$$

4. The contribution of recoil nucleons

According to Pal and Peters (1964) the formation of nucleon isobars of mass in the region of 2300 MeV is dominant in determining the propagation of nucleons through the atmosphere. Assuming this to be so, consider the dynamics of isobar formation shown in figure 3. Using the Lorentz transformation of the total energy of the recoil isobar from the centre of momentum system to the laboratory system gives for the total energy of the recoil N^* in the laboratory system

$$U_{\text{lab}} = (U_{\text{lab}})_{\text{min}} + \frac{M_B M_B c^2}{2M_N}\left(\frac{p_\perp c}{M_B c^2}\right)^2$$

where

$$(U_{\text{lab}})_{\text{min}} = \frac{M_B c^2}{2}\left(\frac{M_N}{M_B}+\frac{M_B}{M_N}\right)$$

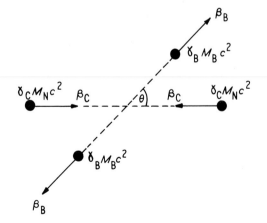

Figure 3. A symmetric nucleon–nucleon collision drawn in the centre of momentum system where both the incident and recoil nucleons are excited into N* states of rest mass $M_B c^2$.

and $p_\perp c$ is the invariant transverse momentum of the produced N*. Assuming that the ground state nucleon after isobar decay has the same Lorentz factor in the laboratory system as the N* its kinetic energy in the laboratory system is given by

$$(E_{\text{lab}})_{\text{nucleon}} \simeq \frac{M_N c^2}{2} \left\{ \left(\frac{M_N}{M_B} + \frac{M_B}{M_N} \right) + \frac{M_B}{M_N} \left(\frac{p_\perp c}{M_B c^2} \right)^2 \right\} - M_N c^2.$$

For $M_B c^2 = 2300$ MeV this gives

$$(E_{\text{lab}})_{\text{nucleon}} \simeq 422 + 1170 \left(\frac{p_\perp c}{938} \right)^2 \text{ MeV}$$

with $(E_{\text{lab}})_{\text{nucleon}} \simeq 422$ MeV for $p_\perp c = 0$ (minimum nucleon kinetic energy in lab) and $(E_{\text{lab}})_{\text{nucleon}} \simeq 752$ MeV for $p_\perp c = 500$ MeV (average nucleon kinetic energy in lab). For $M_B c^2 = M_N c^2$ (elastic scattering) the result is $(E_{\text{lab}})_{\text{nucleon}} \simeq 0$ for $p_\perp c = 0$ (minimum nucleon kinetic energy in lab) and $(E_{\text{lab}})_{\text{nucleon}} \simeq 131$ MeV for $p_\perp c = 500$ MeV (average nucleon kinetic energy in lab).

A number of experiments show that distribution of transverse momentum of nucleons undergoing inelastic interactions is given by

$$N(p_\perp) \, dp_\perp = \frac{p_\perp}{p_0^2} \exp\left(-p_\perp / p_0 \right) dp_\perp$$

for $E > 422$ MeV where the average transverse momentum $\langle p_\perp \rangle = 2 p_0 \simeq 500$ MeV/c (Hayakawa 1969). Using this result and $M_B c^2 = 2300$ MeV the production spectrum of recoil nucleons is found to be

$$N(E) \, dE = \text{constant} \times \exp\left\{ \frac{-(E - 422)^{1/2}}{9} \right\} dE$$

where E is the kinetic energy (MeV) of the recoil nucleon in the laboratory system. It is clear from this expression that the production spectrum of recoil nucleons will drop off rapidly with increasing energy for E greater than 1 GeV and hence will only make a significant contribution to the sea-level nucleon spectrum at energies below 1 GeV.

5. Deductions from available experimental data

Comparing the measured neutron and proton spectra shown in figure 1 it is seen that the intensities of these two components only become equal for E greater than 5 GeV. It is thus concluded that ionization loss in the atmosphere (approximately 2 GeV) can only be neglected in considering the propagation of nucleons which arrive at sea level with E greater than 5 GeV. In §3.1. it was shown that the attenuation length Λ, interaction length λ and elasticity β of high energy nucleon–air nucleus collisions were related by

$$\Lambda = \frac{\lambda}{1 - \beta^{(\gamma - 1)}}$$

where γ is the exponent of the primary cosmic ray differential nucleon spectrum. Ashton *et al* (1970) found $\Lambda = (127 \pm 15)$ g cm^{-2} from measurements of the angular distribution of neutrons of average energy 230 GeV at sea level. Obviously one parameter can be determined from this measurement using the above equation. Accelerator and scattering theory predictions indicate that the inelastic nucleon–nucleon cross section is constant at approximately 30 mb for energies above 2 GeV. Using the data of Williams (1960) and Alexander and Yekutieli (1960) an inelastic nucleon–nucleon cross section of 30 mb corresponds to a mean free path in air of 97 g cm^{-2}. Using a value of $\gamma = 2 \cdot 85$ which is intermediate between the value found for primary cosmic rays (Pinkau *et al* 1970) and that measured for the sea-level neutron spectrum and substituting in the expression for Λ gives $\beta = 0 \cdot 46$. Thus these data indicate that a high energy nucleon retains about 46% of its incident energy in an average inelastic collision with an air nucleus. According to Lebedev *et al* (1963) the average number of inelastic collisions made by a nucleon in traversing an air nucleus is 1·8. This implies that in a single inelastic nucleon–nucleon collision the emergent nucleon retains about 65% of its incident energy on the average.

The parameters given above can be used to calculate the neutron to proton ratio at a given atmospheric depth from the expression $N/P = (1 - \delta_x)/(1 + \delta_x)$ given in §3.2.

Figure 4 shows the expected value of N/P as a function of ω at sea level (1030 g cm^{-2}). Intuitively one would expect $\omega = 0 \cdot 5$ giving $N/P = 0 \cdot 9$ which is not inconsistent with the ratio indicated from the region 30–80 GeV shown in figure 2. In fact, however, the errors are such that all that can really be said from figure 2 is that $\omega \gtrsim 0 \cdot 3$. An independent measurement of ω is $(0 \cdot 3^{+0 \cdot 2}_{-0 \cdot 08})$, Pal and Peters (1964), which is deduced from the measured ratio of interactions of energy above 20 GeV produced by neutrons and charged particles (protons and pions) at mountain altitude. The only direct measurement using accelerators is $\omega = (0 \cdot 39 \pm 0 \cdot 04)$ (Galstyan *et al* 1966) referring to protons on emulsion nuclei at approximately 25 GeV. The evidence is thus that $\omega \simeq 0 \cdot 4$ for energies of several tens of GeV.

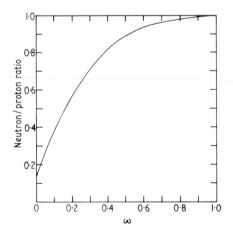

Figure 4. The expected neutron to proton ratio at sea level as a function of the probability ω that a nucleon emerging from an inelastic interaction with an air nucleus is in a different charge state to the incident nucleon.

6. Summary

It is seen that to the precision of the available measurements the high energy (5–1000 GeV) sea-level neutron spectrum can be understood in terms of a nucleon attenuation length of (127 ± 15) g cm^{-2}, an interaction length of about 97 g cm^{-2} and an elasticity of nucleon–air nucleus collisions of about 0·46. The probability that a nucleon emerging from an inelastic interaction is in a different charge state to the incident nucleon is not well determined but is probably about 0·4. Measurements have also been made by Murzina and Afanasiev (1968) of the electron–photon component accompanying nuclear-active particles (neutrons, protons and pions) arriving at sea level with energies above 1000 GeV in which neutrons are not resolved from other nuclear-active particles. These measurements indicate an anomalously large fraction of energy being concentrated in the electron–photon component (gammanization) for nucleon energies greater than 3×10^{13} eV. Obviously it would be useful to extend measurements of the neutron spectrum into this energy range.

References

Alexander G and Yekutieli G 1960 *Nuovo Cim.* **19** 103–17
Ashton F, Edwards H J and Kelly G N 1971 *J. Phys.* A: *Gen. Phys.* **4** 352–66
Ashton F, Smith N I, King J and Mamidzhanian E A 1970 *Acta Phys. Hung.* **29** suppl. 3 25–6
Brooke G and Wolfendale A W 1964 *Proc. Phys. Soc.* **83** 843–51
Cowan E W and Matthews K 1971 *Phys. Rev.* D **4** 37–45
Fan C Y, Gloeckler G and Simpson J A 1968 *Can. J. Phys.* **46** S548–52
Galstyan D A, Zhdanov G B, Tretyakova M E and Tolkachev B V 1966 *Izvest. Akad. Nauk.* **30** 1598
Hayakawa S 1969 *Cosmic Ray Physics* (New York: Wiley) p 235
Hess N H, Patterson H W and Wallace R 1959 *Phys. Rev.* **116** 445–57
Hughes E B and Marsden P L 1966 *J. Geophys. Res.* **71** 1435–44
Janossy L 1950 *Cosmic Rays* 2nd edn (Oxford University Press) p 163
Lebedev A M, Slavatinsky S A and Tolkachev B V 1963 *Sov. Phys.–JETP* **19** 1452–5
Murzina E A and Afanasiev A A 1968 *Can. J. Phys.* **46** S175–7
Pal Y and Peters B 1964 *Mat. Fys. Meddr.* **33** No 15 1–55
Pinkau K, Pollvogt V, Schmidt W K H and Huggett R W 1970 *Acta Phys. Hung.* **29** suppl 1 291–6
Williams R W 1960 *Nuovo Cim.* **16** 762–4

Chapter 5

Muon-neutrinos

J L Osborne

1. Introduction

There are four members of the neutrino family of elementary particles. They are the electron-neutrino ν_e, and its antiparticle $\bar{\nu}_e$, the muon-neutrino ν_μ and its antiparticle, $\bar{\nu}_\mu$. This article describes experiments which have detected muon-neutrinos (ν_μ and $\bar{\nu}_\mu$) in the cosmic ray flux and which have attempted to obtain some information on their interactions.

The flux of cosmic ray muon-neutrinos at ground level has two components: the atmospheric neutrinos and those of extraterrestrial origin. The former come from the decay of pions, kaons and muons which are the secondaries of the interactions between the primary nuclear flux and air nuclei. Extraterrestrial muon-neutrinos are expected to come mainly from corresponding interactions between the primary nuclei and the interstellar or intergalactic gas. It is also possible that some are produced in the central regions of stars having masses several times that of the Sun as they near the end of their life cycle. If the temperature exceeds 10^{12} K, muon pair production can occur and the muon-neutrinos from their decay will carry away energy from the centre of the star. It is almost certain that at ground level the atmospheric neutrinos account for practically all of the muon-neutrino flux above 1 GeV. If this is so one can calculate the energy spectrum of muon-neutrinos at ground level using the knowledge of other components of the cosmic ray flux. The cosmic ray neutrino spectrum extends to essentially limitless energies while the present spectra of machine-produced neutrinos from the Brookhaven and CERN proton-synchrotrons cut off above 10 GeV. The cosmic ray physicist should, therefore, be able to obtain some information on neutrino interactions at energies beyond those attained by these accelerators although the steepness of the cosmic ray spectrum is such that it is very difficult to go much beyond 100 GeV.

The total cross section for interactions between energetic neutrinos and nucleons is a few times 10^{-38} cm^2. For reactions with this cross section an Earth diameter represents only approximately 10^{-4} of an interaction length. The Earth is therefore effectively transparent to neutrinos. Neutrino intensities and angular distributions underground are identical to those at ground level and in particular the flux of neutrinos travelling upwards from the lower hemisphere is identical to that travelling downwards. (This is some justification for the inclusion of an account of experiments performed deep underground in a book on cosmic rays at ground level.) The very small cross section for neutrinos leads to the problems of constructing a large enough detector to get a measurable rate of interactions and at the same time keeping the background rate of other cosmic ray particles sufficiently low. It might at first seem that a prohibitively large detector would be necessary. Markov and Zheleznykh (1961) pointed out, however, that if one is studying neutrino interactions in which a muon is produced and if one does not necessarily require that the interaction itself should be seen inside the detector then there will be an effective target thickness of material surrounding the detector that is equal to the range of the muon in that material. In addition the muon range is approximately proportional to the muon energy. In interactions in which the energy retained by the muon is an approximately constant fraction of the initial neutrino energy this partly compensates for the rapidly falling cosmic ray neutrino energy spectrum. It was concluded that with an underground detector of moderate size it should be possible to measure a significant rate of muons from neutrino interactions.

The cosmic ray background at such an underground detector will be due to the residual flux of high energy atmospheric muons that penetrate the rock above the detector and, to a smaller exent, due to hadrons, electrons and γ-rays produced locally by these muons. The atmospheric muon flux at great depths is attenuated approximately exponentially with depth while the neutrino-induced muon flux remains constant. The observation by Menon *et al* (1963) of zero counts in 30 days for two vertically oriented muon telescopes each of area 1·5 m^2 at a depth of 2800 m at the Kolar Gold Field showed that depths sufficient to reduce the atmospheric muon background to at least the same order as the flux of neutrino-induced muons are in fact attainable in practice. Following this, two experiments to observe cosmic ray muon-neutrino interactions in deep gold mines were proposed, one (Menon 1964) a collaboration between the Tata Institute, Bombay, Osaka City University, Japan and Durham University, UK to be set up at Kolar Gold Field (the KGF experiment), the other, (Reines *et al* 1964) a collaboration between the Case Institute, Ohio, Witwatersrand University and, latterly, the University of California at Irvine (the CWI experiment), at the East Rand Proprietary Mines, South Africa. These two experiments have now been successfully completed and a third experiment by the University of Utah using their rather more sophisticated detector at the Silver King Mine, Park City, Utah is now running (the Utah experiment).

The contents of this article are as follows (for brevity we shall use the word 'neutrinos' to imply 'cosmic ray muon-neutrinos and antineutrinos' unless otherwise stated). In §2 the calculation of the ground-level spectrum of atmospheric neutrinos is described and some estimate of the extraterrestrial flux is made. §3 covers the expected types of neutrino–nucleus interactions and summarizes what is known from the accelerator work. In §4 the three neutrino experiments are described in some detail and the experimental results are given. The interpretation of these results is given in §5 and §6 covers some astrophysical aspects of these experiments.

2. The energy spectrum

2.1. *Atmospheric neutrinos*

The neutrinos produced in the atmosphere come from the decays of pions, kaons and muons:

$$\pi^{\pm} \rightarrow \mu^{\pm} + \nu_{\mu} \, (\bar{\nu}_{\mu}) \tag{1}$$

$$K^{\pm}_{\mu 2} \rightarrow \mu^{\pm} + \nu_{\mu} \, (\bar{\nu}_{\mu}) \tag{2}$$

$$K^{0}_{\mu 3} \rightarrow \mu^{\pm} + \nu_{\mu} \, (\bar{\nu}_{\mu}) + \pi^{\mp} \tag{3}$$

$$K^{\pm}_{\mu 3} \rightarrow \mu^{\pm} + \nu_{\mu} \, (\bar{\nu}_{\mu}) + \pi^{0} \tag{4}$$

$$\mu^{\pm} \rightarrow e^{\pm} + \nu_{e} \, (\bar{\nu}_{e}) + \bar{\nu}_{\mu} \, (\nu_{\mu}). \tag{5}$$

The branching ratios for (2) and (4) are 0·638 and 0·032 of the charged kaon decays and (3) has a branching ratio of 0·268 of the long-lived neutral kaon decays. Other kaon decay modes contribute to the neutrino flux via the pions that they produce. It can be seen that the spectrum of neutrinos at ground level is closely related to the muon spectrum. This has been measured directly using magnetic spectrographs up to about 500 GeV and over the next decade of energy it can be inferred from the dependence of the muon intensity on depth underground provided that the muon energy loss mechanisms are assumed to be understood.

There have been a number of calculations of the ground-level neutrino intensity and angular distribution. Zatsepin and Kuz'min (1962) calculated the neutrino intensity from pion and muon decay and gave the variation with zenith angle from 0 to 90°. There is a considerably greater amount of energy available to the neutrino in the decay of the kaon in the $K_{\mu 2}$ mode than in pion decay, however. A kaon decaying in flight can give up to 95% of its energy to the neutrino while a pion can give only 43% of its energy. This kinematical effect is magnified by the steeply falling energy spectrum of pions and kaons so that an admixture of kaons in the atmospheric meson flux, while having only a marginal effect on the muon intensities, has a considerable effect on the total neutrino intensity. Cowsik *et al* (1966) and Osborne *et al* (1965) calculated the neutrino intensity including those from kaon decay. In the latter work the model for the propagation of the various cosmic ray components is as follows. The nucleons in the atmosphere are assumed to have an attenuation length of 120 g cm^{-2} and to produce pions and kaons with energy spectra having the same form but different intensities. Equal numbers of charged and neutral kaons are assumed to be generated and the attenuation lengths of the pions and kaons are both taken to be 120 g cm^{-2}. Under these assumptions the production spectrum of pions and kaons in the atmosphere can be inferred from the ground-level muon spectrum.

G

The spectrum used was that of Osborne *et al* (1964). One then uses the pion and kaon spectrum with the same assumptions concerning the propagation to derive the ground-level neutrino spectrum. In this way, to a first approximation, the effects of uncertainties in the attenuation lengths of the hadrons cancel out. The main uncertainty in the neutrino spectrum is due to lack of knowledge of the K/π ratio, the ratio of kaons to pions of the same energy produced in the interactions of high energy protons with air nuclei. Studies of the angular dependence of the muon intensity and the γ ray component of the cosmic rays suggest that $K/\pi < 40\%$. A value of 20% was adopted by Osborne *et al* (1965) and the effect of varying the ratio between zero and 40% was studied.

The CERN intersecting storage ring experiments are now beginning to provide information on the production of charged particles in proton–proton collisions at equivalent laboratory energies up to 1500 GeV (Bertin *et al* 1972). From these experiments the ratio of charged kaon to charged pion production as a function of momentum transferred to the particles is obtained. The ratio of charged particles ranges from about 10% to 15% which implies that the ratio of particles both charged and neutral ranges from about 13% to 20%. The ratio that we require is of pions to kaons produced with a given energy averaged over the falling spectrum of protons. When the storage ring data are complete it will be possible to predict a rather precise value for this ratio. At present we may take $20\% \pm 10\%$ as representing a rather generous estimate of the possible spread in values.

In order to derive the flux of neutrinos from muon decay the intensity of muons throughout the atmosphere must first be calculated. One then determines the muon decay spectrum, that is, the intensity of muons of a given energy at a given zenith angle which decay at all heights in the atmosphere. Finally the energy spectrum of neutrinos produced by the decay in flight of a muon of a given energy is folded in. In this case the resulting neutrino spectrum is insensitive to the K/π ratio as the experimentally measured ground-level muon spectrum is used as a datum.

Figure 1 shows the neutrino spectra and angular dependence thus derived for $K/\pi = 20\%$. Figure 1(*a*) shows the spectra at a zenith angle of $90°$. The components from pion, kaon and muon decay are shown separately. One sees that at low energies the latter dominates because of the long path length available for muon decay in the horizontal direction.

The curves show the total intensities of neutrinos and antineutrinos. The ratio of neutrinos to antineutrinos can be simply obtained from the measured charge ratios of the parent particles. Figure 1(*b*) shows the angular distribution of neutrinos as a function of energy normalized to the intensity in the horizontal direction. The uncertainty in the neutrino intensity owing to the range of $\pm 10\%$ in the K/π ratio is a function of zenith angle too. For instance, at 100 GeV the uncertainty in the horizontal direction is from $+5\%$ to -10%, while in the vertical direction it is from $+15\%$ to -25%. This is mainly due to the component from muon decay giving a larger contribution to the total flux at large zenith angles. It can be seen that it is preferable to make measurements in the near horizontal direction where the neutrino intensities are highest and the uncertainties are smallest.

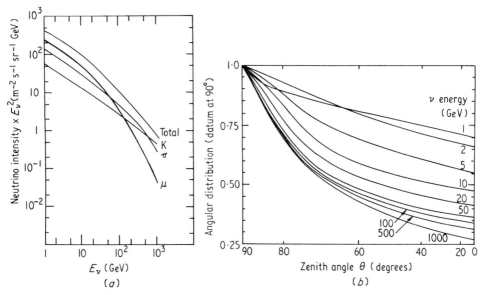

Figure 1. Spectra of neutrinos produced by π, K and μ decay in the atmosphere; (*a*) spectra at $\theta = 90°$, (*b*) angular distribution with respect to $\theta = 90°$ (Osborne *et al* 1965).

It has recently become apparent that a correction is necessary to the above neutrino spectra (Osborne *et al* 1972). The muon spectrum on which they were based was normalized to an intensity at 1 GeV/c of $2 \cdot 45 \times 10^{-3}$ cm^{-2}s^{-1}sr^{-1} (GeV/c)$^{-1}$ given by Rossi (1948). The recent work of Allkofer *et al* (1971) and Ashton *et al* (1972) indicate that this is 10% too low. An increase in the muon spectrum gives rise to a corresponding increase in the predicted neutrino spectrum. This change has been taken into account in the interpretation of the experimental results in §5.

2.2. Extraterrestrial neutrinos

The extraterrestrial neutrinos may be divided into three classes: galactic neutrinos produced as secondary particles in interactions between the nuclear component of the primary flux and the interstellar material; a diffuse background of extragalactic neutrinos some of which may come from similar interactions with the intergalactic material; and those that can be considered to be primaries themselves in that they come from discrete sources. High energy neutrinos (those with energy greater than 1 GeV), both primaries and secondaries, are expected to have their origin in the decay of pions produced in nuclear collisions. They will thus be associated with a corresponding flux of high energy γ rays, provided only that the source region is optically thin to the γ rays. Neutrinos come from the $\pi \to \mu \to e$ decay of charged pions while γ rays are produced by the neutral pions. The calculation of the relative numbers of neutrinos and γ rays is simplified where the density of matter in the source is so low that absorption and energy loss of pions and muons in the source does not occur. If the differential production spectrum of pions is of the form $AE^{-\alpha}$ the ratio of neutrinos to γ rays may be shown to be

$$\frac{F(\nu_\mu + \bar{\nu}_\mu)}{F(\gamma)} = 2 \cdot 34^{(1-\alpha)} + 2 \cdot 34 \left(\frac{5}{3\alpha} - \frac{3}{\alpha+2} + \frac{4}{3(\alpha+3)} \right) (1 - 0 \cdot 575^\alpha). \tag{6}$$

Hayakawa *et al* (1964), using a distribution of atomic hydrogen in the galactic disc from radio-astronomic 21 cm measurements together with the known cosmic ray primary intensity, predict the spectrum of galactic γ rays from π^0 production. For example, the total intensity of γ rays with energy greater than 1 GeV averaged over all directions is 3×10^{-6} cm^{-2} s^{-1} sr^{-1}. From this spectrum of γ rays, Hayakawa *et al* (1965) derive a corresponding spectrum of neutrinos. Equation (6) gives the ratio of neutrinos to γ rays when $\alpha = 2 \cdot 65$ as $0 \cdot 64$ and therefore the intensity of neutrinos with energy greater than 1 GeV is approximately 2×10^{-6} cm^{-2} s^{-1} sr^{-1}. This is about 4 orders of magnitude less than the integral intensity of atmospheric neutrinos above 1 GeV ($3 \cdot 0 \times 10^{-2}$ and $2 \cdot 0 \times 10^{-2}$ cm^{-2} s^{-1} sr^{-1} in the horizontal and vertical directions respectively). The integral spectrum of galactic neutrinos is less steep than the atmospheric one but at 10^4 GeV the difference is still more than two orders of magnitude. Clark *et al* (1971) using the OSO III satellite have made a measurement of the flux of extraterrestrial γ rays with energies greater than 100 MeV. This is the highest energy at which a positive measurement has been made. They observe a peak in intensity towards the galactic centre and a general enhancement in the plane of the galactic disc. The line intensity in the disc is given as $(3^{+1}_{-1 \cdot 2}) \times 10^{-5}$ cm^{-2} s^{-1} rad^{-1}. When this is converted to an effective omnidirectional flux the intensity is slightly greater than Hayakawa's prediction but agrees within experimental error. They also have given an upper limit to the diffuse, possibly partly extragalactic, background of 3×10^{-5} cm^{-2} s^{-1} sr^{-1}. It seems safe to infer from these values that, in the energy region from 1 GeV to several hundred GeV, the fraction of ground-level neutrinos that are of extraterrestrial origin is negligible provided that the sources do in fact produce γ rays as well as neutrinos.

It seems then that the prospects for high energy neutrino astronomy are not good but that because the atmospheric production of neutrinos can be predicted quite accurately one may use it for measurements of the neutrino interaction cross section.

3. Interactions of muon-neutrinos

The cosmic ray neutrino experiments were designed to detect the muon secondaries from the interactions of neutrinos with the surrounding rock. One would expect in only a few cases that the interaction would occur in the detector itself. The experiments therefore measure the overall intensity of neutrino-induced muons underground. The CERN neutrino experiments give information on the neutrino–nucleon interactions up to 10 GeV. This information may be used to predict the intensity of muons underground that are produced by neutrinos with energy up to 10 GeV. Any observed intensity in excess of this prediction will then give information on the behaviour of the cross section at higher energies. Because the target thickness is equal to the muon range one needs to know the mean fraction f of the incident neutrino energy that is retained by the muon. Muons will be produced by the following interactions.

3.1. The elastic interaction

The interaction between a neutrino and a nucleon in which the charge of the lepton changes but no additional particles are produced is termed an 'elastic interaction':

$$\nu_\mu + n \to \mu^- + p \tag{7a}$$

and

$$\bar{\nu}_\mu + p \to \mu^+ + n. \tag{7b}$$

The forms of the cross sections for these interactions have been calculated by Lee and Yang (1960). Below 1 GeV the total cross sections increase approximately linearly with energy, that of (7a) being about three times that of (7b). Near 1 GeV the effects of strong interactions in restricting the four-momentum transfer, q^2, to the nucleon limit this increase and both cross sections tend to the same asymptotic limit. This effect manifests itself as two vector and two axial-vector form factors in the expression for the differential cross section. The 'conserved vector current' hypothesis predicts that the vector form factors are identical to the electromagnetic form factor for electron–proton scattering. The variation with q^2 of the differential cross section for interaction (7a) has been measured in the CERN propane bubble chamber by Budagov *et al* (1969a) confirming that, for this interaction, the vector and axial-vector form factors are similar and that in the asymptotic limit beyond 1 GeV the cross section is $(0\cdot6 \pm 0\cdot2) \times 10^{-38}$ cm². The theory then predicts that the cross section for (7b) is the same and that $f \sim 0\cdot9$.

3.2. The inelastic interaction

As the neutrino energy increases beyond 1 GeV additional hadrons may be generated:

$$\nu_\mu + N \to \mu + N' + \pi + \ldots \tag{8}$$

These are termed 'inelastic interactions'. At energies near 1 GeV an important mechanism is the production of a single pion via the 1236 MeV/c^2 ($\frac{3}{2}$, $\frac{3}{2}$) isobar. The cross section for this has been measured by Budagov *et al* (1969b). It reaches an asymptotic value of $(1\cdot13 \pm 0\cdot28) \times 10^{-38}$ cm² beyond 2 GeV with $f = 0\cdot75$ again due to structure functions.

Inclusive cross sections (elastic and inelastic) for ν_μ in freon (CF_3Br) and propane bubble chambers have been measured by Budagov *et al* (1969c). Recently, data have become available from the freon-filled Gargamelle bubble chamber for both ν_μ and $\bar{\nu}_\mu$ beams (Perkins 1972). The linear dependence of the total cross section on energy that is observed is that predicted for point-like scattering by the nucleon (Bjorken and Paschos 1970). This scale-invariant behaviour is suggested by the experimental data on high energy electron–proton scattering. For high q^2, and energy transfers to the hadron system greater than 1 GeV, the inclusive differential cross section can be parametrized in the following way

$$\frac{d\sigma}{dxd\rho}=\frac{G^2M_p}{2\pi\rho^2}E\left\{K_1\frac{x^2}{2}+K_2(1-x)\mp K_3x\left(1-\frac{x}{2}\right)\right\}$$ (9)

where x is the fraction of neutrino energy, E, transferred to the hadron system, $G^2M_p/2\pi=0\cdot76\times10^{-38}$ cm^2 GeV^{-1}, $\rho=M_pE\,x/q^2$ and K_1, K_2, K_3 are constants to be determined. The $\mp K_3$ gives ν_μ and $\bar{\nu}_\mu$ cross sections respectively. From electron–proton scattering data, $K_1=K_2$, implying that the nucleon is made up of spin-$\frac{1}{2}$ partons. Integrating (9) over all ρ from 0·5 to infinity gives

$$\frac{d\sigma}{dx}=1\cdot53\times10^{-38}E\,K_2\left\{1-\left(1\pm\frac{K_3}{K_2}\right)\left(x-\frac{x^2}{2}\right)\right\}.$$ (10)

The Gargamelle data when converted to a material with $Z/A=0\cdot5$ such as rock give $\sigma(\nu_\mu N)=(0\cdot67\pm0\cdot14)\times10^{-38}\,E$ cm^2 and $\sigma(\bar{\nu}_\mu N)/\sigma(\nu_\mu N)=0\cdot40\pm0\cdot02$. Thus $K_2=0\cdot49\pm0\cdot07$ and $K_3/K_2=-0\cdot86\pm0\cdot04$. Substituting these values in (10) one finds that $f=0\cdot51$ for ν_μ and $f=0\cdot58$ for $\bar{\nu}_\mu$. In previous analyses of the cosmic ray neutrino data (Krishnaswamy *et al* 1971a, Chen *et al* 1971) the cross section for ν_μ measured by Budagov (1969c) was used. This is 20% larger than the present value. In the absence of experimental data $\sigma(\bar{\nu}_\mu N)$ was generally assumed to be equal to $\sigma(\nu_\mu N)$ although the possibility of a smaller value was mentioned.

If the scaling hypothesis is correct the cross sections will continue to rise linearly until the effect of higher order weak interactions imposes a cut-off. Alternatively if the weak interaction is mediated by the intermediate boson, W$^\pm$, of Lee and Yang (1960) then an additional factor

$$\left(1+\frac{M_pEx}{M_W^2}\right)^{-2}$$

multiplies the right-hand side of equation (9). The effect is to reduce the rise of the cross section to a logarithmic dependence on energy, $\sigma\propto\ln(2M_pE/M_W^2)$, for $E\gg M_W^2/M_p$. At the same time f tends to unity.

3.3. Production of the intermediate boson

If the intermediate boson exists it can be produced in the following interactions.

$$\nu_\mu+Z\rightarrow\mu+W+Z$$ (11a)

$$\nu_\mu+N\rightarrow\mu+W+N$$ (11b)

$$\nu_\mu+N\rightarrow\mu+W+N'+\pi\ldots$$ (11c)

The virtual muon and boson are created at a semi-weak vertex and are made real by scattering in the Coulomb field of a nucleus. The minimum momentum transfer to the nucleus is $M_W^2/2E$. At high neutrino energies the momentum transfer is small and the nucleus recoils as a whole. This is termed coherent scattering (11a). At lower energies the momentum transfer may be so large that scattering probably occurs off a single nucleon (incoherent scattering (11b)), and additional hadrons may be produced (inelastic scattering (11c)). Total cross sections for these interactions have now been calculated for M_W up to 20 GeV/c^2 and E up to 1000 GeV (Chen 1970, Brown and Smith 1971). Differential cross sections have also been calculated from which the f value for the muon produced in (11) has been determined (Chen *et al* 1971). Near to threshold $f \simeq M_\mu/(M_W + M_\mu)$ while at very high energies f tends to 0·6.

The W boson decays within 10^{-18} s and a second 'decay' muon may be produced. The ratio of the decay rates $(W \to \mu + \nu_\mu)/(W \to e + \nu_e)$ is expected to be close to unity but the boson may also decay into two or more hadrons and the ratio of leptonic to nonleptonic decays is unknown. This introduces a considerable uncertainty into the rate of muon production. The 'decay' muon will retain 0·25 of the energy of the boson.

For a given neutrino energy the cross section for boson production decreases rapidly with M_W. The negative result of accelerator searches for the boson has lead to a lower limit to the mass at 99 % confidence of $M_W > 1·8$ GeV/c.

4. The neutrino experiments

4.1. The KGF experiment

The experiment was begun in early 1965 and completed in June 1969. Detection of muons from cosmic ray neutrino interaction was reported by Achar *et al* (1965). A full account of the experiment has been given by Krishnaswamy *et al* (1971a) where a complete list of references is given. The apparatus in its final form comprised five telescopes and two magnetic spectrographs (figure 2). These were located in a tunnel as shown in figure 3 at a depth of 2316 m, or $7·0 \times 10^5$ g cm^{-2}, of rock for which $Z/A = 0·495$ and $Z^2/A = 6·3$. Telescopes 1 and 2, the first to be constructed, were each made up of two vertical walls of plastic scintillators of area 3 m × 2 m. Between the walls there were nine trays of neon flash-tubes each containing 210 tubes in 4 layers. The tubes, 2 m long and 1·8 cm in diameter, were placed horizontally so that the projected zenith angle of a particle trajectory could be measured. Two vertical walls of 2·5 cm of lead were included to distinguish electrons from muons. In 1966 telescopes 3, 4 and 5 were added. These had 2 m × 2 m scintillator walls between which were 10 flash-tube trays in a crossed geometry to enable spatial angles to be determined. In these telescopes the absorber was in the form of four 7·5 cm thick iron walls. Spectrographs 1 and 2 were added in 1967. Each had 2 m × 4 m vertical walls of scintillator and twenty trays of flash-tubes disposed around a solid iron electromagnet 40 cm thick. Additional scintillators above the magnet increased the rate of detection of near vertical atmospheric muons. Initially the trigger for all telescopes was a four-fold coincidence between pulses from a pair of photomultipliers viewing 1 m^2 area of one wall and a similar pair on the other wall. For the spectrographs both top–side and side–side coincidences were accepted. From the beginning of 1968 telescopes 3, 4 and 5 were changed to 'one side triggering' demanding a two-fold

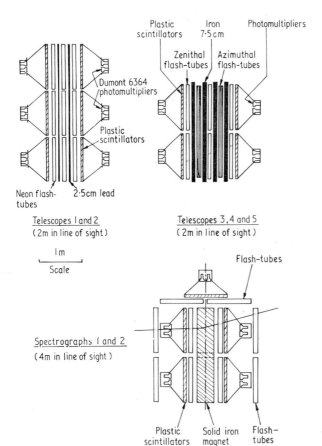

Figure 2. The KGF detectors (Krishnaswamy *et al* 1971a).

coincidence from a scintillation element on one wall only. Although the accidental coincidence rate was then high, genuine events could still be distinguished by the tracks in the flash-tube arrays. The aperture of the telescopes was thereby increased and it was possible to detect neutrino events occurring inside the detector. When a trigger was provided by the scintillators a 30 μs delay was introduced to allow the photomultiplier pulses to be recorded on oscilloscopes and then a high voltage pulse was applied to the electrodes of the flash-tube arrays. The flash-tubes were photographed by open shutter cameras. From the photographs one could measure the projected zenith angle (PZA) of the track and, for telescopes 3, 4 and 5, the azimuth angle to

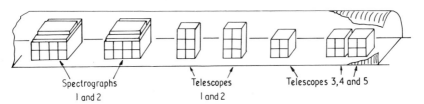

Figure 3. Disposition of the detectors in the tunnel at KGF (Krishnaswamy *et al* 1971a).

within about one degree. The degree of accompaniment of the penetrating particle by an electromagnetic component could be determined and in some cases the sense of direction of the incident particle could also be inferred from secondaries of its interaction in the telescope. A check could be made that the penetrating particle was within the aperture where there was 100% probability of detection. In about 12% of the observed events the penetrating particle passed through one scintillator only, the other two-fold coincidence being provided by accompanying electrons or photons.

A total of 179 'in-geometry' penetrating particle events were recorded (only those 'one side trigger' trajectories passing through more than 1 flash-tube tray were included). The distribution of these events with PZA is shown in figure 4. The distribution depends on the differential aperture of the detectors and the angular distribution of the atmospheric and neutrino-induced muons at the site. At this depth the vertical atmospheric muon intensity is decreasing exponentially with depth and this determines the form of the angular distribution. The best fit to this angular distribution as found by Krishnaswamy *et al* (1971b) is

$$I(\theta) = 1 \cdot 1 \times 10^{-6} \sec \theta \exp \{-9 (\sec \theta - 1)\} \text{ m}^{-2} \text{ s}^{-1} \text{ sr}^{-1}. \tag{12}$$

When this is folded into the aperture of the detectors the left-hand distribution in figure 4, peaking at 22°, is obtained. Coulomb scattering of atmospheric muons, which will have a mean energy of about 300 GeV when traversing the detectors, is negligible. The angular distribution of neutrino-induced muons on the other hand will show a slight peaking in the horizontal direction, accentuated by the differential aperture of the detectors. The precise angular distribution depends on the energy distribution of the neutrinos which produce the observed muons; this in turn depends upon the form of the neutrino cross section. The right-hand curve in figure 4 is for a cross section that we denote by 'case 1' (see §5). It was concluded that the 16 events with PZA greater than 50° were due to neutrinos.

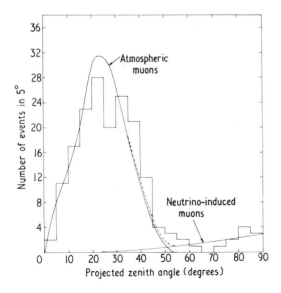

Figure 4. Expected and observed angular distributions of events at KGF.

Of these events 9 were due to single particles, 2 were due to a neutrino interacting within the detector and 5 had multiple particles diverging from an interaction within the tunnel wall. None of these had interaction points sufficiently deep in the rock for the tracks to be ascribed to a pair of muons (the signature of W-boson production and decay). Only two of these neutrino-muons traversed the spectrographs. One had momentum between 1 and 2 GeV/c; the other, illustrated in figure 5, was not less than

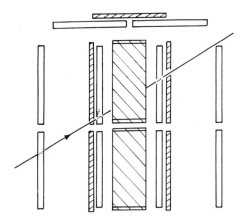

Figure 5. A neutrino-induced muon in the KGF spectrograph, probably upward moving.

4 GeV/c and was probably upward moving as shown by the knock-on electron in the centre tray.

The total exposure for all detectors for PZA greater than $50°$ was $6·2 \times 10^9$ m² s sr. Because the neutrino-induced muon intensity is not isotropic it is not meaningful to quote an overall average intensity. Assuming an angular distribution as for 'case 1' the horizontal intensity is $(3·5 \pm 0·9) \times 10^{-9}$ m⁻² s⁻¹ sr⁻¹.

4.2. The CWI experiment

4.2.1. Stage 1. The experiment was performed in two stages, the first starting in October 1964 and running until August 1967 and the second beginning in 1969 and being completed in November 1971. The apparatus for the first stage was set up in a tunnel at the 76th level in the mine at a depth of $8·71 \times 10^5$ g cm⁻² of rock having $Z/A = 0·499$ and $Z^2/A = 5·5$. The first evidence for neutrino-induced muons was published by Reines *et al* (1965) at the same time as that for the KGF experiment. A full report of the first stage has been given by Reines *et al* (1971a). Initially the detector was made up of two walls of 36 tanks arranged along a tunnel in 6 'bays'. Figure 6 shows two bays and gives the dimensions. The tanks were of lucite filled with liquid scintillator and were viewed by two 5 inch photomultipliers at each end. In 1966 the detector was extended to 54 tanks in 9 bays. Each of these additional tanks had a sensitive length of 4·71 m. The minimum requirement for the recording of an 'event' was a four-fold coincidence between the photomultipliers in one tank. The ratio of the pulse heights from the pair of photomultipliers at one end to the pulse heights from those at the other gave the longitudinal position of the scintillation,

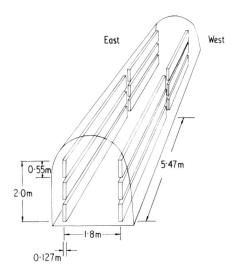

Figure 6. Two of the nine bays of the CWI stage 1 detector.

if due to a single particle, to within ± 0.15 m. The energy deposited could also be measured giving some indication of the angle of incidence. A minimum ionizing muon at normal incidence would deposit 20 MeV. During the run of the experiment a total of 346 events was recorded. They were divided into categories depending on the number of tanks giving a signal and their relative positions, as follows.

Category 1A: 32 events each showing an eight-fold coincidence involving one tank on each side of the tunnel. These were interpreted as single muons with PZA 40° to 50°, 50° to 70° or 70° to 90° depending on the positions, upper, middle or lower, of each of the tanks.

Category 1B: 6 events each involving one tank on one side and two tanks on the other.

Category 2: 11 events involving 4 or more tanks on both sides of the tunnel.

Category 3: 212 events in single tanks anywhere in the array.

Category 4: 81 events each involving 2 or 3 adjacent tanks one above the other, presumably due to near vertical muons.

Category 5: 4 events with two signals from a single tank a few microseconds apart. Detailed studies of these events indicate that it is highly probable that each was due to a muon stopping and decaying in the tank.

The events in categories 1A and 1B were used to obtain the flux of neutrino-induced muons. At the depth of operation the vertical intensity of atmospheric muons must be at least 3 times less than that for the KGF experiment and the angular distribution is steeper. This means that no atmospheric muons would be expected to traverse the apparatus with PZA greater than 40° during the running time of the experiment. Events in categories 1B and 2 could be due either to near horizontal neutrino-induced multiple particles or near vertical showers from atmospheric muon interactions. From a detailed consideration of the geometry it was concluded that probably 4 of the 1B events were neutrino induced and that all the category 2 events were atmospheric muons. The result is that 36 events are taken to be due to neutrino-induced muons passing through both sides of the array. The uncertainty due to ambiguous events is considered to be less than the statistical fluctuation on this number. Again to convert this to a horizontal intensity the angular distribution of neutrino-induced muons is needed. Chen *et al* (1971) using an angular distribution not significantly different from that of 'case 1' obtained a value $(4 \cdot 2 \pm 0 \cdot 7) \times 10^{-9}$ m^{-2} s^{-1} sr^{-1}. Of the single tank events then the ratio of atmospheric to neutrino-induced muons is approximately 2 to 1.

4.2.2. Stage 2. In order to achieve better angular resolution and to remove ambiguities in the interpretation a further development of the detector was undertaken. The new detector was built in a tunnel at the 77th level (depth $8 \cdot 84 \times 10^5$ g cm^{-2}). The same scintillator tanks were used, now arranged in 12 single bays and 4 double bays. The scintillators provided a trigger for a crossed hodoscope of 48 000 neon flash-tubes identical to those used in the KGF experiment. Figure 7 shows two views of a single bay. The three scintillators are surrounded by 27 vertical and 27 horizontal flash-tube 'elements'. Each element contains 56 tubes in a double layer. Photocells attached to the ends of each of the flash-tubes allowed the configuration of tubes that had flashed to be displayed on a lamp board and be recorded photographically. The reconstruction of an actual event is shown in figure 7.

A final report on the stage 2 experiment has yet to be published. Interim results have been given by Sandie *et al* (1970) and F Reines *et al* (1971 unpublished). From an analysis of events with well defined PZA a horizontal neutrino-induced muon inten-

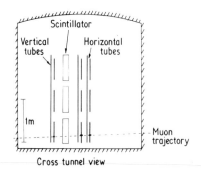

Cross tunnel view

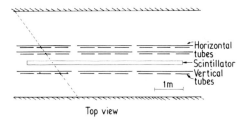

Top view

Figure 7. One bay of the CWI stage 2 detector showing a large zenith angle muon trajectory (Sandie *et al* 1970).

sity of $(4\cdot6\pm0\cdot5)\times10^{-9}$ m^{-2} s^{-1} sr^{-1} has been obtained (H Coxell 1972 private communication).

4.3. The Utah experiment

The Utah detector is situated at a vertical depth of $1\cdot8\times10^5$ g cm^{-2} in a mine in the Wasatch mountain range. At this relatively shallow depth the vertical intensity of atmospheric muons is approximately 2×10^{-3} m^{-2} s^{-1} sr^{-1} and therefore a directional device is needed to pick out upward going neutrino-induced muons. Figure 8 shows two views of the detector. It consists of 4 water-filled Cherenkov counters interspersed with 15 columns of 40 cylindrical spark counters. Light collectors are installed on opposite walls of the Cherenkov tanks. A coincidence between pulses from two left-hand walls or two right-hand walls provides a trigger for the spark counters. The position of the spark along the axis of the counter is determined to an accuracy of about 1 cm by sonic ranging. The vertical resolution of the particle trajectory is limited by the 15 cm diameter of the counters. The Cherenkov wall pulses and spark positions are recorded on magnetic tape. Time of flight measurements on the wall pulses also add to the directional information. Solid iron magnets in which the field runs vertically allow the momentum to be determined up to approximately 100 GeV/c.

The detector was put into operation progressively from 1967 onwards and an improved fast timing system was introduced in early 1969. Up to June 1969 two definite neutrino events had been recorded (Hendricks *et al* 1970). The first of these is shown in figure 8 and indicates an inelastic neutrino interaction within the detector. Wall pulses occurred on the left walls of the two inner Cherenkov counters and the fast timing, which shows a delay of 14 ns between the pulses confirms the leftward

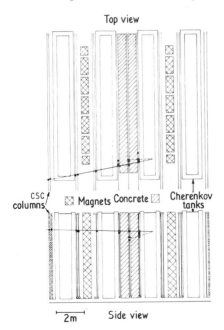

Figure 8. The Utah detector showing a neutrino event (Hendricks *et al* 1970).

travel. The second neutrino-induced muon passed upward through all four tanks at a zenith angle of 99°. A study of its trajectory through the magnets indicated that its momentum was greater than 45 GeV/c, a surprisingly high value in view of the expected low mean energy of neutrino-induced muons.

It can be seen that the Utah detector can give considerably more detailed information about individual neutrino interactions than the KGF and CWI detectors. However, the aperture for neutrino detection is relatively small (approximately 47 m² sr). This aperture is restricted because of the stringent criteria for directional determination.

5. Interpretation of the experimental results

For various assumptions concerning the neutrino–nucleus cross section the underground intensity of muons produced by cosmic ray neutrinos can be calculated. Using the simple detectors described above, the intensity measured in a particular direction is that summed over all muon energies above the threshold for the detector (100 MeV for the KGF telescopes, 20 MeV for the CWI scintillators). The general expression for the intensity at zenith angle θ can be written

$$I(\theta) = \frac{N_A}{A} \int_{E_{min}}^{\infty} N_\nu (E_\nu, \theta) \, R(f E_\nu) \, \sigma(E_\nu) \, dE_\nu. \tag{13}$$

$N_\nu(E_\nu, \theta)$ is the intensity of neutrinos of energy E_ν, N_A/A is the number of nuclei per gram, $\sigma(E_\nu)$ is the total cross section per nucleus for the interaction under consideration, $R(f E_\nu)$ is the effective range in rock of muons of energy $f E_\nu$ that are produced by these neutrinos. E_{min} is the threshold energy of the interaction or of the detector whichever is the lower.

It is apparent that from an observed neutrino-induced muon intensity alone it will not be possible to determine uniquely the behaviour of the total cross section with energy. A model for the extrapolation of the cross section beyond 10 GeV must be taken. Chen *et al* (1971) discuss a number of possibilities. Some of these can now be ruled out on the basis of the recent accelerator data described in §3. Here we shall take two simple models A and B only. In both we take into account the measured ratio of ν_μ and $\bar{\nu}_\mu$ cross sections.

In model A we assume that the neutrino total cross section rises linearly with energy as $(0\cdot67 \pm 0\cdot14) \times 10^{-38} \, E$ cm² until it saturates at an energy E_0. Beyond this energy it is constant. E_0 must be greater than or equal to 10 GeV. Below E_0, f takes the value 0·51 for ν_μ and 0·58 for $\bar{\nu}_\mu$. Above E_0, f tends to unity. One attempts to set an upper limit to E_0 from the observations. In figure 9 the comparison between the observed and predicted numbers is made. The predicted numbers of events are as for the exposure of the KGF detectors. One compares numbers rather than intensities because the conversion from the observed number depends upon the angular distribution and thus upon the assumed model. Predictions are given for $E_0 = 10$ and 100 GeV and for no cut-off. $E_0 = 10$ GeV is the 'case 1' referred to in §4. The CWI results are expressed as equivalent numbers for the KGF experiment and the broken lines show the one standard deviation spread of the weighted mean. It can be seen

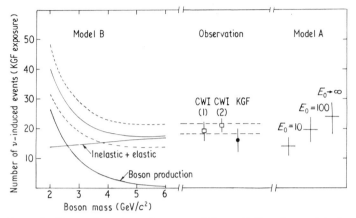

Figure 9. Observed numbers of events and the predictions for models A and B.

that the statistical error is less than the error on the predictions. The latter is compounded of $\pm 21\%$ in the cross sections and $\pm 8\%$ in the neutrino intensity. The observed rate favours a cut-off at about 100 GeV but the case of no cut-off is only 0·7 standard deviations higher.

In model B it is assumed that the intermediate boson exists. The predicted number of events will then depend on its mass. Contributions come from the production of a real boson (11), and the elastic and inelastic interaction. The former gives a number of events that decreases rapidly with M_W. The latter gives a rate slowly increasing with M_W because of the decreasing effect of the boson propagator term. Uncertainties in the inelastic prediction are as for model A; uncertainties in boson production are estimated at $\pm 10\%$ in the cross section and $\pm 15\%$ in energy transferred to the prompt muon combined with the uncertainty in the leptonic branching ratio. The predicted rate is seen to pass through a very broad minimum at 6 GeV/c^2; the broken lines give the one standard deviation spread. Comparison with the observed numbers shows that there is no upper limit to M_W since this corresponds to $E_0 \to \infty$ in model A. The lower limit is 2·2 GeV/c^2 at the 95% confidence level.

6. Some astrophysical aspects of the neutrino experiments

6.1. Extraterrestrial neutrino intensity limit

As stated in §2 it is very unlikely that the extraterrestrial intensity of neutrinos above 1 GeV is a significant fraction of that produced in the atmosphere. However, an experimental upper limit to the overall extraterrestrial intensity can be obtained from the data of figure 9. Case 1, where the neutrino cross section rises no further beyond the presently observed region gives the minimum possible number of events due to atmospheric neutrinos. A comparison of the observed value with this predicted number then gives an upper limit of 1·0 at the two standard deviation level for the ratio of extraterrestrial to atmospheric neutrinos in the energy region from one to a few tens of GeV.

A study of the arrival directions of the neutrino-induced muons in the KGF and CWI experiments gave no evidence for localized sources on the celestial sphere.

A limit can be set on the low energy (100 to 500 MeV) extraterrestrial flux from the number of muons stopping in the CWI stage 1 detector (category 5 events). Tam and Young (1970) have made an approximate calculation of the neutrino spectrum below 1 GeV. The majority of the stopping muons will have been produced by these low energy neutrinos. The observed rate (4 events) is a factor of 4 greater than the predicted rate. In view of the low statistical accuracy and the uncertainty in the predictions this difference cannot be regarded as significant. However, an upper limit to the extraterrestrial flux of approximately 3 times the atmospheric one can be set. Steigman and Strittmatter (1971) have calculated the extraterrestrial flux of low energy muon-neutrinos produced in infrared sources in galactic nuclei under the hypothesis that their energy comes from matter–antimatter annihilation. This flux exceeds the experimental upper limit and it follows that annihilation is most probably not the source of energy.

6.2. Gravitational radiation

An upper limit on high energy neutrinos associated with Weber pulses has been given by Reines *et al* (1971b). Weber (1971) attributes the pulses in his detectors to gravitational radiation, possibly originating in the collapse of objects of stellar mass in the region of the galactic centre. It seems reasonable that some of the energy of the collapse may appear as high energy neutrinos. The times of the neutrino events in the CWI apparatus had been recorded to within ± 2 minutes and these could be compared with the arrival times of gravitational radiation pulses. In 227 complete days of running 2 coincidences occurred while the expected number of random coincidences was 0.7. From this it was estimated that the upper limit to the fraction of total Weber pulse energy appearing as muon-neutrinos, with energy above 1 GeV, is 5×10^{-8}.

7. Conclusions

The cosmic ray muon-neutrino experiments were being planned at the same time that the first accelerator neutrino experiment was being performed at the Brookhaven proton synchrotron (Danby *et al* 1962). In the ten years since then, while the cosmic ray experiments were under way, the accelerator physicists have increased their event rates by a factor of 10^4 due to improved beams and larger bubble chamber detectors. Detailed studies of the neutrino–nucleus interaction are now possible up to 10 GeV. The absolute value of the cross section still has a large error, however, at $\pm 21\%$ mainly due to uncertainty in the absolute value of the neutrino spectrum. By 1974 when the neutrino beam from the National Accelerator Laboratory proton synchrotron is in full operation neutrino interactions up to about 100 GeV should be observed. It seems from the cosmic ray experiments that no great surprises are in store with regard to the behaviour of the total cross section in the decade from 10 to 100 GeV.

If the form of the variation of the cross section with energy is determined then the cosmic ray results will enable its absolute value to be calculated possibly with higher accuracy than can be obtained from the accelerator results alone. This is because it seems that one can calculate the energy spectrum of cosmic ray neutrinos produced in the atmosphere with rather greater accuracy than it is possible to determine the intensity of an accelerator-produced neutrino beam.

References

Achar C V *et al* 1965 *Phys. Lett.* **18** 196–9
Allkofer O C, Carstensen K and Dau W D 1971 *Phys. Lett.* **36B** 425–8.
Ashton F, Tsuji K and Wolfendale A W 1972 *Nuovo Cim.* **9B** 344–50
Bertin A *et al* 1972 *Phys. Lett.* **41B** 201–4
Bjorken J D and Paschos E A 1970 *Phys. Rev.* **D1** 3151–60
Brown R W and Smith J 1971 *Phys. Rev.* **D3** 207–23
Budagov I *et al* 1969a *Nuovo Cim. Lett.* **2** 689–95
—— 1969b *Phys. Lett.* **29B** 524–8
—— 1969c *Phys. Lett.* **30B** 364–8
Chen H H 1970 *Nuovo Cim.* **69A** 585–612
Chen H H, Kropp W R, Sobel H W and Reines F 1971 *Phys. Rev.* **D4** 99–121
Clark G W, Garmire G P and Kraushaar W L 1971 *Proc. 12th Int. Conf. on Cosmic Rays* (Hobart: University of Tasmania) vol 1 91–6
Cowsik R, Yash Pal and Tandon S N 1966 *Proc. Indian Acad. Sci.* **43A** 217–43
Danby G *et al* 1962 *Phys. Rev. Lett.* **9** 36–44
Hayakawa S, Nishimura J and Yamamoto Y 1965 *Prog. Theor. Phys. Suppl.* **32** 104–53
Hayakawa S, Okuda H, Tanaka Y and Yamamoto Y 1964 *Prog. Theor. Phys. Suppl.* **30** 153–203
Hendricks M B *et al* 1970 *Acta Phys. Hung.* **29** suppl 4 313–8
Krishnaswamy M *et al* 1971a *Proc. R. Soc.* **A323** 489–509
—— 1971b *Proc. R. Soc.* **A323** 511–22
Lee T D and Yang C N 1960 *Phys. Rev. Lett.* **4** 307–11
Markov M A and Zheleznykh I M 1961 *Nucl. Phys.* **27** 385–94
Menon M G K 1964 *Proc. Int. Conf. on Cosmic Rays, Jaipur* (Bombay: TIFR) vol 6 152–76
Menon M G K, Ramana Murthy P V, Sreekantan B V and Miyake S 1963 *Nuovo Cim.* **30** 1208–19
Osborne J L, Said S S and Wolfendale A W 1965 *Proc. Phys. Soc.* **86** 93–9
Osborne J L, Wolfendale A W and Palmer N S 1964 *Proc. Phys. Soc.* **84** 911–3
Osborne J L, Wolfendale A W and Young E C M 1972 '*Neutrino '72*' (Hungary: OMKDK-Tech-noinform) vol 2 233–37
Perkins D H 1972 *16th Rochester Conference, Chicago-Batavia September* 1972
Reines F, Jenkins T L, Crouch M F and Sellschop J P F 1964 *Proc. Int. Conf. on Cosmic Rays, Jaipur* (Bombay: TIFR) vol 6 182–8
Reines F *et al* 1965 *Phys. Rev. Lett.* **15** 429–33
—— 1971a *Phys. Rev.* **D4** 80–98
—— 1971b *Phys. Rev. Lett.* **26** 1451–2
Rossi B 1948 *Rev. Mod. Phys.* **20** 537–83
Sandie W G *et al* 1970 *Proc. 6th Interamerican Seminar on Cosmic Rays* (La Paz: Universidad Mayor de San Andres) vol 4 833–46
Steigman G and Strittmatter P A 1971 *Astron. and Astrophys.* **11** 279–85
Tam A C and Young E C M 1970 *Acta Phys. Hung.* **29** suppl. 4 307–12
Weber J 1971 *Phys. Rev. Lett.* **24** 276–9
Zatsepin G T and Kuz'min V A 1962 *Sov. Phys.-JETP* **14** 1294–1300

H

Chapter 6

Electron-neutrinos

E C M Young

1. Introduction

Since its existence was first suggested by Pauli, as early as 1930, the neutrino has remained the most elusive and fascinating of all the elementary particles. It was more than two decades later that the actual experimental detection of the electron-neutrino was achieved by Reines and Cowan (1953). This became possible because large nuclear reactors constructed in the early 1950s produced for the first time very intense beams of antineutrinos with an intensity of the order of $10^{13}\bar{\nu}$ cm^{-2}s^{-1} at the detector. Later accelerator neutrino experiments demonstrated that there are two types of neutrinos, the neutrino (and the antineutrino) associated with the muon (ν_μ, $\bar{\nu}_\mu$) and the neutrino associated with the electron (ν_e, $\bar{\nu}_e$). So far experiments using the cosmic radiation have been carried out to study the interactions of only the muon-neutrino, a situation that is due to the fact that the muon produced in muon-neutrino interactions has a much longer range than that of the electron produced in corresponding electron-neutrino interactions and the effective target thickness is greater.

In this chapter we are concerned with the study of the electron neutrino ν_e and antineutrino $\bar{\nu}_e$. We further limit ourselves to 'natural' electron neutrinos at ground-level, that is the 'artificial' electron-neutrinos from nuclear reactors and accelerators are excluded from our present study.

The natural electron-neutrinos at ground level come from three main sources.

(i) *Terrestrial neutrinos.* The decays of radioactive elements in the earth's crust contribute a small flux of low energy $\bar{\nu}_e$. It is estimated that this flux amounts to only about 7×10^6 cm^{-2}s^{-1}, assuming an effective earth crust thickness of 15 km, and of this flux only about 10^5 cm^{-2}s^{-1} have energies above the threshold for detection by protons (1.8 MeV $+ \bar{\nu}_e + p \rightarrow n + e^+$). This small flux of terrestrial neutrinos will not be considered further here.

(ii) *Extraterrestrial neutrinos.* These are electron-neutrinos produced in the nuclear reactions which are believed to take place in the core of any hydrogen-burning star. The Sun, being the nearest star, is the most intense source of ν_e at the Earth and it is the solar neutrinos which have become the subject of much study. The energies of the solar neutrinos are relatively low, the maximum being 14.06 MeV. It will be seen later that the solar neutrino flux, supposedly intense, which has been studied theoretically in detail and which is being searched for with very large detectors, has still not been detected with absolute certainty. The eventual outcome of the solar neutrino experiment will undoubtedly have far-reaching consequences for our understanding of stellar evolution.

(iii) *Cosmic ray neutrinos.* These are the decay products of muons and, to a small extent, kaons which are produced in the Earth's atmosphere as a result of the nuclear interactions of primary cosmic rays with air nuclei. The energy spectrum of cosmic ray electron-neutrinos extends from the MeV region up to very high energies and calculations of the energy spectra have so far been made up to 1 TeV. At relatively low energies the intensity depends on the geomagnetic rigidity cut-off appropriate to the location in question. This arises from the geomagnetic effect on the intensity of primary cosmic rays. For our present discussion we arbitrarily divide the neutrino spectrum into the low energy region (below approximately 5 GeV) where the geomagnetic effect is noticeable, and the high energy region (above approximately 5 GeV) where this effect is negligible.

It should be noted at the outset that no natural electron-neutrinos have yet been detected experimentally with certainty. While the detection of solar neutrinos will shed light on our knowledge of the solar structure, as mentioned earlier, predictions and estimates of the energy spectra of cosmic ray neutrinos are required in order to separate the genuine solar neutrino signal from its background due to cosmic ray neutrinos as well as to complete the phenomenology of cosmic rays.

2. Solar neutrinos

2.1. Neutrino fluxes

It is generally believed that the Sun's energy is generated by nuclear reactions which fuse light elements into heavier ones. These reactions occur in the interior of the Sun where the temperature is sufficiently high (about 15×10^6 K). Whereas radiations from the Sun come from its surface, solar neutrinos will give us a direct view of the solar core. As the expected energy spectrum of solar neutrinos depends on the solar parameters, such as the constitution, density and temperature of the solar core, the measurement of the neutrino flux will establish these parameters, especially the temperature, more accurately.

There are two distinct processes for fusing four protons to form a helium nucleus with the emission of electron-neutrinos.

(i) *Proton–proton chain*. This is thought to be the dominant source of energy production in the Sun. The first step of the chain is to combine two protons to form a deuteron,

$p + p \rightarrow D + e^+ + \nu_e$ ($E_\nu = 0$–0.42 MeV),

with a small admixture of the 'pep' reaction

$p + e^- + p \rightarrow D + \nu_e$ ($E_\nu = 1.44$ MeV).

This is followed by

$p + D \rightarrow {}^3He + \gamma$.

The next reaction can go in one of three directions

${}^3He + {}^3He \rightarrow {}^4He + 2p$ ($\sim 91\%$)

or

${}^3He + {}^4He \rightarrow {}^7Be + \gamma$ ($\sim 9\%$)

${}^7Be + e^- \rightarrow {}^7Li + \nu_e$ ($E_\nu = 0.86$ MeV)

$\phantom{{}^7Be + e^-} \rightarrow {}^7Li^* + \nu_e$ ($E_\nu = 0.38$ MeV)

${}^7Li + p \rightarrow 2{}^4He$

or

${}^3He + {}^4He \rightarrow {}^7Be + \gamma$ ($\sim 0.1\%$)

${}^7Be + p \rightarrow {}^8B + \gamma$

${}^8B \rightarrow {}^8Be^* + e^+ + \nu_e$ ($E_\nu = 0$–14.06 MeV)

${}^8Be^* \rightarrow 2{}^4He$.

Three of the reactions in the proton–proton chain are of special importance in the solar neutrino experiment. They are the basic proton–proton reaction, the pep reaction and the decay of ${}^8B$. All three reactions produce neutrinos but only those neutrinos from the latter two reactions are energetic enough to be detected by the capture of ${}^{37}Cl$ as in the experiment of Davis (1964 *et seq*). The detection of the pep neutrinos will establish the basic hypothesis that nuclear fusion of protons provides the energy source of the Sun. The neutrinos from the decay of ${}^8B$, being the most energetic, have the largest cross section for being captured. Furthermore, their flux is very temperature sensitive (of the order of T_c^{14}), owing to the high Coulomb barrier which must be overcome to form the parent ${}^8B$ nucleus. It is this fact that suggests the possibility of determining the solar core temperature T_c accurately from a measured neutrino flux from the ${}^8B$ decay.

(ii) *The* CNO *cycle.* This cycle is so named because it involves C, N and O nuclei as catalysts in fusing four protons into a helium nucleus.

$^{12}C + p \rightarrow {}^{13}N + \gamma$

$^{13}N \rightarrow {}^{13}C + e^+ + \nu_e$ $(E_\nu = 0{-}1{\cdot}20$ MeV$)$

$^{13}C + p \rightarrow {}^{14}N + \gamma$

$^{14}N + p \rightarrow {}^{15}O + \gamma$

$^{15}O \rightarrow {}^{15}N + e^+ + \nu_e$ $(E_\nu = 0{-}1{\cdot}74$ MeV$)$

$^{15}N + p \rightarrow {}^{12}C + {}^4He.$

The expected fractions of the solar energy generated in the proton–proton chain and the CNO cycle depend on parameters such as density and especially the temperature used in the solar models. Over the last decade or so, the solar models have been steadily improved (Bahcall 1964a, Sears 1964, Bahcall *et al* 1968, Bahcall and Ulrich 1971, Abraham and Iben 1971). The calculated neutrino fluxes from the various reactions, based on the 'standard' model, and the capture rates in ^{37}Cl are given in table 1 (Bahcall and Ulrich 1971).

Table 1. Solar neutrino fluxes and capture rates in ^{37}Cl (Bahcall and Ulrich 1971)

Source	Neutrino energy (MeV)	Flux on Earth (ϕ in cm^{-2} s^{-1})	Cross section (σ in cm^2)	Capture rate in ^{37}Cl ($\phi\sigma$ in SNU†)
$p + p \rightarrow D + e^+ + \nu_e$	0–0·42	$6\cdot0 \times 10^{10}$	0	0
$p + e^- + p \rightarrow D + \nu_e$	1·44	$1\cdot5 \times 10^8$	$1\cdot72 \times 10^{-45}$	0·26
^7Be decay	0·86	$4\cdot5 \times 10^9$	$2\cdot9 \times 10^{-46}$	1·31
^8B decay	0–14·06	$5\cdot4 \times 10^6$	$1\cdot35 \times 10^{-42}$	7·28
^{13}N decay	0–1·19	$3\cdot3 \times 10^8$	$2\cdot1 \times 10^{-46}$	0·07
^{15}O decay	0–1·74	$2\cdot7 \times 10^8$	$7\cdot8 \times 10^{-46}$	0·21
				$\sum \phi\sigma = 9\cdot13$

† 1 SNU (solar neutrino unit) $= 10^{-36}$ captures per second per target atom.

2.2. The solar neutrino experiment of Davis

Solar neutrinos are electron-neutrinos and their detection is more difficult than that of electron-antineutrinos. This is due to the fact that the detection is based essentially on the inverse β-decay reaction $\nu_e + n \rightarrow p + e^-$, where the neutron must be bound in a nucleus and, for the energy range of solar neutrinos, so is the final proton.

During the last few years a large-scale experiment has been mounted by Davis (1964, 1972, Davis *et al* 1968, 1971, 1972) to detect solar neutrinos. The detection is based on the reaction

$\nu_e + {}^{37}Cl \rightarrow {}^{37}Ar + e^-$ (threshold 0·81 MeV)

which was first suggested by Pontecorvo (1946). The cross section for this reaction increases rapidly with neutrino energy because of its normal quadratic increase with energy above threshold and because of the existence of excited states of ^{37}Ar (Bahcall 1964b). Figure 1 shows the variation of the capture cross section with neutrino energy and the energy spectra of neutrinos from various sources. Also shown in figure 1 is the cross section for neutrino capture based on a reaction with higher sensitivity: ^{7}Li(ν_e, e$^-$) ^{7}Be. It can be seen that most of the neutrino flux, including all those from the basic proton–proton reaction, will not be detected. It is expected that the neutrinos from the ^{8}B decay will constitute the bulk of the capture rate.

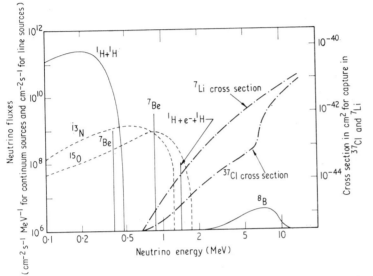

Figure 1. The calculated solar neutrino fluxes and the detection cross sections by capture in ^{37}Cl and ^{7}Li. Neutrinos from the proton–proton chain are indicated by continuous lines and neutrinos from the CNO cycle by broken lines.

In the recent experiments a detection system containing 10^5 gallons of liquid tetrachloroethylene, C_2Cl_4, in a horizontal cylindrical tank, is situated 4925 ft underground (4400 mwe) in the Homestake gold mine in South Dakota, USA. The reason for placing the detector at such a great depth underground is to reduce the background signal due the effect of local interactions of energetic cosmic ray muons. After each exposure of a few months the ^{37}Ar atoms produced are extracted by circulating helium gas through the tank. The helium is allowed to pass through a charcoal trap cooled by liquid nitrogen at 77 K. The argon adsorbed on the charcoal trap is removed. A small low-level proportional counter is then used to search for the ^{37}Ar atoms contained in the purified sample by counting the 2·8 keV Auger electrons from ^{37}Ar decay. The latest results reported (Davis 1972) give a total ^{37}Ar production rate of $0·18 \pm 0·10$ atoms per day in 10^5 gallons of C_2Cl_4 ($2·2 \times 10^{30}$ ^{37}Cl atoms). This total rate includes the background due to the production of ^{37}Ar by cosmic ray muons and neutrinos. It may be noted that the current estimate of the capture rate in ^{37}Cl of 9·1 SNU (table 1) is equivalent to a production rate of 1·7 ^{37}Cl atoms per day.

2.3. Background effects

There are a variety of other processes which can produce ^{37}Ar atoms and they constitute the undesirable background effects. The two main sources of background which cannot be eliminated by experimental precautions are the protons induced by cosmic ray muons and the electron- and muon-neutrinos produced in the atmosphere by cosmic rays. These effects have been recently studied in some detail by Davis *et al* (1972).

The muon background arises from the reaction $^{37}Cl(p, n)^{37}Ar$, where the protons are derived from local interactions of cosmic ray muons. The muon intensity decreases rapidly with the depth underground. At the depth of the neutrino detector (4400 mwe) the mean muon energy is quite high (approximately 300 GeV) and the contribution to the background comes essentially from the 'nuclear interaction' of muons. Using the well known muon intensity–depth relation, the calculated energy spectrum of muons at a given depth and the information on the yield of protons for various muon energies, the ^{37}Ar production rate by muons as a function of depth has been estimated. This rate decreases rapidly with depth. At the present location of the Davis experiment the predicted rate of ^{37}Ar production by muons is 0·065 atoms per day per 10^5 gallons of C_2Cl_4.

The background due to cosmic ray neutrinos arises from the reactions $^{37}Cl(\nu_\mu, \mu^-)^{37}Ar$ and $^{37}Cl(\nu_e, e^-)^{37}Ar$. The predominant contribution comes from neutrinos with energy below 1 GeV, where the neutrino intensity is affected by the local geomagnetic cut-off rigidity. From the estimated cosmic ray neutrino intensities (§3) and the known neutrino cross sections, and making allowance for the fact that the reaction can occur only when the recoil proton has a momentum allowed by the exclusion principle and that there is a reduction in cross section due to the escape of the energetic recoil proton from the nucleus, the background due to cosmic ray neutrinos has been estimated to be 0·024 ^{37}Ar atoms per day per 10^5 gallons of C_2Cl_4. This background is independent of depth underground and it will set a limit to the sensitivity of solar neutrino detectors based on capture by ^{37}Cl.

The main uncertainties in the underground estimation are the depth of the detector underground in terms of mwe of 'standard rock' and the muon intensity–depth relation. Both are required for the estimate of the total muon intensity at the detector. An accurate direct measurement of the muon intensity will eliminate most of the uncertainties in the background. At the present time the total background is estimated to be 0·09 ± 0·03 ^{37}Ar atoms per day for the Davis detector.

2.4. Discussion

The measured total ^{37}Ar production rate (0·18 ± 0·10 ^{37}Ar atoms per day) is less than one standard deviation above the estimated background. It is clear that unambiguous detection of solar neutrinos must await measurements of higher precision or use of a different technique. A promising technique which is currently being explored is based on the reaction $^7Li(\nu_e, e^-)^7Be$. The cross section is higher than that for capture in ^{37}Cl, especially at low energies, and the neutrinos from the pep reaction will have much better chance of being detected. This would test unequivocally the basic ideas of stellar evolution.

The apparent absence of solar neutrinos has created much excitement among astrophysicists. Several possibilities have already been put forward to explain this discrepancy. They include the possible instability of the neutrino (Bahcall *et al* 1972), the possible existence of resonance at some energy below 90 keV for the reaction ^{3}He (^{3}He, 2p)^{4}He (Fowler 1972) which would reduce the flux of ^{7}Be and ^{7}B neutrinos, the possible oscillatory processes between ν_e and ν_μ (Pontecorvo 1968), and the possible short time variation (about 10^6–10^7 years) of the solar interior (Lande *et al* 1972). At the time of writing, this problem is still far from being solved. It is certain, however, that the 'solar neutrino puzzle' will lead to our further understanding of astrophysical processes.

3. Low energy cosmic ray neutrinos

Interactions of primary cosmic rays with air nuclei in the atmosphere lead to the production of pions, kaons and other unstable particles. Neutrinos are then produced as a result of the decays of pions and kaons. Muons from these decays further contribute to the neutrino flux. The predominant contribution to the electron-neutrino flux at low energies, in fact, comes from the decay of the muon: $\mu^\pm \rightarrow e^\pm + \bar{\nu}_\mu(\nu_\mu) + \nu_e(\bar{\nu}_e)$. Although cosmic ray electron-neutrinos have not yet been detected experimentally in view of the short range of the resultant electron from the neutrino interaction, as has been noted before, a knowledge of the energy spectrum is essential for estimating the background effects due to cosmic ray neutrinos in the search for solar neutrinos.

3.1. Geomagnetic effects

The usual procedure in the calculations of the neutrino spectra at ground level is first to deduce the production spectra of the parent particles which decay to give neutrinos. For neutrinos with energy less than 1 GeV the contribution from the kaon decay becomes increasingly negligible and only the muon production spectra need be considered. For energies greater than about 3 GeV the muon production spectra have been derived from the measured energy spectrum of muons at ground-level, but for lower energies, because of the energy loss amounting to about 2 GeV for a muon to arrive at ground-level from its usual region of production at an altitude of around 15 km, the production spectra can only be obtained from measurements of low energy muons at high altitude. With the assumed production spectra the muon spectrum as a function of depth in the atmosphere can be calculated and the total intensity of neutrinos produced from the μ–e decay at various depths in the atmosphere summed.

However, the muon production spectrum is dependent on the geomagnetic latitude. This is due to the fact that as the geomagnetic latitude decreases the threshold rigidity of primary cosmic rays increases and hence the total primary intensity decreases.

As the threshold rigidity of primary particles at a certain location at the Earth's surface varies with the azimuthal as well as the zenith angle, in addition to the enhanced neutrino flux due to the increased path lengths for muon decay at large zenith angles, the neutrino intensity varies not only with the local geomagnetic latitude but also with the direction in space.

It is expected that the geomagnetic effects become significant only in the relatively low energy region. Thus, above about 2 GeV these effects are smaller than the uncertainties in the neutrino intensity estimates (Tam and Young 1970, Osborne *et al* 1965).

The geomagnetic latitude dependence of the muon production spectrum has been given by Olbert (1954) on the basis of experimental measurements of Conversi (1950) on the variation of slow muon intensity with altitude at geomagnetic latitude of 50°N and on the variation of the differential vertical intensity of muons at an atmospheric depth of 300 g cm^{-2} for various geomagnetic latitudes. The production spectrum can be expressed by

$$G(R, \lambda) = 7 \cdot 3 \times 10^4 / (a(\lambda) + R)^{3 \cdot 58} \, \mathrm{g^{-2} \, cm^2 \, s^{-1} \, sr^{-1}}$$

where R is the residual range of the muons, which is related to the muon energy, and the parameter $a(\lambda)$ gives the dependence on the geomagnetic latitude λ. To give the best fit with the experimental measurements the value of $a(\lambda)$ is found to decrease monotonically from 646 g cm^{-2} at the geomagnetic equator to 513 g cm^{-2} at $\lambda = 60°$. The value at $\lambda = 50°$ is 520 g cm^{-2} which is considered most reliable as more experimental measurements have been made near $\lambda = 50°$ than at other latitudes. It can be seen clearly from this expression that the geomagnetic effects decrease with increasing energy.

The muon production spectrum can, of course, be used to derive the sea-level muon spectrum, knowing the survival probability and the energy loss of muons in the atmosphere. It is found that recent measurements of the vertical differential muon spectrum at low energies near the geomagnetic equator at sea level give results in good agreement with the predictions from this assumed expression for the muon production spectrum (Allkofer *et al* 1968, De *et al* 1972). This gives further support for the validity of this expresion.

3.2. *The neutrino spectra*

Calculations of the muon-neutrino spectra for energies from 0·2 GeV to a few GeV have been given by Tam and Young (1970). In these calculations the Olbert expression for the latitude dependence was adopted and the reasonable assumption made that the energy loss for pions from production to decay could be ignored. The electron-neutrino spectra have been derived from similar calculations.

Starting from the assumed muon production spectrum for a given geomagnetic latitude, the depth rate of production of muons is first calculated for both the vertical and the horizontal N–S direction (both have approximately the same threshold rigidity). The energy loss of muons in the atmosphere and the different survival probabilities for muons in the vertical and in the horizontal directions are taken into consideration. The muon decay spectrum, that is, the intensity of muons decaying at a given energy at all heights in the atmosphere is then computed. With the expression for the energy spectrum in the laboratory system of ν_e from muon decay (Zatsepin *et al* 1962), the energy spectrum of the neutrinos for the particular geomagnetic latitude can be obtained.

The calculations have been made for various geomagnetic latitudes. Figure 2 shows the variation of differential intensities of $\nu_e + \bar{\nu}_e$ with the cut-off kinetic energy E_p of the primary particles for various neutrino energies. R is the ratio of the differential intensities for the vertical or the horizontal direction between a location with

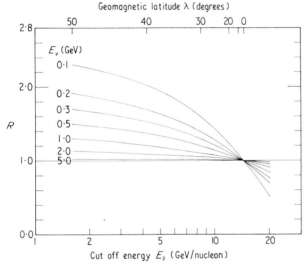

Figure 2. The variation of the intensities of $\nu_e + \bar{\nu}_e$ with the cut-off kinetic energy E_p for various neutrino energies E_ν. R is the ratio of the differential intensities between a location with cut-off energy and that with $E_p = 14 \cdot 2$ GeV.

cut-off energy E_p (the corresponding geomagnetic latitude being λ) and that with $E_p = 14 \cdot 2$ GeV (approximately the cut-off energy for vertical primary protons at the geomagnetic equator). It should be noted that, as the threshold rigidity varies along the same geomagnetic latitude, the neutrino intensity also varies slightly. It can be seen that with the intensity at the geomagnetic equator taken as datum, the geomagnetic effects and hence the ratio R increases with increasing latitude and decreases with increasing energy, as would be expected. Above 5 GeV the effects are practically negligible. From $\lambda = 0°$ to $\lambda = 50°$, while the differential intensity increases by about 130% at 0·1 GeV, it increases by only about 13% at 2 GeV.

The energy spectra of $\nu_e + \bar{\nu}_e$ for the vertical and the horizontal N–S directions are given in table 2. These are for the geomagnetic latitude $\lambda = 50°$ at which the experimental measurements are most numerous. The values for $E_\nu > 2$ GeV are taken from the work of Osborne *et al* (1965) and Osborne (1966). The neutrino spectra at other latitudes can be derived, with the ratios shown in figure 2. The energy spectra in the low energy region for two latitudes $\lambda = 0°$ and $\lambda = 50°$ are plotted in figure 3 which shows clearly the geomagnetic effects on the neutrino intensities at low energies.

Table 2. Energy spectra of $\nu_e + \bar{\nu}_e$ at $\lambda = 50°$ (cm^{-2} s^{-1} sr^{-1} GeV^{-1}) (many of the intensities are very approximate—see the final paragraphs of §4.)

E_ν (GeV)	Vertical intensity	Horizontal intensity
0·1	$1·07 \times 10$	$1·10 \times 10$
0·2	$3·78 \times 10^{-1}$	$4·20 \times 10^{-1}$
0·3	$1·89 \times 10^{-1}$	$2·21 \times 10^{-1}$
0·5	$6·20 \times 10^{-2}$	$8·75 \times 10^{-2}$
0·7	$2·50 \times 10^{-2}$	$4·35 \times 10^{-2}$
1	$9·45 \times 10^{-3}$	$1·93 \times 10^{-2}$
2	$1·34 \times 10^{-3}$	$3·34 \times 10^{-3}$
3	$3·62 \times 10^{-4}$	$1·12 \times 10^{-3}$
5	$6·51 \times 10^{-5}$	$2·76 \times 10^{-4}$
7	$2·09 \times 10^{-5}$	$1·08 \times 10^{-4}$
10	$6·13 \times 10^{-6}$	$3·94 \times 10^{-5}$
20	$5·45 \times 10^{-7}$	$5·15 \times 10^{-6}$
30	$1·31 \times 10^{-7}$	$1·50 \times 10^{-6}$
50	$2·25 \times 10^{-8}$	$2·88 \times 10^{-7}$
70	$7·25 \times 10^{-9}$	$9·41 \times 10^{-8}$
100	$2·23 \times 10^{-9}$	$2·92 \times 10^{-8}$
200	$2·34 \times 10^{-10}$	$2·74 \times 10^{-9}$
300	$5·90 \times 10^{-11}$	$5·28 \times 10^{-10}$
500	$9·48 \times 10^{-12}$	$9·34 \times 10^{-11}$
700	$2·91 \times 10^{-12}$	$2·68 \times 10^{-11}$
1000	$8·48 \times 10^{-13}$	$7·32 \times 10^{-12}$

In these calculations the effect of scattering of the muons has been neglected as it is found that for energies below 1 GeV this effect is small. Thus the bulk of the contribution to the intensity of neutrinos at ground level in the horizontal direction comes from muons which decay in the region of atmospheric depth less than 100 g cm^{-2} where the air density is very low. It is usually difficult to estimate the uncertainties in the calculated neutrino intensities because the accuracy of the parameters used in the calculations is often uncertain. For neutrino energies below 0·3 GeV the greatest uncertainty perhaps arises from the muon production spectrum at low energies. The neglect of the kaon contribution also introduces an error which amounts to a few per cent at 1 GeV and to smaller values at lower energies. All factors included, it is estimated that the uncertainties probably range from 20% at 1 GeV to 40% at 0·1 GeV. For our present purposes, this degree of accuracy is adequate.

4. High energy cosmic ray neutrinos

In the past considerably more attention has been paid to the muon-neutrino intensities as they are a prerequisite for the interpretation of the cosmic ray neutrino experiments designed to detect muons from neutrino interactions. It appears that no attempts have so far been made to detect cosmic ray electron-neutrinos, in view of the low rates arising from the relatively small penetrating power of the resultant electron. Nevertheless, electron-neutrino intensities are of interest and they are usually derived together with those for muon-neutrinos as the calculations necessarily follow similar lines.

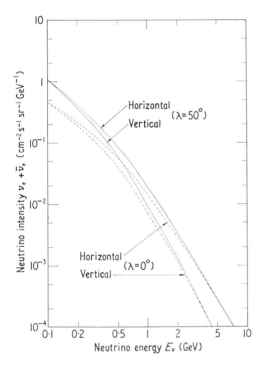

Figure 3. The $\nu_e + \bar{\nu}_e$ intensity in the horizontal and vertical directions at $\lambda = 50°$ and $0°$.

For the energy range from 1 GeV to 1 TeV the expected energy spectra of cosmic ray electron-neutrinos, together with those of muon-neutrinos, have been reported by several workers, notably Osborne *et al* (1965) and Cowsik *et al* (1966). As the main interest lay in the relatively high energy neutrinos, the geomagnetic effects on the low energy part of the spectra were not considered. Since in their calculations the production spectra of the parent particles were based mainly on the measured energy spectrum of muons at sea-level near geomagnetic latitude of 50°, their predicted spectra can be regarded as appropriate for this geomagnetic latitude.

The procedure in the calculations is to assume the most likely model for the propagation of cosmic rays through the atmosphere which is compatible with the measured sea-level muon spectrum. For example in the work of Osborne *et al* (1965) and Osborne (1966) the attenuation length of nucleons in the atmosphere is taken to be 120 g cm⁻² and the ratio of the number of kaons to pions at production, 20%. With the adopted production spectra derived from muon measurements, the neutrino intensities at ground level from the various decays can be computed. The results of the work of Osborne *et al* (1965) and Osborne (1966) have already been shown in table 2.

Several features can be observed. Because the increased path lengths in the horizontal direction enhance the probability of decay and hence the neutrino intensities, the ratio of the horizontal to vertical intensities increases with energy. The relative contribution from kaon decay increases rapidly with neutrino energy. This is due to its greater mass and shorter lifetime which cause its probability of decay to fall much more slowly with increasing energy than that of the muon.

For the muon-neutrino intensities, Osborne *et al* (1965) give typical uncertainties, mainly owing to lack of precise knowledge of the K/π ratios, at 50 GeV of about $\pm 11\%$ in the horizontal direction and about $\pm 30\%$ in the vertical direction. In the electron-neutrino case, pion decay does not contribute directly to the flux and at high energies (above 40 GeV in the vertical direction and above 1000 GeV horizontally) the contribution from kaon decay predominates over that from muon decay, so that the uncertainties in the electron neutrino intensities become very large. Furthermore, mention should be made of the redetermination of absolute muon intensities (see the previous chapter); the effect will be an upward revision of the intensities in table 2 by some 10–20% above about 3 GeV.

5. Conclusions

We have reviewed natural electron-neutrinos in the whole energy range from solar neutrinos to high energy cosmic ray neutrinos. Although the search for the most intense component, the solar neutrinos, has been strenuously pursued for a number of years, up to the present their detection still cannot be confirmed with absolute certainty. If the solar neutrino capture rate is indeed much lower than expected (eg the absence of ^{8}B neutrinos), then recourse must be made to a better technique than the present detection based on capture in ^{37}Cl. The most attractive detector at present seems to be the one based on the ^{7}Li(ν_e, e$^-$) ^{7}Be reaction which has a much higher cross section at low energies than the ^{37}Cl detector. This will increase the detection probability of the pep neutrinos by nearly an order of magnitude. If the results are positive such a detector would test the basic theories of stellar interiors and neutrino reactions and, if the results turn out to be negative, then either our current understanding of stellar evolution needs to be drastically modified or our understanding of the properties of the electron-neutrino is still far from satisfactory (eg the possibility of neutrino decay). Unfortunately the counting of ^{7}Be is difficult but there is no doubt that this will be accomplished in the not too distant future.

There seems to be little prospect in the foreseeable future for the direct detection of electron-neutrinos from cosmic ray interactions in the atmosphere. Nevertheless, the energy spectrum of cosmic ray electron-neutrinos, together with that of muon-neutrinos, is needed to estimate the neutrino background in the present search for solar neutrinos and, indeed, in all searches for extraterrestrial neutrinos. If it turns out that the signal in the solar neutrino detection remains much lower than expected, it is all the more important to have accurate estimates of the various sources of background.

It should perhaps be pointed out that the major source of background, due to cosmic ray muons, in the Davis experiment can be considerably reduced by locating the detector deeper underground. However, the cosmic ray neutrino background is independent of the depth underground. This background will limit the ultimate improvement in the sensitivity of solar neutrino detection by radiochemical techniques. It is useful to note that the background would be a minimum if the experiment were to be carried out near the geomagnetic equator.

The neutrino has so far shown many surprising features since its existence was first postulated some forty years ago. As there are at present many questions still to be answered, perhaps further surprises are yet to be uncovered.

References

Abraham Z and Iben I 1971 *Astrophys. J.* **170** 157–63
Allkofer O C, Andresen R D and Dan W D 1968 *Can. J. Phys.* **46** S301–5
Bahcall J N 1964a *Phys. Rev. Lett* **12** 300–2
—— 1964b *Phys. Rev.* **135** B137–46
Bahcall J N, Bahcall N A and Sahviv G 1968 *Phys. Rev. Lett.* **20** 1209–12
Bahcall J N, Cabibbo N, and Yahil A 1972 *Phys. Rev. Lett.* **28** 316–18
Bahcall J N and Ulrich R K 1971 *Astrophys. J.* **170** 593–603
Conversi M 1950 *Phys. Rev.* **79** 749–67
Cowsik R, Pal Y and Tandon S N 1966 *Proc. Indian Acad. Sci.* **63A** 217–43
Davis R Jr 1964 *Phys. Rev. Lett.* **12** 303–5
—— 1972 *Bull. Amer. Phys. Soc. II* **17** 527
Davis R, Jr, Harmer D S and Hoffman K C 1968 *Phys. Rev. Lett.* **20** 1205–8
Davis R Jr, Radeka V and Rogers L C 1971 *Bull. Amer. Phys. Soc. II* **16** 631–2
Davis R Jr, Wolfendale A W and Young E C M 1972 *Proc. Neutrino '72 Conf.* vol 1 (Budapest: Hung. Phys. Soc.) pp 77–84
De A K, Ghosh P, Mitra S, Bhattacharya P C and Das A K 1972 *J. Phys. A: Gen. Phys.* **5** 1236–42
Fowler W A 1972 *Nature* **238** 24–6
Lande K, Bozoki G and Lee C K 1972 *Proc. Neutrino '72 Conf.* vol 1 (Budapest: Hung. Phys. Soc). pp 87–97
Olbert S 1954 *Phys. Rev.* **96** 1400–7
Osborne J L 1966 *PhD thesis* University of Durham
Osborne J L, Said S S and Wolfendale A W 1965 *Proc. Phys. Soc.* **86** 93–9
Pontecorvo B 1946 *Natn. Res. Coun. Can. Rep. P.D.* 205
—— 1968 *Sov. Phys–JETP* **26** 984–8
Reines F and Cowan C L 1953 *Phys. Rev* **92** 830–1
Sears R L 1964 *Astrophys J.* **140** 477–84
Tam A C and Young E C M 1970 *Acta Phys. Hung.* **29** suppl 4 307–12
Zatsepin G T and Kuz'min V A 1962 *Sov. Phys–JETP* **14** 1294–1300

Chapter 7

Search for quarks, magnetic monopoles and tachyons

F Ashton

1. Introduction

The possible existence of three elementary objects (quarks) from which all known elementary particles are constructed was first proposed by Gell-Mann (1964) and Zweig (1964, 1965). This theory arose from an attempt to understand the observed multiplet structure of elementary particles using group theoretical methods and gives the unusual prediction that fundamental triplet particles may exist having either $\frac{1}{3}$ or $\frac{2}{3}$ the electron charge.

·In contrast the concept of magnetic monopoles arises from considering the possible symmetry between electric charges and magnetic poles. If electric charges exist freely rather than only as electric multipoles is it not possible that free magnetic poles may exist as separate entities even though to date all magnetic phenomena are understandable in terms of magnetic multipoles? The consequences that follow from writing div $B = 4\pi g$ (admitting the existence of monopoles of strength g) rather than div $B = 0$ in Maxwell's equations was first investigated by Dirac (1931, 1948). The conclusion of this work was the somewhat surprising result that there should be a relation between the fundamental electric charge e and some fundamental monopole charge g of the form of $g = \hbar c / 2e$. Thus this work gives some understanding as to why electric charge is observed to be quantized in terms of the electron charge.

Tachyons are postulated objects that travel with a velocity greater than that of light. Mathematically a tachyon observable in cosmic rays at the Earth would have imaginary rest mass but it is not clear what this implies physically. However, it may be that relativistic mechanics as presently formulated is a special case of a more general theory just as newtonian mechanics is a limiting case of relativistic mechanics for $v/c \ll 1$. In this sense it is useful to attempt to detect tachyons in cosmic rays and presently available flux limits are given in §4.

2. Quarks

2.1. Origin of the concept of quarks as fundamental triplet particles

Recent progress in understanding the interactions of elementary particles has been made along two distinct although interlinked lines of thought, these being general dynamical considerations and group theoretical arguments. Scattering theory makes extensive use of Mandelstam variables s, t, u and crossing symmetry to make predictions concerning the energy dependence of total and elastic cross sections which are in reasonable agreement with experiment (eg Barger *et al* 1968). It also leads to the idea that particles with the same isospin and hypercharge should lie on the same Regge trajectory which is traced out on an angular momentum against (mass)^2 plot (Burkhardt 1969). Up to the highest mass and spin values so far investigated both the Regge trajectories for fermions and bosons have approximately the same slope, $\mathrm{d}J/\mathrm{d}m^2 \sim 1$ (GeV)$^{-2}$. According to Cence (1969) the slope for pion–nucleon resonances can be understood in terms of a constant range for the pion–nucleon force coupled with the fact that scattering resonances will occur whenever the angular momentum of the system increases by $\hbar$. Thus general dynamical considerations lead to a scheme for classifying known particles and resonances in terms of Regge trajectories but they give no predictions concerning a possible microstructure of particles.

In contrast group theoretical arguments seek to understand the observed multiplet structure of elementary particles and lead to the suggestion that all elementary particles may be constructed from one or more groups of fundamental triplet particles. Ever since the discovery of the pion attempts have been made to understand the known elementary particles in terms of elementary subunits and as early as the 1940s Fermi and Yang (1949) discussed the possibility that pions were bound states of nucleon–antinucleon pairs. However, after the discovery of strange particles it became clear that some subunit carrying strangeness was also needed and Sakata (1956) proposed that the subunits were the triplet of proton, neutron and lambda zero together with their antiparticles. This model met with some success for a number of years as it was consistent with octet and singlet meson multiplets but it failed to be consistent with the observed octet and decimet multiplets of baryons when these multiplets of baryons became firmly established experimentally. In the Sakata model muons are considered to be bound states of two triplet particles and an anti-triplet particle. In the language of group theory the irreducible representations of the direct product of triplets forming mesons and baryons are

Mesons $3 \otimes \bar{3} = 8 \oplus 1$

Baryons $3 \otimes \bar{3} \otimes 3 = 15 \oplus 6 \oplus 3 \oplus 3$

where $\otimes$ means direct product, $\oplus$ means direct sum and a bar indicates antiparticles. It was first noticed by Gell-Mann (1964) and Zweig (1964, 1965) that although $3 \otimes \bar{3} \otimes 3$ gave the wrong multiplet structure for the baryons the reduction $3 \otimes 3 \otimes 3 = 10 \oplus 8 \oplus 8 \oplus 1$ agreed with observation. This reduction thus indicated that baryons were composed of 3 subunits and immediately led to the idea that the subunits should each carry baryon number $\frac{1}{3}$ so as to be consistent with the well established law of conservation of baryon number and the Gell-Mann–Nishijima relation. Using the Gell-Mann–Nishijima relation

$$Q = T_3 + \frac{B+S}{2} = T_3 + \frac{Y}{2}$$

where Q = charge, T_3 = third component of isospin, S = strangeness and Y = hypercharge, the charges carried by these hypothetical particles (quarks) are deduced; the result is given in table 1. In this deduction it is assumed that the fundamental triplet is composed of a non-strange isospin doublet and a strangeness-carrying singlet as in the Sakata model. In this model mesons are still considered to be triplet–anti-triplet pairs and the reduction $3 \otimes \bar{3} = 8 \oplus 1$ is predicted as in the Sakata model. In what follows quarks will be represented by p, n, λ. The above ideas suggest the quark content of the proton is ppn; of the neutron, pnn; and of the pion triplet, p$\bar{n}$, $2^{-1/2}$(p$\bar{p}$–n$\bar{n}$), $\bar{p}$n. Tables of the quark content of known elementary particles are given by Kokkedee (1969).

As time progresses the quantum numbers of more and more resonances are being evaluated and from time to time the experimental data is reviewed by the Particle Data Group (see PDG (1972) for the most recent review). Tables 2 and 3 are taken

Table 1. Quantum numbers of quarks. The corresponding antiquarks have quantum numbers of opposite sign.

Triplet particle	T_3	B	S	$Y = B+S$	$Q = T_3 + Y/2$	Spin
p	$+\frac{1}{2}$	$\frac{1}{3}$	0	$\frac{1}{3}$	$\frac{1}{2} + \frac{1}{6} = +\frac{2}{3}$	$\frac{1}{2}\hbar$
n	$-\frac{1}{2}$	$\frac{1}{3}$	0	$\frac{1}{3}$	$-\frac{1}{2} + \frac{1}{6} = -\frac{1}{3}$	$\frac{1}{2}\hbar$
λ	0	$\frac{1}{3}$	-1	$-\frac{2}{3}$	$0 - \frac{1}{3} = -\frac{1}{3}$	$\frac{1}{2}\hbar$

Table 2. Established meson octets and singlets as given by the Particle Data Group (1972). Of the two iso-singlets, the 'mainly octet' one is written first followed by a semicolon.

J^p	Nonet members
0^-	possible nonet [π, K, η; η']
0^-	alternative nonet [π, K, η; E]
1^-	[$\rho(765 \pm 10)$, K*, ϕ; ω]
2^+	[A2(1300 ± 20), K$_N$(1420), f'; f]

Table 3. Established baryon octets, singlets and decuplets as given by the Particle Data Group (1972).

J^p	Octet members				Singlet
$\frac{1}{2}^+$	N(939)	Λ(1116)	Σ(1193)	Ξ(1318)	—
$\frac{1}{2}^-$	N(1535)	Λ(1670)	Σ(1750)	Ξ(1825)	Λ(1405)
$\frac{3}{2}^-$	N(1520)	Λ(1690)	Σ(1670)	Ξ(1815)	Λ(1520)
$\frac{5}{2}^-$	N(1670)	Λ(1830)	Σ(1765)	—	—
$\frac{5}{2}^+$	N(1688)	Λ(1815)	Σ(1915)	—	—

J^p	Decuplet members			
$\frac{3}{2}^+$	Δ(1236)	Σ(1385)	Ξ(1530)	Ω^-(1673)
$\frac{7}{2}^+$	Δ(1950)	Σ(2030)		

from this work and show the established meson and baryon multiplets which are quite consistent with those expected from the quark model.

   Further, the quark model leads to a large number of predictions that are in agreement with experiment such as particle masses, magnetic moments, interaction cross sections and decay widths. Apart from the strong interactions the model is also quite successful in understanding the interactions of photons that produce strongly interacting particles. For a review of some aspects of this work see Levin and Frankfurt (1968), Feld (1969) and Morpurgo (1970). Obviously a striking confirmation of the quark model would be the detection of free quarks experimentally. To design an experiment to do this one needs an estimate of the quark mass and production cross section in high energy collisions. These points will be discussed in §2.2. It should be noted that although the simplest interpretation of the SU_3 symmetry is that the fundamental triplet particles should carry fractional charge it is possible that the basic triplet particles have integral charge. In this case the predicted properties of the triplet particles are not unique and there are several possible representations (Lee 1965). Bacry et al (1964) proposed the existence of two sets of triplet particles, t trions and θ trions, where all members have baryon number 1 and integral charge. The two triplets are distinguished by a new additive quantum number D and a generalization of the Gell-Man–Nishijima formula is required,

$$Q = I_3 + \tfrac{1}{2} Y + \tfrac{1}{3} D.$$

   The situation at the moment is that if elementary particles are assumed to contain fractional charge triplet particles then a considerable amount of experimental data can be understood. Examples are the decay widths of baryon and meson resonances and relations between magnetic moments of elementary particles. The agreement obtained to date could possibly be fortuitous but until some sharp contradiction between the quark model and experiment arises the existence of a fundamental triplet carrying fractional charge would seem the more likely.

2.2. The expected properties of free quarks

Comparing the measured masses of elementary particles with their expected quark composition it is found that for bound quarks $M_p \simeq M_n \simeq M$ and $M_\lambda \simeq M + m_\pi$. Also, to account for known decay schemes, it would seem that only the p-type quark is stable, the n- and λ-type quarks decaying to the p-type quark by β-decay and pion emission respectively. The lifetimes indicated for such decays in table 4 are rough orders of magnitude only.

Table 4. Possible decay schemes of quarks

Quark	Decay scheme	Lifetime
p	Stable	Infinite
n	$n \rightarrow p + \bar{e} + \bar{\nu}_e$	$\sim$ sec
λ	$\lambda \begin{cases} p + \pi^- \\ n + \pi^0 \end{cases}$	$\sim 10^{-10}$ sec

2.2.1. Estimate of the quark mass. Assuming mesons are quark–antiquark systems bound in a potential well of radius r Morpurgo (1967) has obtained a rough estimate of the quark mass. Assuming the mesons that provide the binding force between q and $\bar{q}$ are, say, vector mesons with $r = (5\ m_\pi)^{-1}$, then the potential well must have such a depth that the lowest bound level has the mass of the pion. In the preceding equation and in what follows the notation $h = c = 1$ is used. If M is the quark mass and it has momentum p in such a well then the minimum de Broglie wavelength that can resonate in a space of dimension r is $\lambda = 2r = 1/p$. Thus for $r = (5\ m_\pi)^{-1}$, $p = 5\ m_\pi/2$ and

$$\frac{v}{c} = \frac{p}{M} = \frac{5m_\pi}{2M}$$

justifying a nonrelativistic approach to the problem if $M \gg m_\pi$ which it surely is. It is obvious that the above argument holds for any potential similar in shape to a square well but it does not hold for a pure $1/r^n$ potential nor for a pure Yukawa potential because of the singularity at $r = 0$. Indeed it is quite possible that the realistic potential between q and $\bar{q}$ has a short range repulsive core of such radius to make the above argument valid. Assuming an infinitely deep square well potential of radius $(5m_\pi)^{-1}$ the lowest s, p, d energy levels are given by $25m_\pi^2\alpha/M$ where $\alpha = (3 \cdot 14)^2$, $(4 \cdot 5)^2$, $(5 \cdot 76)^2$ for s, p, d states. The energy difference between the first s and p states is of the order of $250m_\pi^2/M$ and experimentally, the difference in average mass of even and odd angular momentum meson multiplets is about 500 MeV giving $M = 10$ GeV. The value obtained for M depends on the square of the assumed range of the q$\bar{q}$ potential and it becomes 20 GeV for a range of $(7m_\pi)^{-1}$ and 5 GeV for a range of $(3 \cdot 5m_\pi)^{-1}$. Obviously the above estimates of the free quark mass are crude but a value in the range 5 GeV to several tens of GeV is indicated.

2.2.2. The expected production cross section of quarks in nucleon–nucleon collisions. The possible production processes of quarks in high energy nucleon–nucleon collisions are listed below:

(i) $N + N \rightarrow N + N + q + \bar{q}$

(ii) $N + N \rightarrow N + 3q$

(iii) $N + N \rightarrow 3q + 3q$

(iv) $\pi + \pi \rightarrow \pi + q + \bar{q}$

(v) $\pi + \pi \rightarrow 2(q + \bar{q})$.

In (i), (ii) and (iii) the total kinetic energy of both incident nucleons in the centre of momentum system is available for quark production (central collisions) while (iv) and (v) are the reactions for a virtual π–π collision so that only a fraction $m_\pi/M_N = 0 \cdot 15$ of the total kinetic energy is available (peripheral collisions). Figure 1 shows the incident nucleon energy threshold kinetic energy for the above reactions as a function of the quark mass.

Processes analogous to (i) that have been studied are proton–antiproton production;

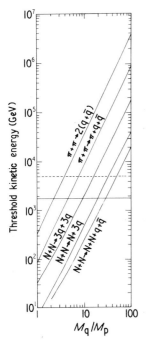

Figure 1. Threshold kinetic energy for quark production in nucleon–nucleon collisions as a function of the quark mass. The full horizontal line represents the energy equal to 30 GeV colliding beams and the broken line the approximate primary cosmic ray energy at which the electron density at the core is 1 m^{-2} at sea level or mountain altitude.

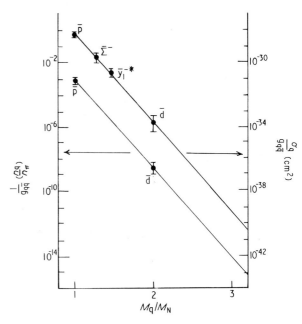

Figure 2. Measured baryon–antibaryon production cross sections in proton–nucleon collisions of approximately 30 GeV energy and a fit of the thermodynamic model to the data (Maksimenko *et al* 1966).

Σ–$\bar{\Sigma}$ production; Y*–$\bar{\text{Y}}$* production; and deuteron–antideuteron production using approximately 30 GeV incident protons. Figure 2 shows the production cross section of the above particles as a function of M/M_N as well as their abundance relative to pions. The variation of production cross section with M/M_N can be understood by assuming that in a nucleon–nucleon collision all the available kinetic energy for secondary particle production is liberated in some small volume determined by the extent to which the mesonic fields of the two nucleons overlap. Assuming a pion gas is initially formed in this small volume so that nucleon–antinucleon pairs will be formed by $\pi + \pi \rightarrow \pi + N + \bar{N}$ it can be seen that in this way deuteron–antideuteron pairs can be formed by appropriate nucleons and antinucleons sticking together. Assuming thermodynamic equilibrium is reached between all possible types of secondary particles an estimate can be made of their relative production cross sections by noting that entropy is a Lorentz invariant quantity. Suppose the entropy of a final state containing only pions is S_π and the entropy of a final state containing only a $q\bar{q}$ pair is S_q. Using the Boltzmann relation

$$S_\pi = k \ln W_\pi + \text{constant}$$

and

$$S_q = k \ln W_q + \text{constant}$$

where W_π and W_q are the probabilities of the indicated states gives

$$S_q - S_\pi = k \ln \frac{W_q}{W_\pi}.$$

But

$$S_q - S_\pi = -\frac{2M_q c^2}{T}$$

so

$$\frac{W_q}{W_\pi} = \exp - \left(\frac{2M_q c^2}{kT} \right).$$

To proceed further account must be taken of phase space, spin and isospin factors and the result obtained is (Maksimenko *et al* 1966)

$$\frac{\sigma_q}{g_{q\bar{q}}} = a \left(\frac{M_q c^2}{kT} \right)^3 \exp - \left(\frac{2M_q^2}{kT} \right) \tag{1}$$

where σ_q is the production cross section of $q\bar{q}$ pairs each of mass M_q, and $g_{q\bar{q}} = (2I+1)(2S+1)$ where I and S are the isospin and spin of the produced particles and a is a constant. Fitting this equation to the measurements shown in figure 2 Maksimenko *et al* find $a = 4 \times 10^{-25}$ cm^2 and $kT = 0.94$ Mc^2. It is clear from figure 2 that the thermodynamic model fits the available data on baryon–antibaryon pair production at an energy of about 30 GeV.

Antipov *et al* (1969) have searched for quarks using 70 GeV protons at Serpukhov and the limits they have obtained on the production cross section are shown in figure 3. Also shown is the production cross section expected on the thermodynamic model. It is clear that this work only limits the quark mass to less than 3 GeV/c^2. A negative result using a 27 GeV proton beam at CERN was also found by Allaby *et al* (1969). Although no results on $q\bar{q}$ production are yet available from the CERN 30 GeV colliding beams an estimate by T Massam and A Zichichi (1968 unpublished) shows that if the thermodynamic model is correct at this energy and assuming a proton luminosity of 10^{30} cm^2 s^{-1} the observation of no quarks in 10 days running time will only set an upper limit on the quark mass of about 4 GeV/c^2.

To establish whether the production cross section of baryon–antibaryon pairs can be much greater than that given by the thermodynamic model at energies very much greater than 30 GeV consider the Feynman diagram (drawn in the C-system)

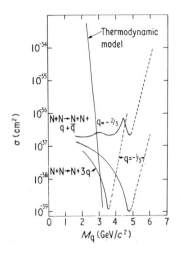

Figure 3. Upper limits to the production cross section of quarks in proton–nucleon collisions of energy 70 GeV (Antipov *et al* 1969). The theoretical curve refers to the process N+N→N+N+q+q̄ and is calculated from equation (1) with $a = 4 \times 10^{-25}$ cm², $g_{q\bar{q}} = 36$ and kT = 0·94 $M_\pi c^2$ (Maksimenko *et al* 1966). The broken lines show the widening of the quark mass range owing to the internuclear motion of the target nucleons.

for pp̄ production shown in figure 4. The pp̄ pair originate from a π–π collision and the threshold energy for an incident nucleon in the laboratory system to produce such a pair each of mass M_N in a virtual π–π collision is

$$2 \left\{ \left(\frac{M_N}{M_\pi} \right)^2 - 1 \right\} \text{GeV} = 91 \text{ GeV}.$$

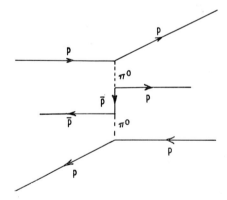

Figure 4. Proton–antiproton pair production.

This energy is in excess of the 30 GeV proton accelerators at CERN and Argonne as well as the 70 GeV accelerator at Serpukhov. However, it is accessible to the CERN 30 GeV colliding beams, which are equivalent to 1800 GeV protons incident on protons at rest in the laboratory system. It is suggested that once the 91 GeV energy threshold is crossed pp̄ pairs will be produced in almost every peripheral collision and preliminary results from colliding beam experiments show p̄/π⁻ of the order of 7% which is a considerable increase of the value p̄/π⁻ at 30 GeV which is of the order of 1%. As the average number of charged secondary particles produced in an 1800 GeV pp collision is 9 a p̄/π⁻ ratio of 7% implies that nucleon–antinucleon pairs are produced in 63 % of all collisions. The above idea is originally due to Peters (1966) who suggested that the two fireballs observed in some high energy cosmic ray nucleon interactions should be pictured as excited nucleon–antinucleon pairs produced in the above manner.

As quarks are more fundamental objects than nucleons, quark pairs rather than p$\bar{\text{p}}$ pairs can be expected to be produced for incident nucleons of energy greater than $2\{(M_q/M_\pi)^2 - 1\}$ GeV in the laboratory system. For 30 GeV colliding beams the above process will only be above threshold for strong q$\bar{\text{q}}$ production if $M_q < 4\cdot6$ GeV/c^2.

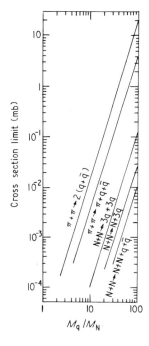

Figure 5. The cross section limit is for one event in three months with a detector of aperture $0\cdot1$ m² sr (flux $= 1\cdot27 \times 10^{-10}$ cm^{-2} s^{-1} sr^{-1}) and assumes all produced quarks are detected. For an aperture of 1 m² sr the limits should be lowered by 10. The curve for each process commences at the kinematic limit of the quark mass for 30 GeV colliding proton beams.

The basic difference between this argument and the thermodynamic model is that it is supposed that the produced baryon and antibaryon have sufficient momentum at production to escape annihilating one another whereas the thermodynamic model assumes they always annihilate producing a pion gas from which further baryon–antibaryon pairs are formed by π–π interactions.

It is clear from the above arguments that the higher the collision energy the more likely is one to observe q$\bar{\text{q}}$ pairs. Cosmic rays provide the only source of available protons of energy greater than 1800 GeV at present and using the known energy spectrum of primary cosmic rays incident on the top of the atmosphere the sensitivity of cosmic ray experiments can be assessed. Assuming all produced quarks would be detected by an apparatus of aperture $0\cdot1$ m² sr and one event is observed in three months' running time, figure 5 shows the limits that can be put on the quark mass for different production processes. Recalling that the inelastic nucleon–nucleon cross section is about 33 mb it is seen that masses of 100 nucleon masses and even higher are accessible to such experiments.

Processes (ii) and (iii) which correspond to the dissociation of either or both of the incident and struck nucleons into quarks may be expected to have a cross section equal to the geometric size of the nucleon core. This can in principle be obtained from an estimate of the high energy asymptotic value of the proton–antiproton annihilation cross section. Collecting together all the available data on proton–antiproton inter-actions shows the upper limit to this cross section is about 2·5 mb. It is seen from figure 5 that cosmic ray experiments can investigate cross sections considerably lower than this even if $M_q/M_N = 100$.

2.2.3. The expected quark–nucleon inelastic cross section and inelasticity. The quark nucleon inelastic cross section is certainly no larger than the nucleon–nucleon inelastic cross section which is about 33 mb and, as can be seen by the following argument, a more likely value is $33/3\ mb = 11\ mb$. Note that the πp inelastic cross section is about 22 mb and that mesons contain 2 quarks and baryons 3 quarks and further assume that constituent quarks interact independently. It can be seen that the expec-ted ratio of the inelastic πp to the inelastic NN cross section is $6/9 = 2/3$ which agrees with the measured ratio and leads to a quark–nucleon inelastic cross section of 11 mb. A discussion of interaction cross sections in terms of the independent quark model is given by Levin and Frankfurt (1968). From the fact that the measured attenuation length of cosmic ray nucleons in air is larger than their interaction mean free path it can be shown that on the average nucleons lose approximately $30\% = 2M_\pi/M_N$ of their energy in nucleon–nucleon collisions. Assuming quarks are surrounded by a mesonic field, the quark–nucleon interaction is predominantly a $\pi\pi$ interaction so the expected inelasticity in analogy with the nucleon–nucleon interaction is $\Delta E/E \sim 2M_\pi/M_q \sim 0\cdot3\ M_N/M_q$. Cocconi (1966) arrives at the same conclusion from more general arguments. It follows from this that the larger the quark mass the more material it is likely to penetrate before being reduced to a nonrelativistic velocity.

2.3. Search for quarks in cosmic rays

Since 1964 a large number of experiments have been performed to search for quarks in cosmic rays and the progress made has been reviewed by Jones (1970), Sitte (1970) and L Jones (1971 unpublished). Briefly, all experiments which have attempted to detect unaccompanied quarks (< 1 accompanying particle/m^2) have been unsuc-cessful. The limit obtained on the quark flux obtained in this way by a number of workers is less than 10^{-10} cm^{-2} s^{-1} sr^{-1}. Experiments to search for quarks in air showers are less numerous and so far have produced conflicting results. The Sydney group (Cairns *et al* 1969, McCusker and Cairns 1969) have reported evidence for quarks with charge $2e/3$ being present close to the cores of extensive air showers initiated by primary cosmic rays of energy greater than 4×10^{15} eV. The detectors used by this group were four cloud chambers each of 30 cm diameter and illuminated depth 5 cm. Three of the chambers were shielded by 15 cm lead while the fourth was unshielded. Air showers were selected by the coincidence of three small Geiger counter trays situated at the apices of a triangle with sides approximately 2 m in length. All the equipment was situated in a hut under a light roof at sea level.

Four quark-like tracks were reported by Cairns *et al* (1969) after one year's running time and a fifth quark-like track by McCusker and Cairns (1969). The five quark candidates were obtained from the observation of 20 000 showers which were selected by a local electron density requirement of greater than 154 m^{-2}. Details of the five quark candidates which occurred at a flux level of approximately 5×10^{-10} cm^{-2} s^{-1} are given in table 5.

Table 5. Characteristics of the 5 Sydney quark candidate events given by Cairns *et al* (1969) and McCusker and Cairns (1969).

Event number	I/I_p for quark candidate	No of δ rays on quark candidate	No of δ rays on equal length of calibration track	No of penetrating particles in chamber	Angle between penetrating points and quark candidate	Electron density at the chamber
62352	0·58 ± 0·05	19	19	3	6°	~300 m^{-2}
64358	0·58 ± 0·12	Not given	Not given	0	No tracks	Not given
64915	0·46 ± 0·08	4	12	Many	6°	~2000m^{-2}
65677	0·46	3	7	Several	10°	~900 m^{-2}
66240	0·48 ± 0·05	3	9	9	1°	~5950 m^{-2}

The claim of the Sydney group that the events observed were genuine quarks was criticized by a number of authors (Wilson 1970, Kiraly and Wolfendale 1970, Adair and Kasha 1969, Rahm and Sternheimer 1969, Rahm and Louttit 1970, Frauenfelder *et al* 1970). The main point of criticism was that the Sydney group had not adequately demonstrated that the five events were well separated in ionization density from the distribution due to plateau or minimum ionizing charge *e* particles where *e* is the electron charge. As a result of this I Cairns and L Peak (1969 unpublished) measured the average number of drops per centimetre of track for 308 plateau ionizing tracks; their results are shown in figure 6. Also shown in figure 6 are the five candidates whose ionization density has been normalized to a value of 30 drops per centimetre for plateau ionizing charge *e* particles. There is some doubt as to the magnitude of the logarithmic rise of ionization density in going from minimum ionizing particles to plateau ionizing particles for the constituents of the cloud chamber gas (argon, 1·4 atm; alcohol, 25 Torr; water vapour, 14 Torr). According to a theoretical estimate by Rahm and Sternheimer (1969) and by Rahm and Louttit (1970) the minimum to plateau ionization density is 0·69 for this gas composition. However, the measured ratio of minimum to plateau ionization density for a gas at atmospheric pressure of composition argon 93% (by molecular concentration), methane 7% gives 0·59 (Ramana Murthy 1968) while the Sternheimer theory predicts 0·63. According to Rahm and Louttit (1970) a realistic estimate of the ratio of minimum to plateau ionization density for the conditions of the Sydney experiment is 0·66. Obviously accurate measurements of the ratio of the minimum to the plateau ionization density of charge *e* particles for the actual gas composition used by the Sydney group is required before their quark candidates can be convincingly shown not to be minimum ionizing charge *e* particles with a downward fluctuation in ionization density.

Stimulated by the Sydney work several groups have searched for quarks in air

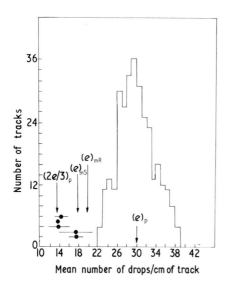

Figure 6. The distribution of the mean number of drops per centimetre of track for 308 calibration tracks given by Cairns and Peak (1969). Mean of the distribution $= 30 \cdot 0$; standard deviation $= 3 \cdot 7$. The 308 calibration tracks are from a sample of 1330 showers while the 5 quark candidates were observed in a sample of 20 000 showers. The mean number of drops/cm for the 5 quark candidates has been calculated using the values of $I/I_{plateau}$ given by Cairns *et al* (1969) and McCusker and Cairns (1969) using $I_{plateau} = 30$ drops/cm of track. $(e)_p$ refers to plateau ionizing charge e particles and $(e)_{mS}$ and $(e)_{mR}$ to minimum ionizing charge e particles according to Rahm and Sternheimer (1969) and Rahm and Louttit (1970) while $(2e/3)_p$ refers to plateau ionizing charge $2e/3$ quarks.

showers. So far only negative results have been reported and these are summarized in table 6. It would seem from this work that either the Sydney events are all spurious or that their estimated flux level is too large.

Chu *et al* (1970) reported a cosmic ray event observed as background in a bubble chamber during an accelerator experiment. They interpreted one of the cosmic ray tracks as that expected from a charge $2e/3$ particle if the particle mass was less than $6 \cdot 5$ GeV/c^2 or a charge $e/3$ particle of mass $(8 \cdot 0 \pm 3 \cdot 0)$ GeV/c^2. However, Allison *et al* (1970) have shown the interpretation of Chu *et al* to be incorrect.

Table 6. Summary of the flux limits for quarks in extensive air showers obtained by different groups. Δ_e is the minimum electron density used as a master trigger.

Group	Technique	Reference	Location	Δe	Flux (10^{-10} cm^{-2} s^{-1} sr^{-1})	
					$e/3$	$2e/3$
Sydney	Cloud chamber	Cairns *et al* (1969)	Sea level	> 154 m^{-2}	—	~ 5
Michigan	Cloud chamber	Hazen (1971)	Sea level	> 150 m^{-2}	< 1	< 1
Livermore	Cloud chamber	Clark *et al* (1971)	Sea level	> 86 m^{-2}	< 3	$< 0 \cdot 3$
Durham	Flash-tube chamber	Ashton *et al* (1972)	Seal level	> 40 m^{-2}	$< 0 \cdot 9$	—
Edinburgh	High pressure (28 atm He) cloud chamber	Evans *et al* (1971/72)	Sea level	> 60 m^{-2}	< 40	—

Experiments have also been performed to search for delayed particles in air showers. The principle of this type of experiment is that the time delay of a particle of rest mass mc^2 and energy E relative to ultrarelativistic particles is $1667 \, (mc^2/E)^2$ ns km^{-1}. Dardo *et al* (1972) working at 70 mwe underground and Tonwar *et al* (1971) working at 2150 m above sea level have claimed definite signals at flux levels of 10^{-8} and 10^{-9} cm^{-2} s^{-1} sr^{-1} respectively. If it is substantiated by further work that the signals observed are indeed due to heavy mass delayed particles it would seem certain they will be found to have integral charge and therefore they may possibly correspond to integral charge fundamental triplet particles.

2.4. Summary

To date there is no strong positive evidence for the existence of quarks with fractional charge. Whether this is due to the fact that they do not exist or due to the fact that their mass is so large or their production cross section so small that they would not have been detected anyway is impossible to say. Obviously any experiment which will depress the limits further is well worth carrying out.

As noted in the text the simplest interpretation of the observed multiplet structure of the elementary particles is in terms of a fundamental triplet of particles with fractional charge. However, it may be that the fundamental triplet particles have integral charge and for such particles searches have only been made so far at non-relativistic velocities ($\beta \sim 0.8$). It is technically quite possible to measure the mass of relativistic charge e particles by measuring their momentum by magnetic deflection and their Lorentz factor by a sufficiently large number of layers (~ 10) of proportional counters. A further possibility is to search for stopping particles that decay with an anomalous Q value. Such measurements have not yet been carried out.

3. Magnetic monopoles

Experiments to search for magnetic monopoles are of interest as their existence seems to be the only way of explaining why electric charge is quantized. According to Dirac (1931, 1948) if the fundamental electric charge is e then monopoles of fundamental strength $g = \hbar c/2e$ should exist. A more recent theory by Schwinger (1966) predicts $g = \hbar c/e$. If quarks with fractional charge $e/3$ should exist then the previous values of g become $3\hbar c/2e$ and $3\hbar c/e$ respectively. Thus the detection of monopoles with $g = \hbar c/2e$ or $\hbar c/e$ would indicate that quarks with fractional charge do not exist. Work on magnetic monopoles prior to 1968 has been reviewed by Amaldi (1968).

The main characteristic of monopoles is their very large rate of ionization loss in matter (Bauer 1951, Cole 1951). For monopoles with $g = \hbar c/2e$ moving with velocity β this is $-dE/dx = 9.4\beta^2$ GeV g^{-1} cm^2 and should be compared with $dE/dx \sim 2/\beta^2$ MeV g^{-1} cm^2 for particles with electric charge e. Thus relativistic monopoles ($\beta \sim 1$) would produce tracks in nuclear emulsions or other visual detectors similar to those produced by high Z nuclei. However, the tracks of monopoles with $\beta \ll 1$ should be resolvable because of the different dependence of dE/dx on β. Table 7 summarizes some expected properties of monopoles.

Monopoles are expected to be produced by processes similar to those producing electron–positron pairs:

$$\gamma + p \rightarrow p + g + \bar{g}$$

$$p + p \rightarrow p + p + g + \bar{g}.$$

Searches for monopoles using 30 GeV proton accelerators (Amaldi *et al* 1963, Purcell *et al* 1963), show that their rest mass is greater than 2·8 GeV/c^2 if they exist. The most recent accelerator experiment (Gurevich *et al* 1972) using 70 GeV protons gives $\sigma < 1\cdot4 \times 10^{-43}$ cm^2 for $M_g < 4\cdot9$ GeV/c^2.

Table 7. Expected properties of magnetic monopoles corresponding to fundamental electric charges e and $e/3$.

Author	Fundamental electric charge	Fundamental monopole strength	dE/dx (GeV g^{-1}cm^2)	Z of nucleus with same dE/dx	Ionization loss in penetrating the atmosphere to sea level
Dirac	e	$\frac{1}{2}\dfrac{\hbar c}{e}$	9·4	69	$9\cdot4 \times 10^{12}$ eV
Dirac	$e/3$	$\frac{3}{2}\dfrac{\hbar c}{e}$	84·6	207	$8\cdot5 \times 10^{13}$ eV
Schwinger	e	$\hbar c/e$	36·6	138	$3\cdot8 \times 10^{13}$ eV
Schwinger	$e/3$	$3\dfrac{\hbar c}{e}$	329·4	414	$3\cdot4 \times 10^{14}$ eV

Monopoles present in the cosmic ray beam in the atmosphere could either be produced in high energy cosmic ray interactions or be present in the primary cosmic radiation. The possibility of monopoles being a component of the primary cosmic radiation at extremely high energies has been pointed out by Porter (1960) and Goto (1963). The main attraction of this hypothesis is that monopoles would be easily accelerated to high energies in weak magnetic fields. In a magnetic field of 10^{-6} Oe a monopole of strength $g = \hbar c/2e$ would gain energy at a rate of 7×10^{16} eV pc^{-1} (1 parsec = 3·26 light years), the corresponding energy loss being only about 5×10^4 eV pc^{-1} for a gas density of one hydrogen atom/cm^3.

Ashton *et al* (1969) searched for magnetic monopoles in the sea-level cosmic radiation using scintillation counters sandwiched between layers of flash-tubes as visual detectors. In this device monopoles should produce a pulse of greater than 4000 times the pulse height produced by a single relativistic muon in the scintillation counter and a single track in the flash-tube layers. For a running time of 628 hours no such events were recorded corresponding to a flux limit of less than $1\cdot3 \times 10^{-10}$ cm^{-2}s^{-1}sr^{-1}. The probability of a monopole undergoing an electromagnetic interaction in the detector or in the atmosphere and producing electron accompaniment at the detector is considered to be negligible at the energies investigated in the above experiment because of the large value of the monopole mass. Subsequent examination of ionization calorimeter data (Erlykin and Yakovlev 1969) gave flux limits of less than $2\cdot5 \times 10^{-12}$ cm^{-2}s^{-1}sr^{-1} for E greater than 10^{13} eV and less than 7×10^{-13} cm^{-2}s^{-1}sr^{-1} for E greater than 3×10^{13} eV for monopoles with $g = \hbar c/2e$. A negative result was also found by Fleischer *et al* (1971) who used an 18 m^2 area Lexan polycarbonate array exposed at sea level and found a flux limit less than $1\cdot5 \times 10^{-13}$ cm^{-2}s^{-1}sr^{-1}. Figure 7 shows the primary cosmic ray spectrum given by Greisen (1966). A possible interpretation is that primary cosmic rays of energy below 10^{18} eV are all galactic while those of energy above 10^{18} eV are all extragalactic. If this is so then extragalactic particles may be present in the low energy radiation at about the 1% level (broken line in figure 7). If these extragalactic particles should all be monopoles then they will be subject to a geomagnetic cut-off at moderate latitudes of about 10^{12} eV which in all cases is less than the minimum energy required to penetrate the Earth's atmosphere. It is clear from figure 7 and the limits quoted above that it would seem unlikely that cosmic rays of energy above 10^{18} eV are monopoles.

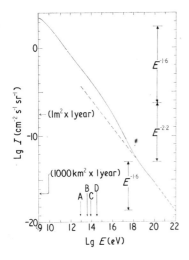

Figure 7. Integral primary cosmic ray energy spectrum according to Greisen (1966). Points A, B, C and D indicate the ionization loss of a monopole traversing the atmosphere. A, B correspond to a fundamental electric charge e and C, D to a fundamental charge $e/3$ according to Dirac and Schwinger respectively.

Extensive searches for monopoles accumulated in stable matter over geological time periods have also been carried out. Workers in this field quote flux limits depending on the monopole energy, for example for lunar materials Alvarez *et al* (1970) find a flux limit of less than 10^{-13} cm^{-2}s^{-1}sr^{-1} for monopoles of energy above 3×10^{14} eV. Kolm *et al* (1971) have searched large quantities of sediment from the ocean bed. Assuming monopoles are bound only to ferromagnetic and paramagnetic materials they find a flux limit of less than $1 \cdot 2 \times 10^{-17}$ cm^{-2}s^{-1} for energies below 4×10^{15} eV.

Noting the strong attractive interaction potential between monopole–antimonopole pairs Ruderman and Zwanziger (1969) point out that close to their kinematic production threshold monopoles may not have sufficient relative momentum to escape immediate mutual annihilation. The expected annihilation products are two or more γ rays. By calculating the invariant mass of groups of γ rays emerging from high energy collisions it may be possible to infer indirectly the existence of monopoles. Such experiments have not yet been carried out.

4. Tachyons

The special theory of relativity is based on two fundamental postulates. (i) If a physical law is valid in one coordinate system then it must remain valid in any coordinate system which moves with constant uniform velocity relative to the first system; (ii) the universal constancy of the speed of light. The second assumption is based on the negative outcome of the Michelson–Morley experiment which showed that the speed of light is independent of its direction of motion relative to the direction of motion of the Earth through space. It should be noted that in the special theory of relativity only the constancy of the speed of light is assumed and the fact that it is the highest possible signal velocity is not an assumption. However, it is implied for material particles as the total energy $E = mc^2/(1 - \beta^2)^{1/2}$ approaches infinity as $\beta \rightarrow 1$. For objects moving with $\beta > 1$ (tachyons) the total energy relation implies that the objects have 'imaginary' rest mass as $E = imc^2/(\beta^2 - 1)^{1/2}$. It is suggestive that β must always be greater than unity for a tachyon can never be slowed down to a speed less than c. For a detailed discussion of the theory of tachyons see Bilaniuk *et al* (1962), Feinberg (1967) and Newton (1967, 1970). One interesting property of charged tachyons is that they would emit Cerenkov radiation in vacuum without violating energy and momentum conservation as normal particles would (Alvager and Kreisler 1968). This property was used by Davis *et al* (1969) to search for tachyon pairs produced in lead by γ rays from a ^{60}Co radioactive source (energy of main components: 1·332 MeV and 1·172 MeV). The detector was the space between two metal plates which was evacuated and an electric field (to accelerate charged tachyons) of 3 kV cm^{-1} was maintained between them. When the vacuum was observed with a photomultiplier, no pulses that could be attributed to tachyon Cerenkov radiation were recorded. The limit on the tachyon pair production cross section by γ rays of about 1·2 MeV energy was found to be less than $1·7 \times 10^{-33}$ cm^{-2} for tachyons having charges between 0·5 and 1·9 electron charges.

A search for tachyons in cosmic ray air showers of primary energy above 3×10^{13} eV has been made by Ramana Murthy (1971) working at an altitude of 2·3 km above sea level. The principle of this experiment was the following. In extensive air showers (EAS) electrons and photons, constituting the major component of EAS, travel with velocities near to or equal to that of light at the very forefront of the EAS forming a well defined shower front (Bassi *et al* 1953). Any tachyons produced in the interactions of the primary or secondary components of EAS particles would arrive ahead of the shower front, the time depending on details such as the height of the point of production and the energy loss of tachyons in air. Taking the average height at which primary protons make their first interaction in the atmosphere as a limiting case tachyons should arrive some time in the period 0–44 μs preceding the arrival of electrons and photons for a detector 2·3 km above sea level. Ramana Murthy (1971) searched for events of this type which deposit energy greater than 40 MeV in a liquid scintillation counter of depth 22 cm in the time domain 0–22 μs preceding the arrival of EAS electrons and photons. Events were observed in this time interval but they were uniformly distributed in time and statistically accountable in terms of the incoherent muon background traversing the detector. Ramana Murthy also used a detector of two aluminium plates of area 80×80 cm^2 separated by 9·5 cm. An electric field of 2·1 kV cm^{-1} was applied between the plates and the air space viewed by photomultipliers. This detector should record the arrival of tachyons moving with velocity close to the velocity of light as they would be accelerated in the applied electric field and radiate energy by Cerenkov radiation (Alvager and Kreisler 1968).

Early pulses in the time domain 0–20 μs preceding the arrival of EAS electrons and photons were observed in this detector but again they could all be explained as due to chance coincidences. Ramana Murthy concluded that using the liquid scintillator detector the tachyon to electron ratio was less than $2 \cdot 6 \times 10^{-4}$ and, using the Cerenkov detector, less than 2×10^{-5} in EAS initiated by primaries of energy above 3×10^{13} eV.

Ashton *et al* (1971) were able to place an upper limit of less than $2 \cdot 2 \times 10^{-5}$ cm^{-2} s^{-1} sr^{-1} at the 90% confidence level on the flux of tachyons in the incoherent sea-level cosmic radiation. This limit was obtained as a by-product of an experiment to establish the precision with which time of flight measurements could be made between two large area scintillation counters and is capable of considerable improvement. For tachyons to be detected in the experiment of Ashton *et al* they were required to deposit energy greater than 2 MeV in each plastic scintillation counter of 5 cm in thickness.

References

Adair R K and Kasha H 1969 *Phys. Rev. Lett.* **23** 1355–8
Allaby J V *et al* 1969 *Nuovo Cim.* **64** 75–94
Allison W W M *et al* 1970 *Phys. Rev. Lett.* **25** 550–3
Alvager T and Kreisler M N 1968 *Phys. Rev.* **171** 1357–61
Alvarez L W, Eberhard P H and Ross R R 1970 *Science* **167** 701–3
Amaldi E 1968 *Old and new problems in elementary particles* ed G Puppi (New York: Academic Press)
Amaldi E *et al* 1963 *Nuovo Cim.* **28** 733–93
Antipov Y M *et al* 1969 *Phys. Lett.* **30B** 576–80
Ashton F *et al* 1969 *Izvest. Akad. Nauk.* **33** 1817–9
Ashton F, Cooper, D A Parvaresh A, and Saleh A J 1973 *J. Phys.* A: *Math. Nucl. Gen.* **6** 577–81
Ashton F, Edwards H J and Kelly G N 1971 *Nucl. Inst. Meth.* **93** 349–51
Bacry H, Nuyts J and Van Hove L 1964 *Phys. Lett.* **9** 120–1
Barger V, Olssen M and Reeder D D 1968 *Nucl. Phys.* **B5** 411–30
Bassi P, Clark G and Rossi B 1953 *Phys. Rev.* **92** 441–51
Bauer E 1951 *Proc. Camb. Phil. Soc.* **47** 777–89
Bilaniuk O M P, Deshpande V K and Sudarsham E C 1962 *Am. J. Phys.* **30** 718–23
Burkhardt H 1969 *Dispersion Relation Dynamics* (Amsterdam: North Holland)
Cairns I, McCusker C B A, Peak L A and Woolcott R L S 1969 *Phys. Rev.* **186** 1394–1400
Cence R J 1969 *Pion–Nucleon Scattering* (Princeton: Princeton University Press)
Chu W T, Kim Y S, Beam W J and Kwak N 1970 *Phys. Rev. Lett.* **24** 917–23
Clark A F *et al* 1971 *Phys. Rev. Lett.* **27** 51–5
Cocconi G 1966 *Proc. 9th Int. Conf. Cosmic Rays* (London: Institute of Physics) **2** 616–8
Cole H J D 1951 *Proc. Camb. Phil. Soc.* **47** 196–206
Dardo M, Navarra G, Penengo P and Sitte K 1972 *Nuovo Cim.* **9A** 319–39
Davis M B, Kreisler M N and Alvager T 1969 *Phys. Rev.* **183** 1132–3
Dirac P A M 1931 *Proc. R. Soc.* **A133** 60–72
—— 1948 *Phys. Rev.* **74** 817–30
Erlykin A D and Yakovlev V I 1969 *Sov. Phys.–JETP* **29** 922–3
Evans G R, Fancey, N E, Muir J and Watson A A 1971/72 *Proc. R. Soc. Edinb.* **A70** 143–53

Feinberg G 1967 *Phys. Rev.* **159** 1089–105
Feld B T 1969 *Models of elementary particles* (Waltham, Mass: Blaisdell)
Fermi E and Yang C N 1949 *Phys. Rev* **76** 1739–43
Fleischer R L, Hart H R, Nichols G E and Price P B 1971 *Phys. Rev.* **4D** 24–7
Frauenfelder H, Kruse U E and Sard R D 1970 *Phys. Rev. Lett.* **24** 33–5
Gell-Mann M 1964 *Phys. Lett.* **8** 214–5
Goto E 1963 *Prog. Theor. Phys.* **30** 700–18
Greisen K 1966 *Proc. 9th Int. Conf. on Cosmic Rays* (London: Institute of Physics) **2** 609–15
Gurevich I I *et al* 1972 *Phys. Lett.* **38B** 549–50
Hazen W E 1971 *Phys. Rev. Lett.* **26** 582–3
Jones L 1970 *Symmetries and quark models* ed R Chand (New York: Gordon and Breach)
Kiraly P and Wolfendale A W 1970 *Phys. Lett.* **31B** 410–2
Kokkedee J J J 1969 *The quark model* (New York: Benjamin)
Kolm H, Villa F and Odian A 1971 *Phys. Rev.* **D 4** 1285–96
Lee T D 1965 *Nuovo Cim.* **35** 933–44
Levin E M and Frankfurt L L 1968 *Sov. Phys. Usp.* **2** 106–29
McCusker C B A and Cairns I 1969 *Phys. Rev. Lett.* **23** 658–9
Maksimenko V M, Sisakyan I N, Feinberg E L and Chernavaskii D S 1966 *Sov. Phys–JETP Lett.* **3** 219–21
Morpurgo G 1967 *Acta Phys. Hung.* **22** 105–28
—— 1970 *Ann. Rev. Nucl. Sci.* **20** 105–46
Newton R G 1967 *Phys. Rev.* **162** 1274
—— 1970 *Science* **167** 1569–74
Particle Data Group 1972 *Phys. Lett.* **39B** No 1 1–145
Peters B 1966 *CERN Report* 66-22
Porter N A 1960 *Nuovo Cim* **16** 958–9
Purcell E M *et al* 1963 *Phys. Rev.* **129** 2326–36
Rahm D C and Louttit R I 1970 *Phys. Rev. Lett.* **24** 279–82
Rahm D C and Sternheimer R M 1969 *Brookhaven preprint* BNL14072
Ramana Murthy P V 1968 *Nucl. Inst. Meth.* **63** 77–82
——1971 *Proc. 12th Int. Conf. on Cosmic Rays* (Hobart: University of Tasmania) **3** 1188
Ruderman M A and Zwanziger D 1969 *Phys. Rev. Lett.* **22** 146–8
Sakata S 1956 *Prog. Theor. Phys.* **16** 686–8
Schwinger J 1966 *Phys. Rev.* **144** 1087–93
Sitte K 1970 *Nuovo Cim.* (suppl) **6** 866–86
Tonwar S C, Naranan S and Sreekantan B V 1971 *Proc. 12th Int. Conf. on Cosmic Rays* (Hobart: University of Tasmania) **3** 1171–6
Wilson J G 1970 *Nature* **225** 1238–9
Zweig G 1964 *CERN preprints* TH401, TH412
—— 1965 *Symmetries in elementary particle physics* ed A Zichichi (New York: Academic Press)

Chapter 8

Extensive air showers below 10^{17} eV

J Wdowczyk

1. Introduction

Extensive air showers have caused a great deal of interest since their discovery in the late nineteen-thirties. At first the interest related mainly to properties of the phenomenon itself, but it soon turned towards questions of the properties of the primary particles and their interactions with matter. These, together with the essential problem of the origin of cosmic rays, form the main physical problems arising in EAS investigations at present.

The astrophysical problems of the nature, origin and mechanism of propagation of cosmic rays are particularly interesting for the highest energy particles initiating EAS. The question of the objects which are able to accelerate particles to such gigantic energies is one of the most important problems of high energy astrophysics.

The present chapter, which is devoted to extensive air showers initiated by particles with energies below 10^{17} eV, will mostly deal with the properties of the phenomenon itself and their relation to high energy physics, as the picture of the phenomenon is determined by the properties of the interactions of high energy particles with matter. The description of the ways of deducing information about the parameters of high energy interactions is an essential part of the presentation, whereas the astrophysical problems are generally not covered.

The interest in deducing information about high energy physics from EAS properties has increased considerably recently, due to progress in experiments with high energy accelerators. The fact that the accelerator energies have already reached the level where the cross section for multiple particle production dominates, has caused theoretical interest in the phenomena characterizing that process. Recently proposed approaches such as Feynman's scaling (Feynman 1969), the limiting distribution hypothesis (Benecke et al 1969) and others (see for example van Hove (1969)) give the possibility of predicting various parameters as a function of collision energy and allow verification of the predictions in wide energy intervals. The wide energy interval often compensates for the fact that the accuracy of various parameters determined from EAS measurements is rather poor and that many of the conclusions are qualitative only.

2. General description of the phenomenon

2.1. Character of the interactions

Extensive air showers are initiated by interactions of primary cosmic rays with nuclei of air atoms. In these high energy interactions secondary particles are produced, most of which are pions. The neutral pions immediately decay into pairs of photons and these photons initiate electromagnetic cascades. The cascades form the most numerous electromagnetic component of EAS. The charged pions together with nucleons and other secondary particles form the cascade of nuclear-active particles. This cascade is the skeleton of the shower, regenerating the electromagnetic component by continuously feeding energy into that component by way of the production of neutral pions. The cascade of nuclear-active particles is also a source of the second most numerous component, the muon component, which is formed via decay of the charged pions.

These three components are the main ones recorded at the various observation levels. In addition one can quote some others produced as result of the passage of the shower through the atmosphere, notably the Cerenkov component and the radio waves emitted by EAS. A detailed discussion of properties of the various components will be given later.

Owing to the high degree of complexity of the phenomena a very important role in understanding EAS is played by detailed theoretical calculations of their development. In the modelling of EAS development the most important factor is the assumed model of high energy interactions. Since full details of such a model are not known, it seems necessary to perform the calculations by a method of successive approximations. In the first stage a simple model is derived by extrapolation from the lower energy region and the results of calculations are compared with the various experimental data. The deviations of the observations from the predictions of the model are used for modifications of it in the later stages. The necessary modifications should be suggested on the basis of a detailed understanding of the sensitivity of various parameters of EAS to different features of the high energy interaction model.

2.2. The 'standard' model

The standard model used in the various calculations is that based on the so-called CKP formula. Properties of the model can be summarized as follows (after de Beer *et al* 1966).

   (i) High energy nucleons lose on average 50% of their energy in each collision and have an interaction mean free path in the atmosphere of 80 g cm^{-2}, both these quantities being independent of energy.

(ii) The secondary particles are mainly pions, there being on average equal numbers of π^+, π^- and π^0 mesons produced.

(iii) The pions have an energy distribution in the laboratory system given by the empirical relation of Cocconi, Koester and Perkins which, when allowance is made for particles emitted in the 'backward cone' can be written as

$$S(E, E_0) = \tfrac{1}{2}\left\{\frac{n(E_0)}{\Gamma}\exp\left(-\frac{E}{\Gamma}\right) + \frac{n(E_0)}{G}\exp\left(-\frac{E}{G}\right)\right\},$$

where $n(E_0)$ is the multiplicity of pions produced, E_0 is the transferred energy, G is the average energy of pions in the backward cone and

$$\Gamma = 2(E_0 - \tfrac{1}{2}n(E_0)G)/n(E_0)$$

is the average energy in the forward cone.

(iv) It is assumed that the fraction of energy lost by a nucleon which does not appear as pions is negligible.

(v) The multiplicity of the secondary pion, n_s, is given by $n_s = 2 \cdot 7 E_p^{1/4}$ with E_p in GeV for $K = 0 \cdot 5$ and $n_s = 2 \cdot 7 \times 2^{1/4}\,(KE_p)^{1/4}$ for all K.

(vi) The distribution in transverse momentum, p_t, of the produced pions is given by the expression suggested by Cocconi, Koester and Perkins

$$f(p_t) = \frac{p_t}{p_0^2}\exp\left(-\frac{p_t}{p_0}\right).$$

The mean transverse momentum $(2p_0)$ is assumed to be independent of energy and equal to 400 MeV/c.

(vii) Pion interactions are assumed to differ from nucleon interactions in that they are catastrophic with interaction length of 120 g cm^{-2}. The energy spectrum of the pions produced in pion interactions is taken to be that given by the same relation as for protons but with $K = 1$, in other words $n_s = 3 \cdot 2\,E_p^{1/4}$.

(viii) Fluctuations are allowed for in the calculations to the extent that variations in the inelasticity of nucleon air nucleus collisions are included as well as the normal statistical fluctuations in the depth in the atmosphere of the interactions.

The adopted form for the inelasticity distribution is

$$f(K) = -(1+\alpha)^2\,(1-K)^\alpha \ln(1-K)$$

with $\alpha = 1 \cdot 414$.

Predictions of this model will be used mostly as the datum in the subsequent discussions of the various EAS phenomena.

3. Review of the properties of EAS components

3.1. The electron component

3.1.1. Lateral distribution. The main parameter characterizing the electron component at the given observation level is its lateral distribution. This distribution is described by a structure function defined as

$$f(r) = \frac{r_1^2 \, \rho(r)}{N}, \tag{1}$$

where N represents the total number of electrons, r_1 is a certain characteristic radius depending on the height of the observation level and $\rho(r)$ is the electron density as a function of distance from the core.

It has been found that the lateral structure function of the electrons in EAS can be described by the function predicted theoretically by Nishimura and Kamata (1952) for pure electromagnetic cascades. This function can be approximated by the following simple expression due to Greisen (1956)

$$f\left(\frac{r}{r_1}\right) = C(s) \left(\frac{r}{r_1}\right)^{s-2} \left(\frac{r}{r_1} + 1\right)^{s-4\cdot5}, \tag{2}$$

where s represents the so-called cascade age parameter and $C(s)$ is a normalization coefficient, values of which are as follows:

s	=0·6	0·8	1·0	1·2	1·4	1·6	1·8
$C(s)$	=0·22	0·31	0·40	0·44	0·43	0·36	0·25.

The fact that the shower lateral distribution can be described well by a function calculated for pure electromagnetic cascades could not be assumed *a priori* but it is not too surprising since EAS is a superposition of electromagnetic cascades.

More surprising is the fact that, contrary to expectation from knowledge of pure electromagnetic cascades, the age parameter of EAS is practically independent of the number of particles in the shower over the very wide range of number: 10^3–10^9 particles. The age parameter over this range is $s = 1\cdot2$–$1\cdot25$ (see, for example, review by Greisen 1960).

The measurements of the electron density in EAS are carried out with detectors of two types: Geiger–Müller counters and scintillators. The lateral distributions obtained with G–M counters represent rather well the actual distribution of particles, whereas those observed with scintillators are slightly steeper owing to the dependence of scintillator response on the energy spectrum of the electromagnetic component. This fact is illustrated in figure 1 where the lateral structure function for $s = 1\cdot2$ is compared with that obtained by Hasegawa *et al* (1962) using scintillators. These workers found that the structure function for scintillators can be described by the formula

$$f\left(\frac{r}{r_1}\right) = \frac{r_1^2}{2\pi \,(120\pi)^{1/2}} \, \frac{\exp\,(r/120)}{r^{1\cdot5}}. \tag{3}$$

It should also be remembered that the equivalent sizes of the showers obtained using scintillators are bigger than the real ones (by 'size' is meant the total number of particles in the shower at the detection level).

3.1.2. Shower age parameter. The theoretical predictions for the shower age parameters as a function of size are given in figure 2 (after Karakula 1968). The results

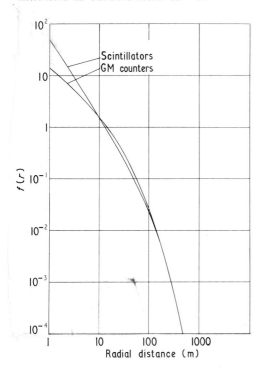

Figure 1. The electron structure functions obtained using G–M counters and scintillators.

were obtained using the standard model. It can be seen that the variation of age with shower size is very small but it seems that the variation is still stronger than that observed experimentally. This can be seen from table 1 where the experimental results of Vernov *et al* (1970) are given. The increase of the age parameter for big showers is interpreted as due to the fact that at large distances from the shower core the structure function becomes flatter than that given by formula (1) . Since the bigger showers on average are recorded further from their cores the apparent increase of age may be expected. Some deviation of the EAS structure function from that obtained for a pure electromagnetic cascade is predicted theoretically. It is found that the EAS structure function is flatter at large distances and steeper at small distances, in

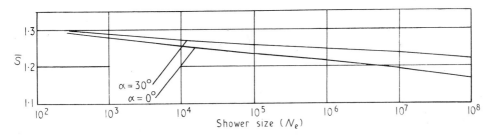

Figure 2. The age parameter variation predicted on the basis of the standard EAS model. The calculations were performed for fixed electron size. Curves for 0° and 30° are marked.

other words the age parameter measured at large distances should be bigger than average and that measured at small distances smaller than average. The last feature has also been confirmed experimentally by the observation that the mean value of the age parameter at small distances (1–20 m) is about 1·15.

Table 1. The shower age parameter and its fluctuations as a function of shower size. Successive columns give shower size, number of showers analysed, mean age parameter, observed fluctuations of the age parameter and that corrected by subtracting the fluctuations due to errors in age determination.

$N_e \times 10^{-5}$	n	$\bar{s}$	$(\sigma_s/\bar{s})_{exp}$	$(\sigma_s/\bar{s})_{corr}$
1·5	496	1·22±0·01	0·14	0·09±0·01
2·5	626	1·19±0·01	0·13	0·09±0·01
5	507	1·18±0·01	0·13	0·09±0·01
10	299	1·18±0·01	0·12	0·09±0·01
20	144	1·21±0·01	0·13	0·09±0·01
40	64	1·22±0·02	0·13	0·09±0·02
70	121	1·31±0·01	0·12	0·09±0·02
150	56	1·29±0·02	0·14	0·10±0·02

The approximate constancy of the mean value of the age parameter is understood as a consequence of an equilibrium between the electromagnetic and nuclear-active components. Such an equilibrium can arise as a result of continuous regeneration of the electromagnetic component by interactions of the nuclear-active component attenuated in the atmosphere at a constant rate. To assure the constancy of the attenuation length it is necessary to assume that in the individual interactions of nucleons only a fraction of their energy is lost on production of the secondary particles, or in other words that the inelasticity coefficient on average is clearly smaller than unity. This observation was taken into account when the standard EAS model described earlier was developed.

3.1.3. Fluctuations. Table 1 also gives fluctuations of the age parameter. One of the main reasons for the interest in these fluctuations is the fact that they are strongly linked with primary mass composition. The measured values of the fluctuations (approximately 10%) can be obtained only if in the primary flux there exists a high proportion of protons. In fact the fluctuations expected for proton initiated showers are of the order of 4–8% depending on the model of high energy interactions used. The fluctuations for heavier nuclei should be quite negligible. However, it should be stressed that the measurements of the fluctuations are complicated by the necessity of separating genuine fluctuations from those due to experimental errors. It is always possible that some sources of errors are disregarded and as a result the genuine fluctuations may be overestimated. In this light it becomes important to examine the method suggested recently by P Catz *et al* (1972 unpublished), which gives the possibility of evaluating a lower limit to the width of the age parameter fluctuations. The basis of the method is the well known existence of a correlation between age parameter and muon content in individual showers. Taking the dependence describing the correlations one can obtain the distribution of age parameter from the distribution of the $N\mu/N_e$

ratio. Since the correlations are expected only for genuine fluctuations the distribution obtained should not be wider than the real one. The distribution calculated by this method is given in figure 3 together with experimental results of Vernov *et al* (1968a). The results are not corrected for the fluctuations due to errors so the fact that they are more widely distributed is not surprising. The fact that the distribution given in figure 3 has a width of at least 5–6% can be treated as one of the stronger indications of the proton domination in the primary flux at energies round 10^{15} eV. The fact that age parameter fluctuations obtained using scintillators are clearly wider is most likely due to fluctuations in scintillator response.

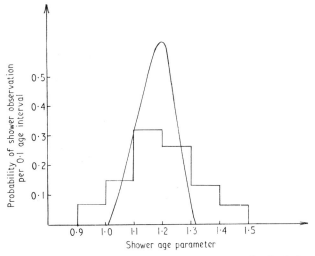

Figure 3. Fluctuations of the shower age parameter for fixed electron size of about 10^5 particles. The histogram gives the upper limit of the width obtained by Vernov *et al* (1968a) and the smooth curve the lower limit obtained by P Catz *et al* (1972 unpublished).

3.1.4. Central electron density. A useful parameter of the electron component of EAS, and one which is strongly related to the mass composition, is the ratio of the central electron density to the total number of particles in the shower. The sensitivity to mass composition is due to the fact that the central density is roughly proportional to the energy per nucleon of the primary particles whereas the total number of particles represents energy per nucleus. The results of experiments performed by Samorski *et al* (1971) are given in figure 4 where the integral distribution of the ratio is given. It can be seen that the results are in agreement with predictions based on the assumption of the domination of protons in the primary flux and they are in clear contradiction with the predictions for heavy primaries.

3.1.5. Shower intensity as a function of height. Another important parameter is dependence of the shower intensity on height. EAS observations are carried out at various levels in the atmosphere: at sea level, at mountain altitudes up to 5200 m and on aeroplanes at heights of the order of 10 km. The observations show that the maxima

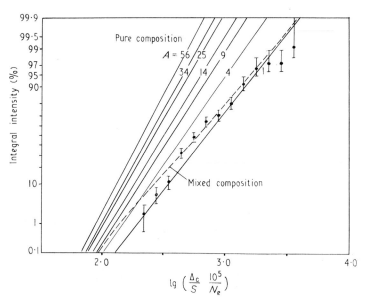

Figure 4. The integral distribution of the ratio of central electron density to the shower size. The lines represent expectations for various primary mass compositions (after Samorski *et al* 1971).

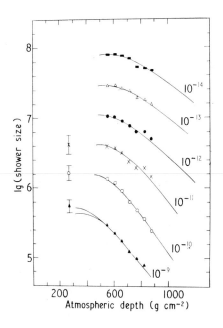

Figure 5. Longitudinal development curves obtained from constant intensity cuts on size spectra obtained at various atmospheric depths.

of the showers are situated relatively high in the atmosphere. From the observations on aeroplanes it is also found that the shower maxima are rather broad. These facts are illustrated in figure 5 where the cascade curves (dependence of size on height) obtained at Chacaltaya (Bradt *et al* 1966) by measurement of the EAS intensity as a function of angle are plotted together with the data of Antonov *et al* (1971) obtained at a height of 10 km. The cascade curves obtained indicate that the electromagnetic cascades initiated by individual interactions of nuclear-active particles are relatively short and that they are subject to large fluctuations. The shortness of the cascades indicate a fast division of the energy of the nuclear-active component or, in other words, high multiplicity of the secondary particles.

3.2. The muon component

3.2.1. Information from muon studies. Owing to their relatively weak interaction with matter, muons are able to give information about the early stages of EAS development. In fact the amount of information about the primary particles, and about the mechanism of their interactions, carried by the muon component is much higher than that carried by electrons. It is well known that the total number of muons represents the energy of the primary particle in individual showers much better than does the total number of electrons. This is particularly the case when observations are carried out at sea level. Because muons represent the directions of emission of their parent particles rather well it is possible by studying lateral distributions of various energy muons to gain information about transverse momenta of those parent particles and also about the longitudinal EAS development. The fact that the information is difficult to collect is due to the low muon density. The construction of large and relatively expensive well shielded detectors is necessary in order to ensure high accuracy of measurement and separation from the much more numerous electrons. The shielding of detectors is obtained by covering with protecting material, usually lead, which is a very efficient absorber of the electromagnetic component or by operating the detectors underground. The thickness of the shielding material determines the threshold energy of the recorded muons. Another type of detector is the magnetic spectrograph in which the muon momentum is determined from its deflection in a magnetic field. The limited sizes of these detectors makes their use rather restricted, however.

3.2.2. Relation of muon number to electron number. The total number of muons in a shower is approximately proportional to the number of electrons raised to the power 3/4. This proportionality is valid over a relatively wide interval and the index is not very dependent on the muon energy threshold (in general it decreases very slightly with increase in energy). The value of the index comes from two other indices in the formulae

$$N_e \sim E^\beta \qquad \text{and} \qquad N_\mu \sim E^\gamma$$

where β is about 1·25 and γ slightly less than unity. The coefficient α in the proportionality $N_\mu \sim N_e^\alpha$ can be evaluated as $\alpha = \gamma/\beta$. The weak variation of α as a function of threshold energy is explained since the deviation of the muon number from proportionality to primary energy is small for all threshold energies.

3.2.3. Lateral distribution of muons. For practical reasons, instead of analysing the total number of muons (as that quantity is difficult to measure) it is better to deal with muon densities at various distances from the shower core. Many measurements have been made of the muon lateral distributions at various threshold energies. The result of some of these are summarized in figures 6 and 7 where the muon lateral distributions are given for 1 GeV threshold and for 10 GeV threshold. It is difficult to summarize the results of various experiments together since the problems of normalization

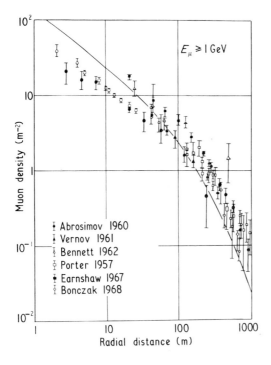

Figure 6. The muon lateral distribution for 1 GeV energy threshold. All data are normalized to the shower size $N_e = 2 \times 10^7$ particles. The continuous curve was calculated according to Greisen's formula (see text).

are rather essential but in general it may be said that no serious deviation from the formula proposed by Greisen and co-workers over 10 years ago (Bennett *et al* 1962) is observed, especially in the region above 20 m from the shower core. At distances smaller than 20 m the distribution seems to be on average slightly flatter. (The observation in various experiments of strong flattening is perhaps partly due to errors in EAS core localization.) The above-mentioned formula has a form

$$\rho_\mu = \frac{14 \cdot 4 r^{-0 \cdot 75}}{(1 + r/320)^{2 \cdot 5}} \left(\frac{N}{10^6}\right)^{0 \cdot 75} \left(\frac{51}{E + 50}\right) \left(\frac{3}{E + 2}\right)^{0 \cdot 14 r^{0 \cdot 37}}$$

where r is expressed in metres and E is in GeV. The formula is valid for muons with energies from 1–10 GeV. Predictions of the formula are also plotted in figures 6 and 7.

In respect of the comparison of muon lateral distributions with theoretical predictions in general it can be said that the lateral distributions expected on the basis of the standard model are slightly narrower than the experimental ones. In order to obtain wider lateral distributions it would be necessary to assume either higher pion transverse momenta or to modify the assumptions in such a way that the muons would be produced higher in the atmosphere. It seems that the more likely possibility is the second one, since the low energy muons come from pions produced in interactions with energy of order 10^{12} eV where the transverse momenta are known. The faster development of EAS, which is in agreement with the observations about the height of shower maximum described earlier and with some indications from measurements of height

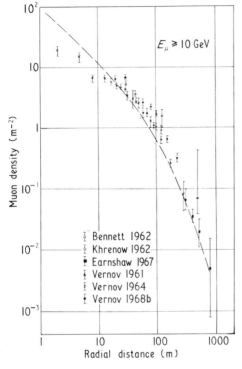

Figure 7. The muon lateral distribution for 10 GeV energy threshold. All data are normalized to the shower size $N_e = 2 \times 10^7$ particles. The continuous curve was calculated according to Greisen's formula.

of the muon generation level, could occur as a result of a multiplicity of the secondary particle production higher than that assumed.

Attention should be called to the interesting fact that the expected width of the muon lateral distribution depends on the mean transverse momenta of the particles in the last interaction and the height of the muon origin on the multiplicity in the very first interactions in a shower. This fact clearly indicates that in order to make some conclusions about transverse momenta it is necessary to make observations of high energy muons, whereas some observations of the low energy muons give indications about multiplicity in the first interactions of the primary particle.

3.2.4. Fluctuations of muon parameters. An important role in the picture of the muon component is played by fluctuations. The fluctuations in the muon to electron numbers have been widely investigated. Results of the investigations are given in figures 8 and 9. In figure 8 a parameter characterizing the width of the fluctuations of the muon number for a fixed electron size is plotted as a function of that size and in figure 9 the analogous parameter characterizing the width of electron fluctuations for fixed muon size. The expected curves shown in the figures were calculated using the standard model for two different assumptions concerning the primary composition;

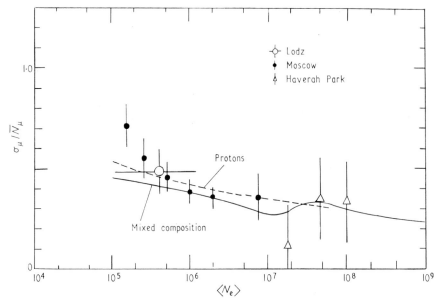

Figure 8. Relative standard deviation of N_μ for fixed N_e. The data were taken from papers by Gawin *et al* (1968), Vernov *et al* (1968a) and Pidcock (1967).

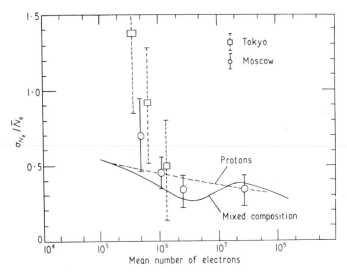

Figure 9. Relative standard deviation of N_e for fixed N_μ. The data were taken from Hasegawa *et al* (1962), and Vernov *et al* (1968a).

these are a pure proton flux and the so-called 'modulated mass spectrum' (see de Beer *et al* 1968). The comparison shows that the expected width of the fluctuations is in good agreement with experimental data and this indicates that the applied model of fluctuations in EAS is reasonable. It can also be seen that fluctuations in muon to electron ratio are not a good indicator of the primary mass composition, if in the primary flux protons play an important role, which is the case for both trial mass compositions. However, it seems that the fluctuations are clearly wider than those expected in the case of all primary particles being heavy nuclei.

The observed fluctuations of the ratio are mainly caused by fluctuations of the electron number. The fluctuations of the muon component are small. In the case of the muon component the fluctuations of their lateral distribution seem to be more important than the fluctuations of their total number for fixed primary energy. Recently it has been shown experimentally that the muon lateral distribution fluctuates strongly at small distances from the core and that its shape is strongly correlated with age of EAS (Iliyna *et al* 1971). This observation is particularly interesting because it is another piece of information indicating that in the primary flux at about 10^{15} eV an important role is played by protons.

3.2.5. High energy muons. Some interesting results have been obtained by the registration of high energy muons in EAS. These muons come directly from the early interactions of the primary particles and their properties are related to the parameters of those interactions. Owing to the fact that the intensity of the muons is very low investigation of them together with EAS is difficult. The highest threshold energy of muons recorded together with showers so far is 600 GeV (Chatterjee *et al* 1966) and the registrations were carried out with small detectors. Much more comprehensive are the results of the registration of groups of high energy muons not correlated with the simultaneous registration of EAS (Cannon and Stenerson 1971). Detailed theoretical analysis has shown that the lateral distribution of muons can give information about the mean transverse momenta of pions produced in interactions of energy around 10^{14}–10^{15} eV (Adcock *et al* 1970) and that the spectrum of numbers of the recorded parallel muons is related to the multiplicity of the pion production at the primary energies quoted (Adcock *et al* 1971).

A direct measurement of the lateral distribution is not practicable but very good information about the lateral distribution can be obtained from a measurement of the rate of coincidences between two detectors as a function of their separation (the decoherence curve). Results of measurements of the decoherence curve together with theoretical predictions for various mean transverse momenta are given in figure 10 (all other high energy interaction characteristics were taken from the standard model of EAS). A detailed comparison shows that the best agreement is obtained when the mean transverse momentum is assumed to be 0.6 GeV/c and the transverse momentum distribution on the side of large p_t is described by a function of the type $\exp(-p_t/p_0)$ and not by a function of type $\exp\{-(p_t/p_0)^2\}$. The error in the mean p_t determination is about 0.05 GeV/c.

Figure 11 shows the ratio of the number of events when three parallel muons were recorded to the number of events when two such muons passed through the Utah

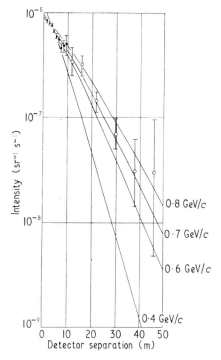

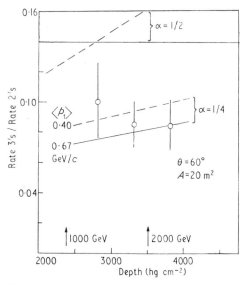

Figure 10. The decoherence curve for high energy muons (threshold energy 1050 GeV, zenith angle 45°). The theoretical curves were calculated for different assumptions about the mean transverse momentum.

Figure 11. Ratio of rates of 3's to 2's as a function of depth (Cannon and Stenerson 1971) compared with theoretical predictions for two different multiplicity laws ($n_s \sim E^\alpha$ with $\alpha = 0.25$ and $\alpha = 0.50$). The 2's represent the case of simultaneous registration of two muons by the detector and the 3's the case of simultaneous registration of three muons.

detector. It can be seen from the figure that the ratio is not very sensitive to the mean transverse momentum and is clearly sensitive to the assumed multiplicity. The data clearly support the so-called $E^{1/4}$ multiplicity law ($n_s = 2.7E^{1/4}$ where E is expressed in GeV).

3.3. The nuclear-active component

3.3.1. Role of hadrons. Hadrons in EAS are far less numerous than the other particles and their separation from electrons is only possible on the basis of energy difference. Only for low energy hadrons are other methods such as neutron detectors used. The higher energy hadrons are detected by calorimetric methods which give not only their numbers but also their spectra.

The role of the nuclear-active component (NAP) in the development of EAS is essential. As was mentioned earlier the hadrons form the skeleton of the shower and the properties of the electromagnetic and the muonic components reflect the

properties of the nuclear-active component. Owing to the existence of that equilibrium some conclusions which were drawn on the basis of properties of the electromagnetic component are really related to properties of the hadron component.

The equilibrium is illustrated in figure 12 where there are given $N_{\pi}{}^{\pm} - N_e$ diagrams
for two different primary energies, calculated on the basis of the standard model.
The results presented are related to sea level and to hadrons of threshold energy
10 GeV (J Kempa 1972 private communication). It can be seen that the correlations

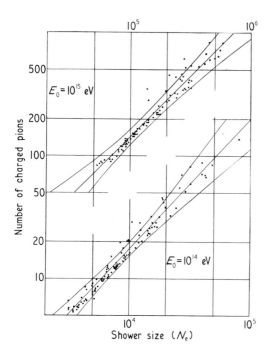

Figure 12. Correlation of the low energy charged pions with total number of electrons for two primary energies. The curves represent the least squares fit and the boundary of errors of the fit.

are very strong and that the electron size is determined by the number of nuclear
active particles almost independently of the primary energy. The same type of
regularity is observed for hadrons with higher energies. Obviously in those cases the
fluctuations are bigger since the numbers of particles involved are small.

3.3.2. Experimental data from NAP *experiments.* The experimentally observed properties of nuclear-active particles in EAS are illustrated in figures 13, 14 and 15. In
figure 13 there are given examples of dependences of the nuclear-active particle
numbers on shower sizes for three different energy thresholds. The results were
obtained in three different experiments (Kameda *et al* 1966, Vedenev 1968, Matano
1970). Good proportionality is observed except for the highest energy thresholds
(1700 GeV) where the number of nuclear-active particles is increasing slightly faster
than the shower size. Figures 14 and 15 give the lateral distributions and energy
spectra of hadrons in EAS. The lateral distributions, which are collected from different

L

experiments and correspond to different shower sizes and different heights of observation, can be well described by exponential functions. The energy spectrum given in figure 15 is compared with theoretical predictions of the standard model; the agreement is seen to be good.

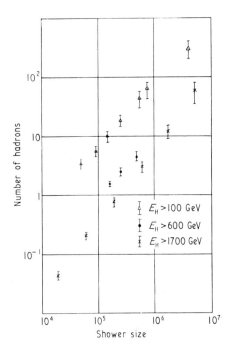

Figure 13. Number of hadrons plotted against shower size for three different threshold energies.

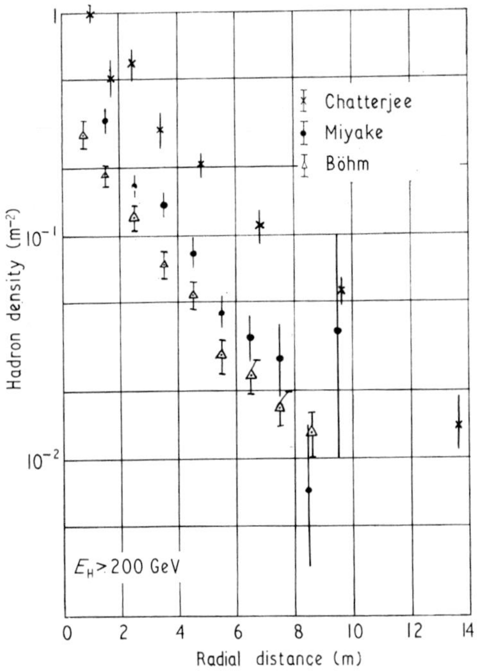

Figure 14. The hadron lateral distributions for 200 GeV energy threshold and three different shower sizes. The data come from the work of Chatterjee *et al* (1968), Miyake *et al* (1970) and E Böhm *et al* (1972 unpublished).

3.3.3. Transverse momenta. One of the most direct pieces of information about high energy interactions which one may hope to get from properties of the nuclear-active component is that concerning the transverse momenta of the secondary particles. This information is slightly wider than that obtained from the high energy muons as it is related to all secondary hadrons, not only to pions. From the observations of the multicore structure of EAS (see, for example, Dake *et al* 1971) conclusions are drawn about the existence of hadrons with extremely high transverse momentum (about 10 GeV/c). This observation is still in doubt, however, since the rates of the multiple cores are very different in different experiments and since the existence of the high transverse momenta has not yet been confirmed in experiments where the lateral distributions of hadrons are measured directly. For example, recent measurements by E Böhm *et al* (1972 unpublished) indicate that the lateral distribution of

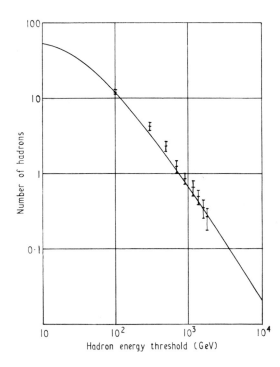

Number of hadrons

Hadron energy threshold (GeV)

Figure 15. Energy spectrum of hadrons in EAS. Experimental data according to E Böhm *et al* (1972 unpublished), theoretical curve calculated using standard model based on CKP formula.

hadrons with energies above 200 GeV can be well described by the distribution expected on the basis of the CKP formula when allowance is made for a small increase of mean p_t (from 0·4 to 0·5–0·6 GeV/c).

3.3.4. Gammanization. In connection with the nuclear-active component one more observation should be made. A detailed study of the hadron content in EAS and the size distribution of showers accompanying the high energy nuclear-active component led S I Nikolski (1967) to arrive at the conclusion that the hadron properties can be better explained if it is assumed that in high energy interactions above a few times 10^{13} eV there exist some interactions where γ rays are produced directly ('gammanization process'). This interesting conclusion needs further investigations however.

3.4. The Cerenkov component

The Cerenkov radiation, emitted by shower particles during their passage through the atmosphere, is investigated mainly because of the possibility of getting information about EAS at various stages of their development from the observations at one level alone. This is due to the fact that in clear air absorption and scattering of the Cerenkov light is negligible. Recent theoretical investigations (Giler 1972) have confirmed good proportionality of the total flux of the Cerenkov light to the primary energy but it has been shown that the lateral distribution of the radiation fluctuates strongly and that the fluctuations are correlated with shower size for fixed primary energy. These

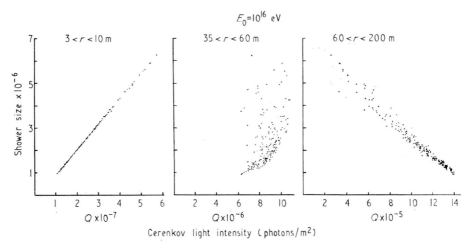

Figure 16. Correlations of the Cerenkov radiation intensity and total electron size for fixed primary energy and three distance intervals (sea level).

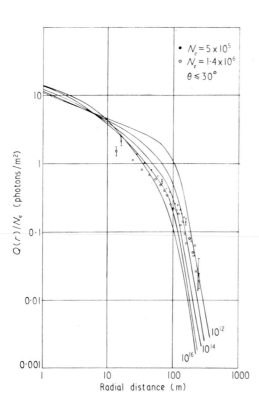

Figure 17. The lateral distributions of the Cerenkov radiation in EAS calculated on the basis of the standard EAS model in comparison with experimental data of Chudakov *et al* (1960).

correlations are negative correlations of the width of the Cerenkov lateral distribution and the shower size. At small distances the density of Cerenkov radiation is positively correlated with size and at large distances from the core those quantities are negatively correlated. This fact is illustrated in figure 16 where plots of N_e against Q are shown for fixed primary energy, 10^{16} eV, and for three different distance intervals. Particularly striking is the strict correlation observed for the interval 3–10 m from shower core.

The lateral distribution of Giler (1972) is compared with the experimental data of Chudakov *et al* (1960) in figure 17. It can be seen that the theoretical distributions are clearly narrower than those observed. It seems that it would be very difficult to account for the divergence in terms of inaccuracies in measurements or calculations as the calculations were performed without any crude assumptions (except for uncertainties in the model of high energy interactions) and the errors of the experimental results are small. If the observed discrepancy is genuine then it would appear to indicate that EAS develop faster in the atmosphere than expected. This conclusion is in good agreement with the earlier observations concerning the electron and muon components of EAS.

4. The EAS size spectrum

The size spectrum of EAS is investigated mainly for the information it contains about the energy spectrum of the primary cosmic rays. The main feature of the sea-level EAS size spectrum is a sudden change of its slope at about $3–5 \times 10^5$ particles. Around that point in a narrow interval the spectral index changes from a value of about 1·5 to about 2. A similar characteristic appears in the EAS size spectrum observed at higher elevation in the atmosphere. For example the spectrum observed at Mt Chacaltaya shows a change of slope at about $1–2 \times 10^6$ particles. The most likely explanation of the change of slope is that it reflects a change in shape of the primary spectrum. The striking feature of the 'kink' in the size spectrum is its sharpness. Such a sudden change in the slope of the size spectrum has to lead to an even sharper change in the slope of the primary spectrum as the transition from primary energy to shower size must lead to some smearing out due to existing fluctuations in EAS development. A detailed discussion of the astrophysical implications of the change of the primary spectrum slope has been given by Bell *et al* (1972).

The primary energy spectrum deduced from measurements of the EAS size spectra at various levels and also from measurements of other EAS and general cosmic ray components has been summarized by Greisen (1966). According to that summary the cosmic ray spectrum up to about 10^{15} eV can be described by a single power law with spectral index 1·6 and with intensity about 10^{-4} particles per m^2 s sr above 10^{14} eV, and beyond 10^{16} eV by a power law with index 2·2 and intensity about 2×10^{-10} particles per m^2 s sr above 10^{17} eV.

In fact the spectrum deduced from the sea-level size spectrum, on the basis of the relation of N_e to E_0 calculated using the standard model, gives intensities lower by a factor of about two.

An analytical representation of the EAS primary spectrum has been given recently by Nikolski (1970):

$$F(>E_0) = \frac{1 \cdot 9 \times 10^{-5}}{E_0^{1 \cdot 6}} \frac{1 + E_0/3 \times 10^6}{1 + (E_0/10^3)^{0 \cdot 6}} \text{ cm}^{-2} \text{s}^{-1} \text{sr}^{-1},$$

where E_0 is expressed in TeV. The formula gives essentially the same result as the spectrum suggested by Greisen. Nikolski also gives a more general formula where some assumptions about the primary mass compositions are incorporated. It seems, however, that the information about the primary mass composition is still too scarce to predict energy spectra for the various masses separately.

5. Concluding remarks

One of the main aims of the discussion given in the previous sections was to illustrate methods of deducing information about high energy interactions from EAS data. The essential point of that task seems to be the choice of parameters which are most sensitive to the appropriate features of high energy interactions. The most favorable situation occurs when the chosen parameters practically fully describe the analysed feature. An example here is the lateral distribution of high energy muons which is practically determined by the transverse momenta of the produced pions alone. With some objections, which will be discussed later, one may also quote the relation between the height of the shower development maximum and the multiplicity of the secondary particles in the high energy interactions.

The main characteristic which appears in investigations of the various EAS components is the fact that showers seem to develop faster than expected, a fact that appears to indicate that the multiplicity in the extremely high energy interactions increases even faster than the $E^{1/4}$ law. A similar conclusion was obtained by Hillas *et al* (1971) on the basis of the experimental data about muons in EAS recorded by the Haverah Park array (a detailed description of the Haverah Park device and the water Cerenkov detector techniques employed there are outside the scope of the present work since that experiment is clearly related to the energies above 10^{17} eV).

The conclusion about multiplicity is important since various theoretical models (in particular Feynman's scaling hypothesis) require a logarithmic increase. The way out of the dilemma suggested by Wdowczyk and Wolfendale (1972), that the average primary mass is increasing with the primary energy, seems also to be insufficient in the light of the observations described earlier which indicate that protons dominate the primary particles at energies about 10^{15}–10^{16} eV. According to the suggestion at the quoted energies the average primary mass should be about 10. The scaling hypothesis is also strongly contradicted by the observations showing some increase of the mean transverse momentum with the energy of the primary particles, whereas the hypothesis predicts almost absolute constancy of that parameter.

In conclusion it may be said that EAS investigations are a good tool for the analysis of extremely high energy interactions. Further experimental investigations and detailed analysis of EAS, in addition to giving information about the properties of the primary particles, will certainly increase our knowledge of parameters of the high energy elementary process.

References

Abrosimov A T *et al* 1960 *Sov. Phys.–JETP* **38** 100
Adcock C, Coats R B, Wolfendale A W and Wdowczyk J 1970 *J. Phys.* A: *Gen. Phys.* **3** 697
—— 1971 *J. Phys.* A: *Gen. Phys.* **4** 276
Antonov R A, Ivanenko I P, Samosudov B E and Tulinova Z I 1971 *Proc 12th Int. Conf. on Cosmic Rays* (Hobart: University of Tasmania) p 2194
de Beer J F, Holyoak B, Wdowczyk J and Wolfendale A W 1966 *Proc. Phys. Soc.* **89** 567
de Beer J F *et al* 1968 *J. Phys.* A: *Gen. Phys.* **1** 72
Bell M C, Osborne J L and Wolfendale A W 1972 *Proc 3rd European Symp. on Cosmic Rays, Paris* unpublished
Benecke J, Chou T T, Yang C N and Yen E 1969 *Phys. Rev.* **188** 2159
Bennett S, Delvaille J, Greisen K and Kendziorski F 1962 *J. Phys. Soc. Japan* **17** AIII 196–202
Bończak B *et al* 1968 *Can. J. Phys.* **46** No 10 102
Bradt H *et al* 1966 *Proc. 9th Int. Conf. on Cosmic Rays* (London: Institute of Physics) p 715
Cannon T M and Stenerson R O 1971 *J. Phys.* A: *Gen. Phys.* **4** 266
Chatterjee B K *et al* 1966 *Proc. 9th Int. Conf. on Cosmic Rays* (London: Institute of Physics) p 627
Chatterjee B K *et al* 1968 *Can. J. Phys.* **46** No 10 136
Chudakov A E 1960 *Proc. 6th Int. Conf. on Cosmic Rays* (Moscow: USSR Acad. Sci.) vol 2 p 46
Dake S *et al* 1971 *Proc. 12th Int. Conf. on Cosmic Rays* (Hobart: University of Tasmania) p 948
Earnshaw J C *et al* 1967 *Proc. Phys. Soc.* **90** 91
Feynman R D 1969 *Phys. Rev. Lett.* **23** 1415
Gawin J *et al* 1968 *Can. J. Phys.* **46** 104–6
Giler M 1972 *PhD thesis* University of Lodz
Greisen K 1956 *Progress in Cosmic Rays Physics* vol III (Amsterdam: North Holland) p 1
—— 1960 *Ann. Rev. Nucl. Science* **10** 63
—— 1966 *Proc. 9th Int. Conf. on Cosmic Rays* (London: Institute of Physics) p 609
Hasegawa H *et al* 1962 *J. Phys. Soc. Japan* **17** A–III 189
Hillas A M, Hollows J D, Hunter H W and Marsden D J 1971 *Proc. 12th Int. Conf. on Cosmic Rays* (Hobart: University of Tasmania) p 1007
van Hove L 1969 *Nucl. Phys.* **B9** 331
Iliyna N P *et al* 1971 *Proc. 12th Int. Conf. on Cosmic Rays* (Hobart: University of Tasmania) p 2109
Kameda T *et al* 1966 *Proc. 9th Int. Conf. on Cosmic Rays* (London: Institute of Physics) p 681
Karakuła S 1968 *PhD thesis* University of Lodz
Khrenow B A 1962 *Izvest. Akad Sci. USSR* **26** 5
Matano T 1970 *Acta Phys. Hung.* **29** suppl 451
Miyake S *et al* 1970 *Acta Phys. Hung.* **29** suppl 463
Nikolski S I 1967 *Izvest. Akad. Sci. USSR* **31** 1505
—— 1970 *Izvest. Akad. Sci. USSR* **35** 1645
Nishimura J and Kamata K 1952 *Prog. Theor. Phys.* **1** 185
Pidcock J K 1967 *PhD thesis* University of London
Porter N A *et al* 1957 *Phil. Mag.* **2** 900
Samorski M, Staubert R, Trümper J and Böhm E 1971 *Proc. 12th Int. Conf. on Cosmic Rays* (Hobart: University of Tasmania) p 959
Vedenev O V 1968 *Proc. Tashkent Conf.* (Moscow: Lebedev Institute) vol 1–2 p 105
Vernov S N *et al* 1961 *Sov. Phys.–JETP* **41** 340
Vernov S N *et al* 1964 *Izvest. Akad Sci. USSR* **28** 1886
Vernov S N *et al* 1968a *Can. J. Phys.* **46** No 10
Vernov S N *et al* 1968b *Izvest. Akad. Sci. USSR* **32** 458
Vernov S N *et al* 1970 *Acta Phys. Hung.* **3** 429
Wdowczyk J and Wolfendale A W 1972 *Nature, Phys. Sci.* **236** No 63 29

Chapter 9

Extensive air showers above 10^{17} eV

K E Turver

1. The importance of studies of large air showers

Interest in large extensive air showers (EAS) is stimulated by the possibility of determining the energies, directions of arrival and hence possible origins of primary particles of energy approaching the limits known to man. Such information complements that available from other forms of observational astronomy and adds to our general understanding of the universe; this has been termed by Greisen (1960) the 'large scale quest' in his excellent review of the subject. Of no less importance is the so-called 'small scale quest' which involves the study of those ultrahigh energy interactions occurring only in the air shower environment. Recent advances in accelerator studies of interactions of particles with energies up to 1500 GeV have given no indication of a decrease in the importance of studies at the super-high shower energies. Indeed, it may well be the case that considerations of interactions at energies many orders of magnitude above those available for machine experiments are now of increased importance in attempts to resolve current problems in high energy physics. For example, the validity over a large range of energy of the scaling hypothesis suggested by Feynman (1969) may be amenable to test by air shower studies. Furthermore, some understanding of ultrahigh energy interactions will very much improve the possible astrophysical interpretations of shower data and may even be a necessary prerequisite for any satisfactory astrophysical studies based on measurements of large showers.

It is the intention in this chapter to summarize the data from recent measurements of those infrequent large showers produced by particles of energy in excess of 10^{17} eV, together with the results of computer simulations of such events. In the view of the present author, such simulations have played a vital part of the development and clarification of the field in the last decade and may well continue to do so, aiding in the first instance the design of experiments, and later the analysis of the data obtained.

2. The detection and recording of large air showers

The detection of large air showers became possible in the late 1950s as a result of the combination of the techniques of density sampling using many linked particle detectors (Williams 1948), fast timing using spaced scintillation counters (Bassi *et al* 1953), and digital computers both for the analysis of the recorded data and for shower simulations to aid their interpretations. Many experiments initially made use of large numbers of small area plastic scintillation counters (for example, those operated by

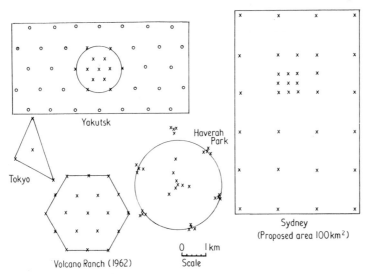

Figure 1. Sketch maps of large shower arrays. Detector systems which are, or have been, in use are shown × ; planned extensions to the arrays are shown thus ○.

the MIT groups at Agassiz, El Alto, Volcano Ranch and Mount Chacaltaya) and this trend has been continued in recent experiments at Tokyo (Kawaguchi *et al* 1971) and at Yakutsk (Yegerov *et al* 1971). Other experiments have been developed using quite different techniques; for example, at the Haverah Park experiment large area deep water Cerenkov detectors form the basic shower recorder.

The geometries of some of the detector arrays operated during the past decade are shown in the sketch plans of figure 1; the specifications of the arrays together with primary particle energies to which the arrays respond and other useful data are given in table 1.

2.1. Conventional particle detector arrays

Considerations of the data in figure 1 and table 1 indicate that the largest arrays in operation or planned will have collecting areas for showers of no more than 10^8 m². The extent of the Haverah Park array, having a useful area for the detection of EAS of 12×10^6 m², is indicated in detail in the aerial photograph shown in figure 2. The complexity of the equipment necessary for accurate recording of large showers may be

Table 1. Characteristics of large EAS arrays.

Array	Latitude and atmospheric depth (g cm^{-2})	Type of detector (thickness g cm^{-2})	Detector area (m^2)	Number of detectors	Typical detector spacing (m)	Array radius (m)	Enclosed area (km^2)	Primary energy range (eV)	Zenith angle range (deg)
Agassiz	42° N 1040	Plastic scintillator (8)	0·9	15	200	250	0·10	3×10^{15}–3×10^{18}	0–40
El Alto	16° S 630		0·9	12	200	350	0·40	8×10^{14}–3×10^{17}	0–50
Chacaltaya	16° S 500		0·9	25	150	150	0·07	8×10^{14}–3×10^{17}	0–50
Volcano Ranch (1962)	35° N 820		3·3	19	(i) 400 (ii) 800	900 1800	2 8	10^{17}–3×10^{19}	0–39
Haverah Park	54° N 1016	Water Cerenkov (120)	34 13·5 9	4 25 3	— — —	2000	12	10^{17}–5×10^{19}	0–60
Sydney	31° S 1016	2 × liquid scintillators (6–15) plus shielding (375)				1600 m cells	40	10^{19}–10^{20}	0–75
			2 × 6	34 pairs	1600	4 × 800 m 4 × 400 m cells	2·6	10^{17}–10^{19}	0–75
Yakutsk	62° N 1020	2 × plastic scintillators (8)	2 × 2	13 pairs	500	1000	3·3	10^{17}–10^{19}	0–40
Tokyo	36° N 1020	2 × plastic scintillators (4)	2 × 2	4 pairs	1000	1000	~1	10^{17}–10^{19}	—
Volcano Ranch (1970)	35° N 820	Plastic scintillator (8)	0·8	79	150	600	1·23	10^{16}–5×10^{18}	—

appreciated from a brief description of this system which comprises 510 m² of water Cerenkov detector (120 g cm⁻² deep), deployed as 32 interlinked detectors spread over a circular area of radius 2×10^3 m. Measurements are made with each detector of the energy lost in the deep detector together with the time of arrival of the particles for those showers fulfilling rigorous triggering requirements. Sufficient information is then available to locate the central core region of each shower with high precision and estimate the energy deposited in 120 g cm⁻² of water at a distance of 500 m from the core. This latter quantity, a useful measure of the primary particle energy, has been

Figure 2. An aerial view of the Haverah Park EAS array. (Reproduced by permission of the West Riding County Council and Meridian Airmaps Ltd).

identified after careful study of the array's performance. In addition to the main particle detectors, the experiment incorporates a 12·5 m² electron and muon density detector, a magnetic spectrograph for studies of the momentum and charge of muons, and multiple antennae for measurement of the radio frequency emission from showers.

It seems likely that an array of sensitive area approaching 10^8 m², as is proposed by the University of Sydney group, represents a limit to the size of conventional arrays in the foreseeable future. Primary particles of the highest energy of interest, greater than 10^{20} eV, will be detected using such large arrays at a rate of about one per year. It seems unlikely, therefore, that reasonable fluxes of events of energy greater than 10^{20} eV will be available from conventional particle detector arrays.

2.2. Recent attempts to detect the larger showers using novel techniques

To overcome the requirements for large arrays necessary to record, at reasonable rates, showers arising from particles of energy approaching 10^{20} eV, suggestions were made by Greisen (1966a) to use the atmosphere itself as a scintillator which would register the arrival of large showers and also allow the cascade development to be tracked. This means of detection arises from the ionization of the air produced by the many shower electrons with a subsequent excitation of the air molecules; one mode for their de-excitation involves the emission of fluorescent light which may be detected by ground-based sensors. Systematic studies of the fluorescence effect by A Bunner (1965 unpublished) showed that the nitrogen molecules of the air were primarily involved, that Cerenkov light would add a strongly coned contribution and, under the optimum atmospheric conditions, large showers up to 20 km distant should be detected and their development recorded. Attempts to make such measurements have been described by Porter *et al* (1970) who have made extensive simulations of the expected shower signals, and Hara *et al* (1970a) who have reported the successful detection of scintillation light from nearby showers. No evidence has yet been presented, however, for such devices fulfilling their early promise as economic and efficient detectors of very large showers.

The detection of the radio-frequency signal from small air showers by Jelley *et al* (1965), and the subsequent studies on larger showers to be described in §3, have given rise to the hope that this new technique may also provide a method of economically detecting large showers. Such a scheme would be based upon the use of many cheap and simple radio antennae separated by distances typical of, or greater than, those used in particle counter arrays (many hundreds of metres), so producing at low cost a large area sensitive to EAS. Unfortunately, as the radio signal in large air showers was parametrized, it became clear that the steep lateral distribution of the radio signals at the useful frequencies (30–60 MHz), depicted by the data of Allan *et al* (1971) in figure 3, required very many antennae systems to cover a large sensitive area efficiently and at present the technique offers no advantage over conventional particle detection methods.

Further unsuccessful attempts to develop economic detection schemes for large

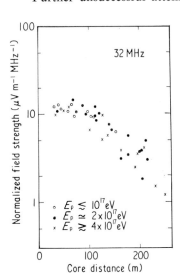

Figure 3. The lateral distribution of the radio signal in large showers (Allan *et al* 1971).

showers have been reported based upon the high ionization produced by the many shower electrons near the shower core (eg at distances of less than 10 m from the core of 10^{18} eV showers ionization densities of greater than 2×10^9 m^{-3} are to be expected). In the radio echo experiment of Hara *et al* (1970b) false reflections of the radio beams radiated from Loran transmitters made studies difficult, whilst attempts by M L T Kannangara and K E Turver (1971 unpublished) to measure the disturbing effect on the Earth's potential gradient directly, as suggested by Wilson (1957), were shown to be difficult owing to the instability of the ambient potential gradient.

2.3. The accuracy of shower measurements

The main aim of present large shower experiments is to measure the primary energies and celestial arrival directions of energetic primary particles. The accuracy of such measurements depends upon the precision of the measurement of the shower at the observational level, and, in the case of the primary energy determination, upon the certainty with which the observation can be converted to a primary energy estimation. This latter point will be discussed in detail in §6.

The parameter of the shower measured as an indication of the primary energy in each of the four current shower arrays is different; at those arrays operated by the MIT group, the so-called conventional particle size N has been measured, based upon the scintillation detector lateral structure function data; at Haverah Park the quantity ρ_{500}, the signal at a specific core distance of 500 m recorded in the deep water Cerenkov detector, is measured; at Sydney the total muon size N_μ is derived from the lateral structure of muons recorded by the buried scintillation counters, and the Yakutsk array measures both the total particle size N and the optical Cerenkov light signal $\phi(r)$ at core distances of 200–500 m.

It has been estimated by Clark *et al* (1960) that the accuracy of the Agassiz array measurement of N was $\pm 10\%$. Linsley (1964) estimates that the size measurements of Volcano Ranch were accurate to $\pm 30\%$ for sizes of the order of 10^8 particles and the uncertainty increases to a factor of about 2 for the largest showers. In a recent alternative analysis of the Volcano Ranch data, Hillas *et al* (1971) have suggested a possible systematic underestimation of the order of two in size, arising from uncertainties in the measured lateral distribution function. The recently completed modifications at Volcano Ranch to provide a close pitched array (J Linsley 1970 private communication) will provide a density sample within 50 m of most shower cores and so remove the earlier uncertainty, which arose from a lack of measurements close to the core.

The accuracy of the Haverah Park measurement of ρ_{500} is estimated by Evans (1972) for those showers used in primary spectrum work to be ± 15–30% for energies of 3×10^{17}–10^{19} eV; this small value arises mainly from the array geometry which ensures good measurements of the detector signal at distances of about 500 m in all showers. In addition, the statistical accuracy of such energy loss detector measurements shows an improvement over, for example, thin scintillation counters owing to the response of the detector to the numerous photons. Typical values for this improvement are approximately 40% at core distances of 500 m (Hollows 1968).

The accuracy of N_μ measurements at the Sydney array, according to Bell *et al* (1971), depends upon an effective measurement of the lateral structure function for muons in individual showers and is $\pm 30\%$; this will decrease in the larger showers when the number of measurements in the widely spaced detectors increases. It may be expected that the uncertainty of the present shower size measurements at the Yakutsk experiment, incorporating data on the structure function measurements by Linsley (1964), may be similar to those of the early Volcano Ranch array discussed above and the optical Cerenkov measurements, under conditions of clear atmosphere, should involve only small fluctuations and measurement inaccuracies.

It should be reasonable to assume that the accuracy of arrival directions based upon the fast timing measurements would be similar in all experiments, although timing inaccuracies in those experiments measuring small densities with small detectors may increase as a result of the 'sampling' effect described in studies of the profile of detector signals by A A Watson and J G Wilson (1972 private communication). Experience at the Haverah Park array (Hollows 1968) indicated that terrestial arrival directions are measured to better than $\pm 4°$ in zenith at angles less than 60°, and in most cases about $\pm 7°$ in azimuth, although this may increase for events recorded with zenith angles less than 20°. Such uncertainties, arising from errors of typically ± 40 ns in the timing of the arrival of the shower front, are made up from about $\pm 20\%$ uncertainties of instrumental origin, the remainder being of possible physical origin and arising from the variations in the shape of the shower front and sampling effects.

The accuracy of energy estimation has always been of considerable importance, being of similar magnitude to the statistical uncertainty inherent in primary spectrum measurements at high particle energies. The accuracy of arrival direction measurements was of interest until recently primarily as a necessary requirement of accurate shower analysis and primary energy estimation; recent interest in the possible correlation of arrival directions of large showers with the directions of closely situated pulsars has produced a requirement for an increased accuracy. Such studies will require accuracies of arrival direction much greater than is currently available if the normal precision of astronomical observation is to be approached (for example, at Haverah Park the uncertainty in solid angle of arrival for showers incident at zenith angles θ is quoted by Hollows (1968) as 2×10^{-3} sec θ sr).

3. The electron–photon component

The main interest in this component during the early studies of large showers was in the lateral spread of electrons which provided a substantial contribution to the signal recorded by conventional 'thin' particle counting detectors; lately, the interest has spread to the lateral development of the photons as a result of the consideration of deep water Cerenkov detectors and even scintillation detectors as essentially energy-measuring devices (Hillas 1970). Furthermore, the advent of studies, particularly by Allan (1971) at Haverah Park, of the radio-frequency signal from showers and by Yegerov *et al* (1971) at Yakutsk of the atmospheric Cerenkov signal generated by the shower electrons in the atmosphere, have caused renewed interest in the detail of the longitudinal development of the electron component.

3.1. The lateral distribution function

The distribution of electrons and photons has received considerable theoretical treatment in the past by Kamata and Nishimura (1958) and their results have been summarized by Greisen (1960). An expression representing the electron lateral distribution function well at distances 5 cm–1500 m in showers of size less than 2×10^9 particles recorded at atmospheric depths of up to 1800 g cm^{-2} (zenith angles at sea level as large as 55°) has been given by Greisen (1960) as

$$\rho(N, r) = \frac{0.4N}{r_1^2} \left(\frac{r_1}{r}\right)^{0.75} \left(\frac{r_1}{r+r_1}\right)^{3.25} \left\{1 + \left(\frac{r}{11.4r_1}\right)\right\}$$

where r_1 is the Molière unit (80 m at sea level).

Experimental data on the measured distributions, particularly at those great distances from the core important in studies of large showers, are very sparse. The data from the only such measurements, made using supplementary plastic scintillation counters at the Haverah Park experiment by Dufresne *et al* (1966) and later by Kellermann and Towers (1970), are shown in figure 4. The measurements refer to showers of primary energy 2×10^{17} eV arriving within 30° of the zenith.

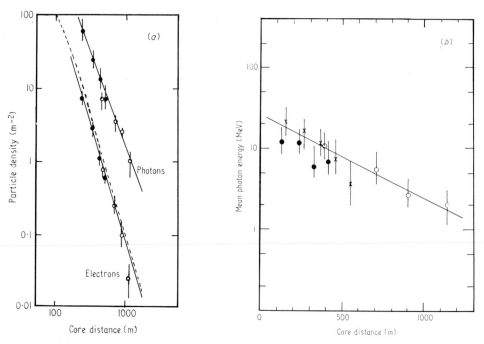

Figure 4. (*a*) The lateral distributions of photons and electrons (Kellermann and Towers 1970); the broken line shows the form of the theoretical electron structure function suggested by Greisen (1960). (*b*) The variation of the mean photon energy with core distance in large showers (Kellermann and Towers 1970).

The other experimental measurements which are influenced greatly by the electrons and photons are the lateral structure functions for the energy deposited in a deep water Cerenkov detector of the type used in the Haverah Park experiment, or in a plastic scintillation detector as used, for example, in the Volcano Ranch experiment. Figure 5 shows the deep water detector lateral structure function measured at Haverah Park; the indication of that part of the response arising from the soft component and that from the muon component is based upon the data from simulations by A M Hillas (1971 private communication), when due allowance is made for the response of the Cerenkov detector. The lateral structure function for the signal from a plastic scintillator of the type used in the MIT experiments and of thickness 8 g cm⁻², considered as an energy loss detector, is also shown in figure 5.

3.2. The 1-D electron cascade development

Although it has not yet been possible to measure at different depths the total electron size of a shower passing vertically through the atmosphere, similar information has

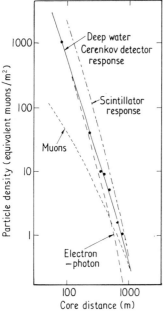

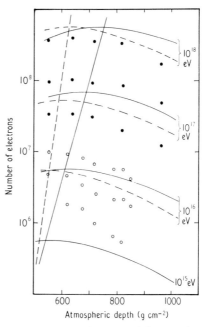

Figure 5. The lateral structure function for the energy deposited in a water Cerenkov detector of depth 120 g cm⁻². The data represent that typically available at the Haverah Park array for a shower of primary energy about 10¹⁸ eV; The solid lines are from the simulations of A M Hillas (1971 private communication) and show the various contributions to the detector response. For comparison, a curve for a thin scintillation detector (thickness 8 g cm⁻²) is shown.

Figure 6. The development of showers through the atmosphere (La Pointe *et al* 1968). The solid curves are from simulations for proton-initiated showers of the energy indicated using the model described in §5; the broken curves represent simulation data for showers in which the produced particle multiplicity increases as the square root of the energy of the incident particle. The straight lines connect the maxima of the cascades.

M

been obtained at the high altitude shower experiments by making equi-intensity cuts in the size spectra recorded at different zenith angles (Linsley *et al* 1962, La Pointe *et al* 1968). Such data derived from the Chacaltaya experiment by La Pointe *et al* are shown in figure 6, where they are compared with the predictions of recent model simulations (H E Dixon *et al* 1972 unpublished). The mean height of maximum shower development together with individual fluctuations in this quantity contain information on the rate of development of showers which in turn reflects the nature of the primary particle and details of the high energy interactions. Showers initiated by primary protons or light nuclei will show longitudinal developments fluctuating greatly so that although the size at maximum remains constant, the depth at which the maximum is reached may vary, as shown by the simulation data of figure 7. A consequence of the

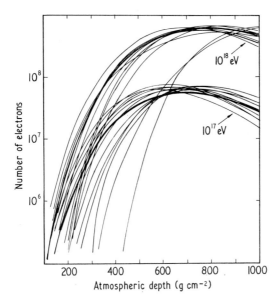

Figure 7. The longitudinal development of the electron component of showers initiated by primary protons of energy 10^{17} and 10^{18} eV. A sample of ten simulations is shown for each primary energy; the heavy lines represent the average of many such showers.

incidence of a heavy nucleus as a primary particle may be a decrease in the average depth of maximum development together with a lack of large fluctuations in the observed showers. It has been suggested by Kaneko *et al* (1971) that the measurements of La Pointe *et al* indicate that there is no satisfactory explanation of the 1-D development of the electron cascade on the basis of data from shower simulations using models, typified by that described in §5, which have had considerable success in explaining many other aspects of showers. In particular, these authors suggest that a more rapid development of the shower is necessary to account for the observations, as indicated in figure 6.

3.3. *The atmospheric Cerenkov radiation*

A large proportion of the electrons in showers are sufficiently energetic to emit visible Cerenkov radiation in air. The first measurement of this light was made by Galbraith and Jelley (1953) and subsequent work by Chudakov *et al* (1960) has been confined to showers smaller than 10^7 particles.

To date there have been only two reports of measurements of the photon fluxes present at large core distances in high energy showers. Such visible photons are the most numerous component at core distances of about 200 m in large showers and reach densities of 10^7 photons/m² at sea level for showers of energy in excess of 2×10^{17} eV, although climatic conditions may present significant experimental problems in their measurement. The information carried by such photons differs from that contained in the more energetic locally produced photons since the optical signal is derived from all electrons in the shower and so reflects the total development of the shower through the atmosphere; it thus relates well with the primary particle

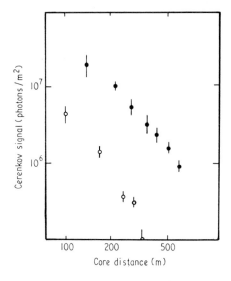

Figure 8. The lateral distributions of optical Cerenkov light at sea level and mountain altitude in showers of primary energy about 3×10^{17} eV. Full circles, O C Diminstein *et al* (1972 private communication); open circles, Krieger and Bradt (1969).

energy and mirrors the longitudinal development of the shower. It is in the context of primary particle energy estimation that the optical measurement at the Yakutsk array is made. Figure 8 shows the measured lateral distributions of optical photons at sea level in showers of energy greater than 10^{17} eV (O C Diminstein *et al* 1972 private communication), together with the distribution of the smaller signal arising from the less developed showers but of similar primary particle energy, based upon the data of Krieger and Bradt (1969) from mountain altitudes.

3.4. The radio-frequency emission from showers

Following the pioneer work in small showers by Jelley *et al* (1965), significant advances in the understanding of the radio emission from showers came from the work in large, fully measured showers, particularly by Allan and colleagues at the Haverah Park experiment. Measurements made by this group and that at Calgary (Prescott *et al* 1970) have shown that the radio signal comes predominantly from the conditions of coherence necessary for the production of a radio signal and arising from the geo-magnetic separation of the electrons and positrons, since there is good correlation of the pulse amplitude with the strength of the geomagnetic separation of electrons and positrons, as shown in figure 9.

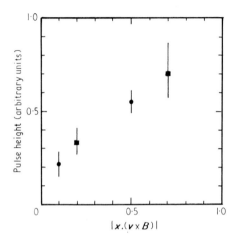

Figure 9. Radio signals at 22 MHz showing their dependence on the relative orientation of the shower axis and the earth's magnetic field (Prescott *et al* 1970).

The lateral distribution of the radio signal has been shown, at frequencies in the range 30–60 MHz, to fall away rapidly with core distance (see figure 3) and to indicate field strengths in agreement with expectation from simulations made by J H Hough (1972 unpublished). More recently the shape of the lateral distribution has been shown by G B Khristiansen (1972 private communication) to change with the stage of development ('the age') of the shower. The lateral distribution function for radio signals steepens for those showers developing low in the atmosphere, as indicated by a decrease in the N_μ/N_e ratio. The sensitivity of the shape of the radio signal structure function to the depth of maximum development of the shower suggested by Allan (1971) and evaluated by J H Hough (1972 unpublished) is confirmed. Recent predictions for radio signal strengths and the measurements by G B Khristiansen (1972 private communication) at low frequencies are in good agreement, suggesting that the early experimental work which indicated very large signals was probably in error, as indicated by Allan (1972). Initial hopes that measurements of the signal at low frequencies, typified by its broad lateral distribution, will be practicable and offer an economic means of detecting large showers seem unlikely.

4. The muon component

Although muons comprise only some few per cent of the total charged particle flux at small core distances, at the large distances at which measurements in large showers are typically made they represent a significant proportion of the total particles and at core distances of 1000 m the muons are the dominant shower component. The weak interaction of the muon makes it unique in showers in delivering to sea level details of the shower at higher altitudes. The form of the distribution in transverse momentum of the parent pions causes the density of muons of known momenta and distance from the shower core to be sensitive to their heights of origin.

Most of the measurements of the muon component in large showers have been made using either the absorption technique where muons of energy in excess of some threshold are recorded (usually the threshold is between 0·3 and 1·0 GeV, although some work under thicker absorbers giving a threshold of 5 GeV has been carried out), or the magnet spectrograph technique employed initially in shower studies by Bennett and Greisen (1961) and in recent years by Rochester and co-workers at the Haverah

Figure 10. The Haverah Park solid iron magnet spectrograph.

Park experiment (Earnshaw *et al* 1967). The Haverah Park solid iron magnet spectrograph, after modifications made in 1970 to improve the momentum resolution, is shown in figure 10.

Such different experiments have provided data for the distribution in core distance of the densities and the heights of origin of all muons, with additional information on particles of specific momentum being confined to data from spectrograph experiments.

4.1. The lateral distribution of muons

The density of muons of energy in excess of 1 GeV measured by Clark *et al* (1958) and at the Cornell experiment by Greisen formed the basis for the empirical lateral distribution function proposed by Greisen (1960). Subsequent measurements made at Moscow (Abrosimov *et al* 1960), at Haverah Park by the Durham group (Earnshaw 1968) and the Nottingham group (Blake *et al* 1971) and at Sydney (Fisher 1970) have all indicated general agreement with this formulation, particularly at core distances in excess of 150 m. Measurements at Haverah Park which contain data from a wide range of core distances for events of similar primary energy are shown in figure 11,

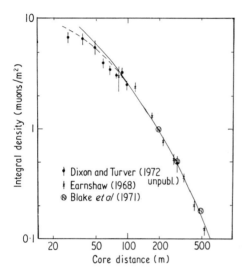

Figure 11. The lateral distribution function for muons of energy above 1 GeV in showers of energy $1 \cdot 4 \times 10^{17}$ eV incident at zenith angles less than 40°. The solid line represents the relation given in the text; the broken line shows the expected effect of core location uncertainties of ± 20 m (after A A Watson 1972 private communication).

where, after correction for the small effects of core location errors of ± 20 m which are important at lateral distances of less than 35 m, they are compared with the curve of the form suggested by Greisen (1960). These measurements and the results of computer simulations indicate that the lateral distribution may be expressed, following Greisen, by a general expression of the form

$$\Delta_\mu (>1 \text{ GeV}, X, r) = f(X) \, r^{-0 \cdot 75} \left\{ 1 + \left(\frac{r}{320} \right) \right\}^{-2 \cdot 5}$$

where the variable X may represent any of the measures of 'shower size' used in the various arrays and in which case the function $f(X)$ takes the form given in table 2, for values corresponding to primary energies in the range 10^{17}–10^{18} eV.

Adding to these data the information of particle momentum from magnetic spectrograph measurements enables the energy spectra shown in figure 12 to be derived; there is good agreement between the original data of Bennett and Greisen (1961), which was obtained for showers covering a wide range of size but including few large showers, and the data from the Haverah Park experiment which are confined to a range of primary energies of 10^{17}–5×10^{17} eV. The measurements in large showers at core distances about 200 m are complemented by the data from the burst experiment of Suga *et al* (1970) at Mt Chacaltaya who obtained a differential energy spectrum for muons at core distances of 100 m of the form

$$N(\epsilon_\mu, r \sim 100 \text{ m}) \, \mathrm{d}\epsilon_\mu \propto \epsilon_\mu^{-2 \cdot 2} \, \mathrm{d}\epsilon_\mu$$

Table 2.

Measure of primary energy, X	$f(X)$
Shower size, N	$f(N)=\left(\dfrac{N}{4\cdot4\times10^4}\right)^{0\cdot75}$
Muon number, N_μ	$f(N_\mu)=\left(\dfrac{N_\mu}{3\cdot5\times10^3}\right)$
Deep detector signal, ρ_{500} (equivalent muons/m^2)	$f(\rho_{500})=\left(\dfrac{\rho_{500}}{8\cdot8\times10^{-4}}\right)^{0\cdot86}$
Primary energy, E_p (GeV)	$f(E_p)=\left(\dfrac{E_p}{5\cdot92\times10^5}\right)^{0\cdot94}$

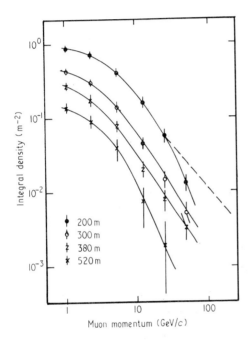

Figure 12. The integral momentum spectrum of muons in large showers. The data are from the Haverah Park experiment (Machin *et al* 1970) and refer to primary particles of energy $1\cdot4\times10^{17}$ eV incident at zenith angles less than 40°. The broken line represents the data of Suga *et al* (1970).

valid over the range 20–300 GeV and which agrees well with the value from the corresponding spectrograph measurements at sea level.

4.2. The heights of origin of muons

Measurements of the mean height of origin of muons of energy in excess of $0\cdot3$–$1\cdot0$ GeV have been derived by de Beer (1960) from measurements of angular separations of muons using spark chamber telescopes, by Linsley and Scarsi (1962) from time-delay measurements on individual muons with respect to the tangent front of showers, by Suri (1966) from studies of shower front curvature and by Baxter (1967) from studies of the profile of signals from large deep water Cerenkov detectors. These data are summarized in figure 13 after reduction to a common threshold energy of $0\cdot3$ GeV, together with the results of the spectrograph measurements of Earnshaw *et al* (1973) reduced to a similar threshold energy. There is agreement between the measurements and they show the expected increase in the mean height of origin with increasing core distance.

The data of Earnshaw *et al* from magnetic spectrograph experiments in which the muon's momentum and its arrival direction with respect to the shower core direction were measured and the heights derived from trigonometrical considerations are shown

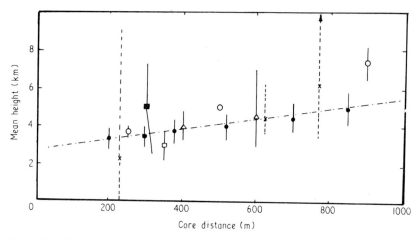

Figure 13. The mean height of origin of muons of energy greater than 0·3 GeV recorded at various core distances in large showers. ● Earnshaw *et al* (1973), ⬦ D R Pickersgill (1972 unpublished), ○ Suri (1966), △ Baxter (1967), × Linsley and Scarsi (1962), □ de Beer (1960).

in figure 14; the increase in mean height with increasing muon momentum is evident. Using the same magnetic spectrograph, measurements have been made of the distortion of the charge ratio of muons in specified regions of the shower front in events incident at known angles to the lines of the geomagnetic field, arising from the interaction between the muons and the geomagnetic field. A necessary requirement of such a method of determining the height of origin is a knowledge of the muon charge ratio and lateral distribution function in the absence of the geomagnetic field and these have been taken as those values measured for all showers. The initial measurement of the charge ratio of muons of energies recorded in wide ranges of showers made by Bennett and Greisen (1961) of 0·96 ± 0·08 has been supplemented by measurements at Haverah Park which indicate that the ratio is unity for all muons (1·02 ± 0·03) and no significant deviation from this value occurred in any of the intervals of muon energy or core distance. The mean heights of origin determined by this method are also shown in figure 14.

4.3. Fluctuations in the muon component

Measurements of the muon component and its fluctuations have in general been made in one of two circumstances; firstly, those measurements in showers chosen to be at the maximum of their development which may be expected to show little fluctuation

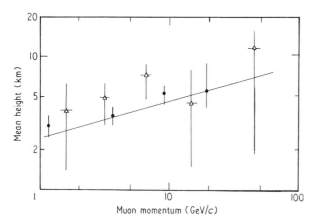

Figure 14. The mean height of origin of muons of various momenta recorded at about 300 m from the cores of showers of primary energy $\sim 10^{17}$ eV. Triangles, from geomagnetic effects; circles, from trigonometric considerations.

in the electron size (for example, the work of Linsley *et al* (1962) and Suga *et al* (1970)) and secondly, those measurements in showers which have developed past their maximum, which therefore show appreciable fluctuations in shower size as studied by Fukui *et al* (1960) and Kaneko *et al* (1971).

The measurements of Suga *et al* made at the Chacaltaya array using a large area (60 m²) muon detector are shown in figure 15 which gives the frequency distribution of events with various values of the ratio of the observed muon density to that expected for the average shower in a given size band. The variations in the ratio are well represented by a gaussian of width 25–30% and the authors suggest that such small fluctuations, being fully accounted for by the statistics of detection, may only arise from a beam of primary particles with a narrow distribution in mass number. Furthermore, measurements at sea level of showers initiated by primary particles of similar energy which have been attenuated by the increased depth in the atmosphere give values of the ratio of observed predicted muon densities which show large fluctuations (Fukui *et al* 1960). The data on muon fluctuations in showers of fixed sizes at various atmospheric depths have been summarized by Hara *et al* (1970b) and their summary is reproduced in figure 16.

5. Computer simulations of large showers

The complexity of the shower development together with the large numbers of particles to be considered in showers with primary energies in excess of 10^{17} eV prevented the rigorous simulation of 3-D cascading until the 'step-by-step' procedure was suggested independently by Hillas (1966) and Dedenko (1966). In this procedure the average distribution in energy and position in the atmosphere of all pions was obtained from numerical evaluation of the appropriate analytical relations. Such data allow lateral distribution functions, together with the temporal characteristics of muons and

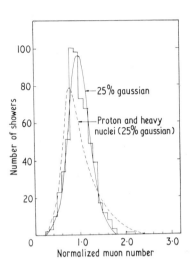

Figure 15. The distribution in the number of muons in 592 showers with sizes larger than 5×10^7 particles incident at zenith angles less than 30° (after Suga *et al* 1970).

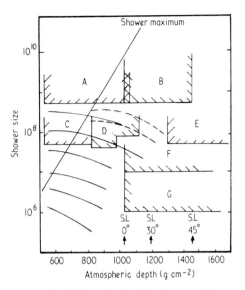

Figure 16. The longitudinal development of EAS and the fluctuations of muons at various atmospheric depths (after Hara *et al* 1970b). Each hatched area represents the range of sizes and atmospheric depths considered in different experiments. Experiments A and C (made at Mt Chacaltaya) and D (made at Volcano Ranch) found no muon fluctuations; experiments B, F and G (made at the Institute of Nuclear Study, Tokyo) and E (made at Volcano Ranch) detected fluctuations.

the approximate 1-D development of electron cascades, to be evaluated. The procedure formed the basis of work on energetic muons by Orford and Turver (1970) and was further extended by Hillas *et al* (1970) to include the 3-D treatment of the electron–photon cascade, a study of the response of the Haverah Park and Volcano Ranch arrays in detail and some effects of fluctuations in shower development arising from fluctuations in points of interaction of the leading nucleons. To date, rigorous Monte Carlo methods, applied with great success to simulations of lower energy showers, have not been applicable at energies greater than 10^{16} eV.

The importance of simulations to studies of large showers is contested; it is the opinion of the present author that they form an integral part of the design of experiments and the interpretation of data, despite the lack of precise knowledge of the nature of the very high energy interactions involved.

5.1. The importance of the model for high energy interactions

The longitudinal development of air showers depends upon the rate of degradation of the energy in the nuclear cascade and so is governed by the mean free paths of nucleons and pions, the coefficients of inelasticity in nucleon–air nucleus and pion–air nucleus collisions, and the number of secondaries produced together with their distribution in energy. The values assumed for all these quantities in computer simulations of showers depend upon extrapolations, over many decades in energy, of the results of measurements made using accelerators up to energies of 1500 GeV and in cosmic rays to energies of 10^4–10^5 GeV. The consequences of these extrapolations

Table 3. Details of 'preferred model' parameters for high energy nuclear interactions.

Nuclear mean free path	$\lambda_p = 80$ g cm^{-2}
Nucleon–air nucleus coefficient of inelasticity	$P(K_p)\,dK_p = \{(1+\alpha)^2\,K_p^{\alpha}\,\ln K_p\}\,dK_p$ with $\langle K_p \rangle = 0.5$
Pion mean free path	$\lambda_\pi = 120$ g cm^{-2}
Pion–air nucleus coefficient of inelasticity	$K_\pi = 1.0$
Total number of produced secondaries (pions) in nucleon–air nucleus collisions	$n_{\pm_0} = 3.75\,E_p^{1/4} - 1.0$
Distribution in energy of secondary particles (after G Cocconi *et al* 1961 unpublished)	$f(\epsilon_\pi)\,d\epsilon_\pi \propto \left\{\dfrac{1}{T}e^{-\epsilon_\pi/T} + \dfrac{1}{u}e^{-\epsilon_\pi/u}\right\}d\epsilon_\pi$ where T and u are the mean energies of the particles moving forwards and backwards in the CMS.
Distribution in transverse momentum among produced secondaries	$f(p_t)\,dp_t \propto \left(\dfrac{p_t}{p_0}\right)^{3/2} e^{-p_t/p_0}\,dp_t$

becomes more important the higher the primary particle energy. For example, at an energy of 10^{17} eV the multiplicity expected from the initial nucleon–air collision if the data from machine experiments are extrapolated as the square root of the incident particle energy is about 5000. This is larger by a factor of almost 100 than the number expected if the multiplicity increases more slowly with energy as may be expected from the scaling hypothesis. Similar strong sensitivities to other assumed values are shown at these high energies, and so, on the one hand, the importance of using the correct model in studies of astrophysics cannot be overstressed, but, on the other hand, there is considerable potential for studies of the high energy interactions themselves.

The representation of high energy interactions specified in table 3 and used as a preferred model by H E Dixon *et al* (1972 unpublished), is similar to the standard model adopted in many simulations (de Beer *et al* 1966, Hillas *et al* 1971). The model was arrived at after a survey of data on nucleon and pion interactions and has the additional characteristic of predicting shower parameters which are in agreement with observations in many experiments.

5.2. Typical simulation data

The data presented here typify those available from recent computer simulations and are taken from the work of H E Dixon *et al* (1972 unpublished) unless otherwise stated. The simulations are made with a model of high energy interactions characterized by the details given in table 3 and using a computational procedure in which the

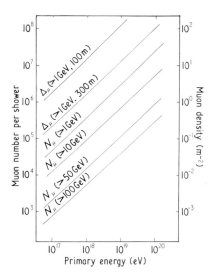

Figure 17. The total numbers and densities of muons of energy above different thresholds in showers initiated by primary protons of energy 10^{17}–10^{19} eV (HE Dixon *et al* 1972 unpublished).

interactions of nucleons are considered fully using Monte Carlo procedures and the subsequent shower development arising from the interaction of pions is treated by the 'step-by-step' procedure. The average characteristics for the 1-D and 3-D development of showers initiated by primary protons of energy between 10^{17}–10^{19} eV are shown in figure 17. In recent years a marked advance in simulation studies, as a result mainly

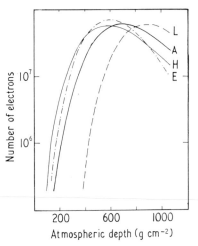

Figure 18. The longitudinal development of the electron cascades in showers. Showers A, E and L refer to the proton-initiated showers which show average, early and late development in the atmosphere; shower H is typical of that for a heavy primary nucleus (assumed mass number 56).

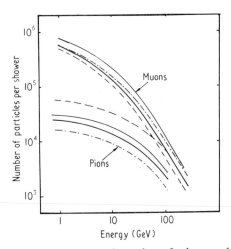

Figure 19. The total number of pions and muons in the specimen showers.

of the work of Hillas *et al* (1970, 1971), has been the extension of the simulations to include the detailed response of particle detectors; consideration of detectors as energy loss measuring devices has enabled many measurements to be interpreted with increased confidence.

Table 4. The approximate fluctuations in showers initiated by primary protons (after Hillas *et al* (1971) and H E Dixon *et al* (1972 unpublished)

Primary energy (eV)	N_e (S.L.)	N_μ	ρ_{500}	Δ_μ(100 m)	Optical Cerenkov signal (300 m)
		Fluctuations (relative dispersion)			
10^{17}	67%	12%	14%	10%	~10%
10^{18}	32%	9%	12%	10%	—
10^{19}	~25%	8%	9%	—	—

The magnitude of the fluctuations to be expected for various observable aspects of sea-level proton-initiated showers of greater than 10^{17} eV are summarized in table 4.

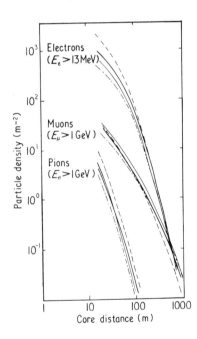

Figure 20. The lateral distributions of electrons, muons and pions in the specimen showers.

In an attempt to present the information on the fluctuations from shower to shower the characteristics of four specific showers are given in figures 18–22. The four showers considered, each initiated by a primary particle of energy 10^{17} eV, are:

Shower A —a shower which is typical of the average of a large sample of proton-initiated showers.

Shower H —a shower typical of those produced by a primary iron nucleus.

Shower E —a shower developing high in the atmosphere which may be expected to occur as a consequence of the normal fluctuations of proton-initiated showers some 5% of the time.

Shower L —a shower developing low in the atmosphere as may be expected to arise for a primary proton-initiated event from normal fluctuation effects some 5% of the time.

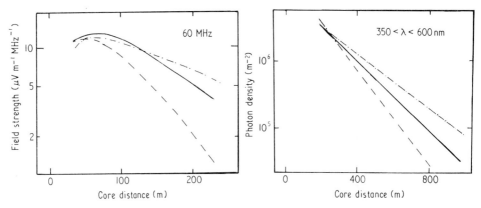

Figure 21. The lateral distribution of the radio field strength in the specimen showers (shower H varies little from shower E), after J H Hough (1972 unpublished).

Figure 22. The lateral distribution of the optical Cerenkov signal in the specimen showers (shower H varies little from shower E), after G J Smith (1972 unpublished).

6. The primary energy spectrum

6.1. The measurement of primary particle energy

Measurement of the energy of the primary particle initiating a shower depends upon the accurate measurement at the observation level of some parameter related to the primary energy and the reliable conversion of this parameter to the primary energy, perhaps based upon data derived from computer simulations of showers. The various measurements and their typical accuracies have been discussed in §2; it is of interest that the four predominant large shower experiments measure four different primary energy sensitive parameters. These four different measures of primary energy each have particular advantages and disadvantages for ease and accuracy of measurement and conversion to primary energy. At the Haverah Park experiment the observed quantity is ρ_{500}, the deep water Cerenkov detector signal at a distance of 500 m from the core. It has been shown by Hillas *et al* (1971) that this quantity on average relates to the primary energy independent of the mass of primary particle assumed and the fluctuations in the value for showers initiated by proton primary particles of energy 10^{17} eV are typically $\pm 15\%$. On the other hand, the measurement made at the Volcano Ranch array, the total number of charged particles in a shower, relates to primary energy in a way which depends upon primary particle mass. In the case of proton primary particles the fluctuations in the observation for fixed primary energy, say

10^{18} eV, may be small at shower maximum (some $\pm 18\%$) but increase for a shower past maximum development to a value at sea level of $\pm 32\%$. The total number of muons in a shower, being the basic measurement of the Sydney array, is expected to show smaller fluctuations for a fixed primary energy ($\pm 9\%$ according to Hillas *et al* (1971)); if the quantity measured in, for example, a 10^{18} eV shower would be the muon density at a specified core distance of 100 m, then the fluctuations would be approximately $\pm 10\%$ as suggested by the data of H E Dixon *et al* (1972 unpublished) in figure 19. However, all aspects of the muon component of showers reflect some sensitivity to primary particle mass—this indeed may be the basis for experiments to determine the nature of the primary particle—and so reliable conversions of N_μ to E_p may only be derived from simulations with a pre-knowledge of the nature of the primary particle. The Yakutsk array is unique at present in that it selects and records showers using scintillation detectors and estimates the total number of charged particles in the shower, but it relates an event of given shower size to its primary particle energy in the region 10^{17}–10^{18} eV via measurements at core distances 200–500 m of the average optical Cerenkov signal generated in the atmosphere. The latter quantity is characterized by showing little fluctuation in the measurement from shower to shower (see figure 22). The sensitivity to the nature of the primary particle assumed, following the data of figure 22, suggests differences of about two in the signal arriving from showers initiated by primary protons and heavy nuclei. An estimate of the fluctuations in the signal at 300 m from the core of 10^{17} eV proton-initiated showers would be about $\pm 10\%$ (G J Smith 1972 unpublished).

The simulation results of H E Dixon *et al* (1972 unpublished) suggest relationships between the average measured quantities in the four main experiments and the primary energy for a proton-initiated shower as indicated in figure 23.

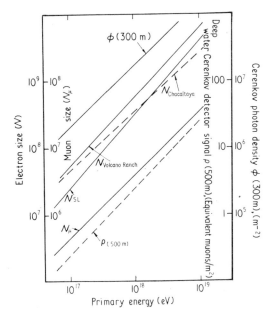

Figure 23. The relationship between the various observable measures of 'shower size' and the primary particle energy. The primary particles have been assumed to be protons and the showers arrive in the vertical direction.

6.2. The spectral shape

The pioneer work on the spectral shape at very high energies was that at the Volcano Ranch array, reported by Linsley (1964). The information from this experiment together with that from measurements made by the MIT group at Agassiz and El Alto and the unpublished work from the Cornell experiment form the basis upon which Greisen (1966a) produced the representation of the primary spectrum shown in figure 24. This representation was confirmed at the energies 10^{17}–10^{18} eV by the data from the Chacaltaya experiment (La Pointe *et al* 1968) and the early data from the Haverah Park experiment (Hollows *et al* 1968). No further data at the highest energies and

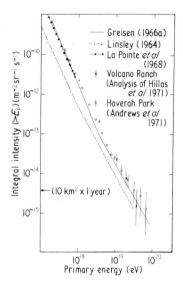

Figure 24. The integral primary energy spectrum.

in particular no comment upon the flattening of the spectrum at energies greater than 10^{18} eV indicated by the original Volcano Ranch data were available until 1969, when measurements made at the Tokyo, Haverah Park and Sydney arrays were reported.

The Tokyo measurement reported by Hara *et al* (1970b), based upon decoherence experiments made with large detector separations and incorporating results from the lateral structure function from the Volcano Ranch experiment, required that the sea-level size spectrum show a change of slope, as was suggested by the original Volcano Ranch data. The preliminary measurements from the Sydney array (Brownlee *et al* 1970a) indicated an even more marked flattening of the energy spectrum such that the integral spectrum exponent at energies in excess of 10^{19} eV was $1 \cdot 0^{+0 \cdot 3}_{-0 \cdot 4}$. A similar trend leading to an exponent of $1 \cdot 6$ for energies in excess of 5×10^{17} eV was derived from the measurements at Haverah Park (Andrews *et al* 1970).

An excellent survey of the data available for the size spectra of showers was made by Hillas (1970) and is reproduced as figure 25; with the aid of model simulations this was converted into a primary energy spectrum which is shown as figure 26. An alternative analysis of the Volcano Ranch data has been made by Hillas *et al* (1971) and suggests an approximate two-fold increase to the energies ascribed to the events by Linsley (1964).

It is interesting to note that not so much as a consequence of increased statistics, but rather as a direct result of improvements of the analysis techniques, and in particular the knowledge of the lateral structure function of the few high energy events,

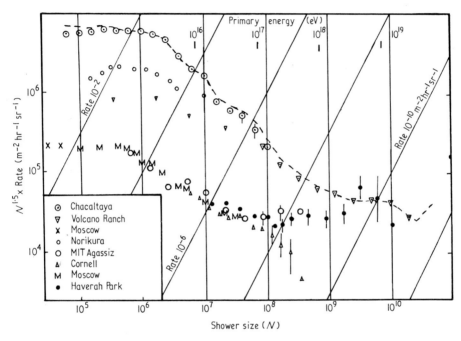

Figure 25. The rate R of showers of more than N particles (plotted as $R \times N^{1.5}$) observed at various altitudes and the derived energy spectrum. Data: Haverah Park: Hollows *et al* (1968) and Andrews *et al* (1970); Volcano Ranch: Linsley (1964); Moscow: Vernov and Khristiansen (1968), Mishnev and Nikolskii (1960); Chacaltaya: Bradt *et al* (1966); Cornell: Delvaille *et al* (1960); MIT: Clark *et al* (1960); Norikura: Katsumata (1964). (After Hillas 1970.)

the improved data presented by Andrews *et al* (1971) indicated no significant change in slope of the spectrum up to energies of 10^{19} eV. Similarly, basic data from the Sydney experiment have been reanalysed (Bell *et al* 1971) and the spectrum for muon sizes also shows no change in slope from the value of about 2·2 to muon sizes of 10^9, corresponding to energies about 10^{19} eV. The recent data from those experiments are shown in figure 24; the Sydney muon data after conversion to primary energy using the same model simulations as used at the Haverah Park experiment give a spectrum of slope in agreement with that found at the Haverah Park experiment.

The recent data indicate a primary energy spectrum constant in slope (corresponding to an exponent for the integral spectrum of about 2·2) for all energies from less than 10^{16} eV to 10^{19} eV, in contradiction to the earlier indications of the flattening of the spectrum coming from the Volcano Ranch experiment. Absolute fluxes at

N

sea level may be represented by the spectrum derived from the Haverah Park experiment (Andrews *et al* 1971):

$$I(>E_p) = (4 \cdot 5 \pm 0 \cdot 2) \times 10^{-10} \left(\frac{E_p}{10^{17}} \right)^{-2 \cdot 24 \pm 0 \cdot 04} \quad \text{m}^{-2} \text{ s}^{-1} \text{ sr}^{-1}$$

for $3 \times 10^{17} < E_p < 10^{19}$ eV.

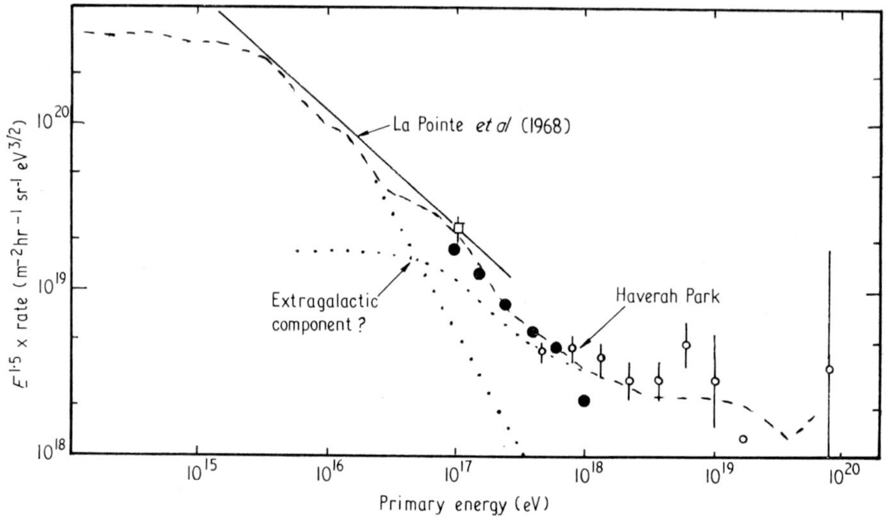

Figure 26. The primary integral energy spectrum $R(E)$ plotted as $E^{1 \cdot 5} \times R$. The broken line is derived from figure 25 and the continuous line and points from theoretical models applied to particular shower groups observed at Chacaltaya and Haverah Park (after Hillas 1970).

6.3. The highest energy events

The frequency of recorded energetic events in the energy region beyond 10^{19} eV is of interest in connection with the possible cut-off for the spectrum at such large energies. This cut-off was suggested by Greisen (1966b) to arise as a consequence of interactions between high energy protons and low energy photons which constitute the universal black body radiation of temperature 3 K. High energy primary protons would be removed from the primary flux by this interaction provided that the primary particles travelled across distances large compared with the characteristic distance for the interaction (about 10^{25} cm), as will be the case if they were of extragalactic origin.

The numbers of energetic events recorded at the various experiments are summarized in table 5, together with the highest energy shower recorded by each experiment.

6.4. The nature of the primary particles

The difficulty in the measurement of the nature of energetic primary particles is reflected by the paucity of data. To date four measurements at energies just above 10^{17} eV have been interpreted to give indications of the primary particle composition.

Table 5. The highest energy showers.

Array	Total number of events $E_p > 10^{19}$ eV	$E_p > 5 \times 10^{19}$ eV	Largest recorded shower energy (eV)
Volcano Ranch (Linsley 1964)	97	7	10^{20}
Volcano Ranch (Linsley 1964 analysed by Hillas *et al* 1971)	~25	2	~10^{20}
Haverah Park (Zenith angle < 30°) (Andrews *et al* 1971)	16	2	~7×10^{19}
Sydney (Zenith angle < 33°) (Bell *et al* 1971)	1	0	1.5×10^{19}
Tokyo (Kaneko *et al* 1971)	—	—	4×10^{21}
Tokyo (J Garmston and A A Watson analysis (1972 private communication))	—	—	$\lesssim 4 \times 10^{19}$
Yakutsk (O C Diminstein *et al* 1972 private communication)	4	0	3×10^{19}

Similar measurements of muon fluctuations in showers of constant electron size at shower maximum and in showers beyond shower maximum have both suggested a purely protonic primary beam. Fluctuations of the muon component at the Moscow State University experiment (Khristiansen *et al* 1966) have produced evidence in favour of the normal mixed composition found at low energies; data consistent with this finding was produced from studies of horizontal muons by Alexander *et al* (1968), although it should be pointed out that the small data sample referring to primaries of energy in excess of 10^{17} eV required that particles be heavier than protons. A similar conclusion was reached by Orford and Turver (1970) on the basis of the lateral spread of energetic muons in near vertical showers.

Many of the authors realize the limitations of their approach to this difficult problem and accept the low degree of confidence put in the interpretations.

7. The arrival directions of high energy cosmic rays

Prior to 1960 the only information on the time variations of large showers was that from the Harwell experiment (Cranshaw and Galbraith 1954, 1957) and the Manchester experiment (Crawshaw and Elliot 1955). Both experiments employed Geiger counters, had an angular resolution of about 0·5 sr and provided no evidence for anisotropies in arrival direction.

More precise arrival direction measurements (typically 10^{-2} sr solid angle accuracy) were made at the fast timing experiments at Agassiz, Cornell and El Alto, but again no significant evidence for anisotropy was forthcoming. Measurements for the highest energy showers made at Volcano Ranch (Linsley 1964) and Sydney (Brownlee *et al* 1970b) together with data for events of slightly lower primary energy but having much improved statistics from the Haverah Park experiment (Blake *et al* 1968), again gave indication of isotropic arrival for all particles. A summary of available data is given in table 6.

Table 6. Time variations of high energy cosmic rays. The analysis is made in right ascension and, unless otherwise stated, shows the amplitude and maximum of the first harmonic.

Experiment	Energy threshold (eV)	Amplitude (%)	Maximum (deg)
Harwell (Cranshaw and Galbraith 1954)	$> 5 \times 10^{16}$	$4 \cdot 9 \pm 1 \cdot 5$	—
Manchester (Crawshaw and Elliott 1955)	$> 10^{17}$	$7 \cdot 5 \pm 6$	—
Harwell (Cranshaw and Galbraith 1957)	$> 10^{17}$	Standard error of harmonic	$0 \cdot 7 \%$
	$> 3 \times 10^{17}$		$3 \cdot 0 \%$
Agassiz (Clark *et al* 1960)	$> 6 \times 10^{16}$	Isotropic arrival	
	$> 3 \times 10^{17}$	Isotropic arrival	
Cornell (Delvaille *et al* 1962)	$> 10^{17}$	$17 \pm 4 \cdot 8 \%$ Semi-diurnal (145°, 325°)	
	$> 5 \times 10^{17}$	Minimum at 180–240° with probability of $7 \cdot 5 \%$	
El Alto (Hersil *et al* 1962)	$> 10^{17}$	14 ± 10	—
Volcano Ranch (Linsley (1964) analysed by Hollows (1968))	$> 10^{18}$	$13 \cdot 3 \pm 4 \cdot 4$	247
	$> 10^{19}$	16 ± 14	150
Haverah Park (Blake *et al* 1968)	$7 \times 10^{16} < E_p < 3 \times 10^{17}$	$0 \cdot 4 \pm 1 \cdot 5$	90
	$3 \times 10^{17} < E_p < 10^{18}$	$3 \cdot 4 \pm 2 \cdot 8$	240
	$E_p > 10^{18}$	$3 \cdot 9 \pm 2 \cdot 7$	140
Haverah Park (Hollows 1968)	$> 3 \times 10^{17}$	No preferred directions at	N. galactic pole, spiral arm in, spiral arm out, galactic anti-centre
Sydney (Brownlee *et al* 1970b)	$> 10^{18}$	Isotropic arrival	

All the above analyses were made for convenience in right ascension, and the importance of scrutinizing regions of the sky of potential importance has been mentioned by Hollows (1968). The data from the Haverah Park experiment—the most significant sample available to date—gave no indication of any excess of events from regions about the galactic north pole, the spiral arm in or out direction, or the galactic anti-centre (Blake *et al* 1968).

Recent attempts to correlate the arrival directions of high energy primaries with the directions of pulsars have provided no evidence for correlation (Brownlee *et al* 1970b, J L Osborne and A W Wolfendale 1972 unpublished, U Lapikens 1972 unpublished).

8. Future work

The primary energy spectrum measurements at the large arrays should improve our knowledge so that in 5–10 years we may expect the spectrum up to energies of

5×10^{19}–10^{20} eV to be well known and statistically accurate to better than 10%. Many of the current experiments are also able to recognize and record the largest events, and the presence or absence of a few events of energy in excess of 10^{20} eV may constitute the only evidence for or against the proposed cut-off at large energy. Such events should be detected on the total sensitive area of the four main experiments (some 10^8 m²) at a rate of about one per year if the spectrum at lower energies is maintained to such high energies. There appears at present to be no satisfactory novel method of detection of large showers with which to extend the spectrum measurements beyond 10^{20} eV; the considerable efforts to employ atmospheric scintillation measurements, radio emission or radio-echo experiments during the past decade do not suggest the successful application of these techniques in the foreseeable future. The arrival direction studies may be expected to benefit from improvements in statistics so that the measurements at energies of about 10^{19} eV, at which energy the effects of magnetic fields on the trajectories is decreasing, may be made with the significance presently attached to events of energy 10–100 times lower. It is likely that the present analyses of convenience in right ascension will give way to attempts to correlate arrival directions with directions of celestial objects and this will demand an improved accuracy in directional measurements.

The largest advances in the astrophysical studies of EAS data may come from the attempts to determine the nature of the primary particles—a field neglected in the past. The information presently available consists of hints as to the nature of the primary particle from some four experiments, most of which are confined to energies just above 10^{17} eV, and are contradictory. The possibility of new experiments to provide, at energies in the region of 10^{18} eV, new information on this problem is attractive; recent measurements and simulations, however, indicate that the experiments will be difficult to make if definite data are to be obtained. Attempts to ascertain the presence of any protons or light nuclei in the primary beam may be approached via a search for those extreme fluctuations in the longitudinal development of showers arising from different rates of degradation of the energy in the nuclear cascade which are a consequence of the possible widely spaced interactions of the nucleons. For a high degree of confidence in the data on showers developing very low in the atmosphere two or three simultaneous measurements must be made, each identifying the fluctuation event. For example, in the data of figures 19–22, the shower developing low in the atmosphere, shower L, is identified by a high electron/muon ratio, a steeply falling lateral distribution function for radio emission and visible Cerenkov photons, a large number of pions and a slow arrival time distribution for the particles at the detectors far from the shower core. Measurements of two or three such effects would produce convincing evidence for a shower developing low in the atmosphere, which is thought likely only if some of the primary nuclei are light. A quantitative study of such showers to determine the proportion of light nuclei in the primary beam may be possible as experience accumulates.

Attempts to determine the mean mass number or the distribution in mass numbers for the primary beam seem to be much more difficult; the difference in many shower parameters between the average of many light or heavy nucleus initiated showers is small. Ratios of muon to electron densities measured using large area detectors (about 100 m²) or perhaps measurements of whole showers using arrays sensitive to different components, would be required; there may be no marked differences in the shapes of the average lateral distributions of the radio or optical Cerenkov signals measured in many showers initiated by light or heavy nuclei.

Studies to date of high energy interactions using shower data have suggested that the mean transverse momentum of secondary particles rises as the energy of the interacting particle increases (de Beer *et al* 1968) and that the shower develops faster than would be expected if the multiplicity of produced secondaries increased as the quarter power of the incident particle energy (Kaneko *et al* 1971). Current data from accelerator experiments do not contradict the concept of scaling for the momentum distributions of the produced secondaries suggested by Feynman (1969) and which leads to values of mean transverse momentum effectively constant at EAS energies, together with only a slow increase in the total multiplicities of secondaries with increasing energy of the incident particle. Shower studies are therefore very relevant to the question of the applicability of the scaling hypothesis at the very highest energies, where the differences in measurable shower parameters arising from acceptance of the scaling concept or other representations of high energy interactions are largest.

References

Abrosimov A T, Bazilevskaya G A, Solovieva V I and Khristiansen G B 1960 *Sov. Phys.–JETP* **11** 74–9

Alexander D, Holyoak B, Thompson M G and Turner M J L 1968 *Can. J. Phys.* **46** 273–7

Allan H R 1971 *Proc. 12th Int. Conf. on Cosmic Rays* (Hobart: University of Tasmania) **3** 1108–12
—— 1972 *Nature* **237** 384–5

Allan H R *et al* 1971 *Proc. 12th Int. Conf. on Cosmic Rays* (Hobart: University of Tasmania) **3** 1097–101

Andrews D A *et al* 1970 *Acta Phys. Hung.* **29** Suppl 3 343–8

Andrews D A *et al* 1971 *Proc. 12th Int. Conf. on. Cosmic Rays* (Hobart: University of Tasmania) **3** 995–1000

Bassi P, Clark G and Rossi B 1953 *Phys. Rev.* **92** 441–51

Baxter A J 1967 *PhD thesis* University of Leeds

de Beer J F 1960 *PhD thesis* University of Potchefstroom

de Beer J F, Holyoak B, Wdowczyk J and Wolfendale A W 1966 *Proc. Phys. Soc.* **89** 567–85

de Beer J F *et al* 1968 *Can. J. Phys.* **46** 737–41

Bell C J *et al* 1971 *Proc. 12th Int. Conf. on Cosmic Rays* (Hobart: University of Tasmania) **3** 989–93

Bennett S and Greisen K 1961 *Phys. Rev.* **124** 1982–7

Blake P R *et al* 1968 *Can. J. Phys.* **46** 78–80

Blake P R, Ferguson H and Nash W F 1971 *Proc. 12th Int. Conf. on Cosmic Rays* (Hobart: University of Tasmania) **3** 1050–5

Bradt H *et al* 1966 *Proc. 9th Int. Conf. on Cosmic Rays* (London: Institute of Physics) **2** 715–7

Brownlee R G *et al* 1970a *Acta Phys. Hung.* **29** Suppl 3 377–82

Brownlee R G *et al* 1970b *Acta Phys. Hung.* **29** Suppl 3 383–8

Chudakov A G, Nesterova N M, Zatsepin V I and Tukish E I 1960 *Proc. 6th Int. Conf. on Cosmic Rays* (Moscow: USSR Acad. Sci.) **2** 50–7

Clark G W *et al* 1958 *Nuovo Cim.* suppl **8** 628–52

Clark G W *et al* 1960 *Phys. Rev.* **122** 637–54

Cranshaw T E and Galbraith W 1954 *Phil. Mag.* **45** 1109–18
—— 1957 *Phil. Mag.* **2** 804–10
Crawshaw J K and Elliott H 1955 *Proc. Phys. Soc.* A**69** 102–9
Dedenko L G 1966 *Proc. 9th Int. Conf. on Cosmic Rays* (London: Institute of Physics) **2** 662–3
Delvaille J, Kendziorzki F and Greisen K 1960 *Proc. 6th Int. Conf. on Cosmic Rays* (Moscow: USSR Acad. Sci.) **2** 101–5
—— 1962 *J. Phys. Soc. Japan* **17** AIII 76–83
Dufresne R, Kellermann E W and Towers L 1966 *Proc. 9th Int. Conf. on Cosmic Rays* (London: Institute of Physics) **2** 689–90
Earnshaw J C 1968 *PhD thesis* University of Durham
Earnshaw J C *et al* 1967 *Proc. Phys. Soc.* **90** 91–108
Earnshaw J C, Machin A C, Pickersgill D R and Turver K E 1973 *J. Phys.* A: *Math. Nucl. Gen.* **6** to be published
Evans A C 1972 *PhD thesis* University of Leeds
Feynman R P 1969 *Phys. Rev. Lett.* **23** 1415–7
Fisher A J 1970 *PhD thesis* University of Sydney
Fukui S *et al* 1960 *Suppl. Prog. Theor. Phys.* **16** 1–53
Galbraith W and Jelley J V 1953 *Nature* **171** 349–50
Greisen K 1960 *Ann. Rev. Nucl. Sci.* **10** 63–107
—— 1966a *Proc. 9th Int. Conf. Cosmic Rays* (London: Institute of Physics) **2** 609–15
—— 1966b *Phys. Rev. Lett.* **16** 748–50
Hara T *et al* 1970a *Acta Phys. Hung.* **29** Suppl 3 369–77
Hara T *et al* 1970b *Acta Phys. Hung.* **29** Suppl 3 361–8
Hersil J *et al* 1962 *J. Phys. Soc. Japan* **17** Suppl AIII 243–6
Hillas A M 1966 *Proc. 9th Int. Conf. Cosmic Rays* (London: Institute of Physics) **2** 758–61
—— 1970 *Acta Phys. Hung.* **29** Suppl 3 355–60
Hillas A M, Hollows J D, Hunter H W and Marsden D J 1970 *Acta Phys. Hung.* **29** Suppl 3 533–8
Hillas A M, Marsden D J, Hollows J D and Hunter H W 1971 *Proc. 12th Int. Conf. on Cosmic Rays* (Hobart: University of Tasmania) **3** 1001–6
Hollows J D 1968 *PhD thesis* University of Leeds
Hollows J D, Hunter H W and Suri A N 1968 *J. Phys.* A: *Gen. Phys.* **2** 591–604
Jelley J V *et al* 1965 *Nature* **205** 327–9
Kamata K and Nishimura J 1958 *Suppl. Prog. Theor. Phys.* **6** 93–100
Kaneko T *et al* 1971 *Proc. 12th Int. Conf. on Cosmic Rays* (Hobart: University of Tasmania) **3** 945
Katsumata I 1964 *J. Phys. Soc. Japan* **19** 800–14
Kawaguchi A *et al* 1971 *Proc. 12th Int. Conf. Cosmic Rays* (Hobart: University of Tasmania) **3** 994–5
Kellermann E W and Towers L 1970 *J. Phys.* A: *Gen. Phys.* **3** 284–95
Khristiansen G B *et al* 1966 *Proc. 9th Int. Conf. on Cosmic Rays* (London: Institute of Physics) **2** 799–801
Krieger A S and Bradt H V 1969 *Phys. Rev.* **185** 1629–35
La Pointe M *et al* 1968 *Can. J. Phys.* **46** 68–71
Linsley J 1964 *Proc. 8th Int. Conf. on Cosmic Rays* (Bombay: TIFR) **4** 77–9
Linsley J and Scarsi L 1962 *Phys. Rev.* **128** 2384–92
Linsley J, Scarsi L and Rossi B 1962 *J. Phys. Soc. Japan* **17** Suppl AIII 91–101
Machin A C, Orford K J, Pickersgill D R and Turver K E 1970 *Acta Phys. Hung.* **29** Suppl 3 579–83
Mischnev S I and Nikolskii S I 1960 *Zh. Exp. Teor Fiz.* **38** 257–8
Orford K J and Turver K E 1970 *Acta Phys. Hung.* **29** Suppl 3 585–2
Porter L G *et al* 1970 *Nucl. Inst. and Meth.* **87** 87–99
Prescott J R, Hough J H and Pidcock J K 1970 *Acta Phys. Hung.* **29** Suppl 3 717–24
Suga K *et al* 1970 *Acta Phys. Hung.* **29** Suppl 3 423–28
Suri A N 1966 *PhD thesis* University of Leeds
Vernov S N and Khristiansen G B 1968 *Can. J. Phys.* **46** 345–98

Williams R W 1948 *Phys. Rev* **74** 1689–706
Wilson R R 1957 *Phys. Rev.* **108** 155–6
Yegerov T A *et al* 1971 *Proc. 12th Int. Conf. on Cosmic Rays* (Hobart: University of Tasmania)
    3 946

Chapter 10

The neon flash-tube technique

J M Breare

1. Introductory remarks

The neon flash-tube was first introduced by Conversi and Gozzini (1955) during a decade which saw the invention of several important techniques for particle detection. Of these the bubble chamber (Glaser 1952) and the spark chamber (Cranshaw and de Beer 1957) have proved particularly relevant to accelerator experiments while the flash-tube has contributed significantly in cosmic ray experiments.

In operation, the neon flash-tube is similar to the spark chamber which followed it. It requires an auxilliary detector such as a Geiger–Müller tube or a scintillator to register the passage of a particle. After this, a high voltage pulse of several kilovolts per cm peak field and a few microseconds length is applied to metal sheet electrodes. Between the electrodes are placed an array of sealed glass flash-tubes usually containing a mixture of neon and helium. A typical flash-tube is 1 m long, outside diameter 1·8 cm and filled with gas at 600 Torr. One end of the tube has a flat window for observing the discharge but apart from this the tube is painted black to avoid light spreading to adjacent tubes. The track of the particle through the array is indicated by a light flash occurring in those tubes through which the particle has passed. The other tubes in the array do not flash. A large array of more than 10 000 tubes is shown in figure 1 where tracks of several cosmic rays and their interactions are clearly visible.

The neon flash-tube has often found favour with the cosmic ray physicist at the expense of the spark chamber for a number of reasons. High on this list is the sealed envelope of the flash-tube which makes it an ideal detector for long experiments which would otherwise require the constant attention of a gas flow or recycling system. The long life and robust characteristics of flash-tubes are associated with the tube being constructed of glass which is a relatively strong material. These are also highly desirable properties bearing in mind that tubes have been subjected to the cold of a mountain altitude and to the heat and humidity of an Indian gold mine. As far as long life is concerned Coxell and Wolfendale (1960) found that tubes had characteristics essentially unchanged after 10^6 pulses. Whereas the relatively thick glass envelope of the flash-tube may be unacceptable in many accelerator experiments involving predominantly nuclear-active particles, the weakly interacting muons and electrons of cosmic radiation have little difficulty in penetrating them.

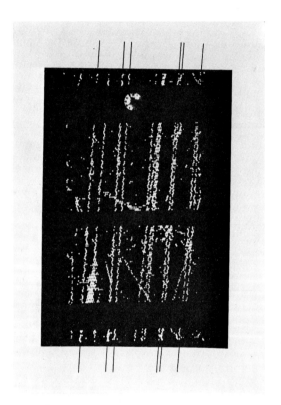

Figure 1. Cosmic ray shower passing through a large flash-tube array of more than 10 000 tubes. High energy knock-on electrons and a small cascade are clearly visible (Ashton *et al* 1971b).

The general form of the flash-tube and a study of its properties were made principally in Durham up to 1961. More recently, digitization methods have been developed to replace the usual film recording technique. This further increases the flash-tube's potential use in large arrays and long time duration experiments. As far as cost is concerned, it is very much a matter of the electronic sophistication, but a favourable comparison can be made with spark chambers, with the added advantages of long life, low maintenance and ease of operation.

2. The nature of the discharge in flash-tubes

2.1. The initiation of the discharge

Although tubes have been filled with a variety of gas mixtures and a range of pressures which vary from 200 Torr up to 3 atmospheres, the basic discharge mechanisms do not change significantly over this pressure range since even the lowest pressure is considered high when referring to spark formation theory. Furthermore, changes in gas mixture affect the basic mechanism only slightly.

In common with most detectors, the flash-tube utilizes some of the energy given up by the charged particle as it passes through the gas. Typically, with a gas density of 1 mg cm^{-3}, a particle losing energy at the rate 2 MeV gm^{-1} cm^2 will deposit approximately 2 keV in the gas of a flash-tube. This energy will be distributed amongst the various forms appropriate to the particular gas. Generally speaking, a little will go into thermal motion of the atoms but the majority will result in electronic excitation (which will include metastable states in the case of noble gases) and ionization. If the gas is molecular, dissociation may take a significant proportion of the energy and vibrational and rotational excitation will also occur. As far as the subsequent discharges are concerned, only the ionization component need be considered at this stage because it is the free electrons which are responsible for the initiation of the subsequent discharge. Electrons released by collision of metastables can also contribute but are usually small in number and can be neglected as far as the basic discharge mechanism is concerned. Although the actual numbers will depend on gas composition and pressure, it is normal to expect up to 30 electrons to be produced in a flash-tube by the passage of a charged particle through it.

In the time interval between the production of the electrons and the application of the high voltage pulse an electron may be removed from the gas by one of several processes. Motion to the walls of the tube, either as diffusion or as drift in an electric field, actually removes the electron, but it can also be effectively removed if it becomes attached to an electron-attaching molecule in the gas. Such molecules, for example oxygen, may be added deliberately or may constitute an impurity. Any electron remaining in the tube when the high voltage pulse is applied may initiate a discharge. It is clear from the work of Townsend (1947) and Raether (1964) that a discharge can form from a single initial electron. However, it must be pointed out that the probability of this occurring depends on the position of the electron in the tube at the time of application of the high voltage pulse.

2.2. Discharges without streamer formation

When an electric field is applied across a flash-tube, electrons will be swept towards the positive electrode and in so doing they will gain energy from the field. They rapidly lose this energy by collisions with gas atoms and hence secondary ionization is caused. An avalanche will thus build up, and the number of electrons at a distance x from the initial position of the first electron will be given by the familiar Townsend equation

$$n = n_0 \exp(\alpha x)$$

where n_0, in this case, can be taken as unity; α, Townsend's first ionization coefficient, is shown in figure 2 for the noble gases used in flash tubes. It is seen that for the range of values of E/P normally applicable, α increases with field implying that the discharge will build up more rapidly with large fields.

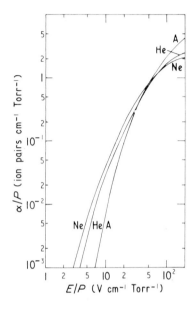

Figure 2. Electron ionization coefficient α/P as a function of the field, E/P for noble gases (von Engel 1965).

Whereas the starting conditions and the initial rate of growth of discharges can be explained fully in terms of the Townsend multiplication process, the later stages of the discharge are not readily accounted for. When the number of electrons (n) in the avalanche head reaches a value in the region of 10^8, the electric field due to the charges themselves is usually a significant fraction of the applied field (fields of a few kilovolts per cm are assumed). From that time the discharge grows at a modified rate. Most of the light, both the ultraviolet and the visible, is emitted during the later part of the discharge when the avalanche has built up to a large number of electrons. The light is caused by emission from excited atomic levels, the excitation being caused in the first place by collisions between electrons and ground state atoms.

The likelihood of 10^8 electrons being produced in the avalanche before it reaches the walls of the tube will depend principally on the diameter of the tube and on the applied electric field. Hampson and Rastin (1971) found that in small tubes (6 mm internal diameter) at a high pressure of 3 atm, the avalanche reached the wall of the tube without attaining this number of charges. However, in larger tubes at pressures in the region of 1 atm the avalanche has a greater distance available to it and these space charges can occur under normal flash-tube operating conditions. Having reached the wall of the flash-tube, the avalanche would die out unless it generated secondary avalanches of its own. This is very likely to occur by photoelectric emission and Harries and von Engel (1954) showed that the photoelectric yield from glass was 0·01. The number of ultraviolet photons available in the discharge, all of which must eventually reach the glass, will be comparable with the number of electrons in the avalanche. In fact Corrigan and von Engel (1958) calculated the number of photons emitted in a discharge in helium to be greater than the number of ion pairs produced in the discharge. Thus a copious supply of secondary electrons is to be expected, originating principally around the first discharge, but also spreading along the tube. The secondary avalanches will subsequently cross the tube and cause a further generation of new avalanches at still greater distances from the initial discharge (see figure 3). In this way the discharge spreads along the tube and its velocity of propagation has been measured by Ayre *et al* (1972) to be $6 \cdot 7 \times 10^8$ cm s^{-1} in the case of high pressure tubes. The appearance of the discharge, looking into the side of the tube, is that of a continuous diffuse glow filling the whole tube. It is not possible to distinguish individual avalanches. An indication of the speed with which an avalanche crosses the

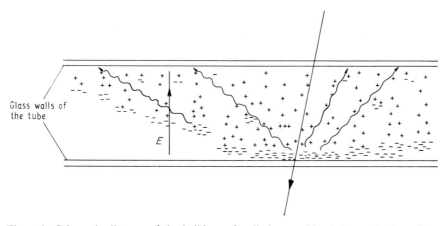

Figure 3. Schematic diagram of the build up of a discharge without the production of streamers. E is the applied field. Each individual avalanche is not, by itself, large enough to cause distortion of the electric field, but successive avalanches build up a charge on the wall capable of counteracting the field.

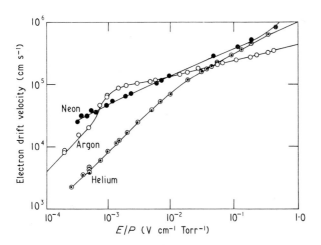

Figure 4. Drift velocities of electrons in noble gases (Pack and Phelps 1961).

tube can be obtained from figure 4 which shows electron drift velocities as a function of electric field. Transit times of 50 ns are typical.

If the electric field applied to the small high pressure tubes had been greater, the first avalanche would have attained 10^8 electrons and space charge effects would be expected. This occurs under normal conditions in the larger diameter 600 Torr tubes where the appearance of the discharge, shown in figure 5, is by no means a uniform discharge filling the whole space of the tube. In fact the discharge is in the form of individual streamers and they can be qualitatively accounted for by the 'streamer theory' developed by Raether (1964) and by Meek and Craggs (1953).

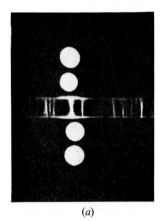
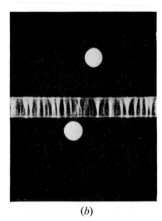

(a)   (b)

Figure 5. Photographs of discharges in 1·6 cm inside diameter flash-tube filled with 98% neon and 2% helium at 600 Torr. The circular flashes signify the trajectory of the triggering particle, which was located using similar tubes at right angles to the tube under inspection. HT pulse parameters: peak field 3·9 kV cm^{-1}. $\tau = 40$ μs (J Webster, Durham University).

2.3. Streamer formation

The streamer theory relies very much on enhancement of the electric field both in front of and behind the bunch of electrons in the avalanche head. In these enhanced field regions the discharge spreads at a much faster rate causing further field distortion and a consequent increase in ionization. Figure 6 shows a schematic diagram of streamer growth. Although the origin of the enhanced fields is now understood qualitatively, the origin of the suitably placed electrons away from the avalanche head is still a matter of some conjecture. Photoionization in the gas, collisions of metastable atoms with ground state atoms and electron diffusion are all possible processes and each probably contributes to the very fast build up of the discharge when field distortion occurs. A requirement of the streamer theory is that a large applied field is necessary if 10^8 electrons are to be produced in the short distances available in a flash-tube. The Raether criterion for streamer formation can be written as $\alpha x \simeq 20$. This is derived in simplified form from the fact that $\exp(20) \simeq 10^8$. Taking $x = 1$ cm for a flash-tube a value of the field in neon or helium necessary for streamer formation can be obtained from figure 2—a field of 5·5 kV cm^{-1} at a pressure of 600 Torr in neon is indicated. This, however, will be an overestimation because the streamers will be formed from more than one initial electron. In fact, as stated earlier, there may be more than 30 electrons, all in a line across the tube, caused by the passage of the charged particle. Each of the electrons will form its own avalanche and this will grow until it joins on to the tail of the one ahead of it. Field distortion will occur more easily as the avalanches influence one another and a conducting path is produced close to the track of the initial ionization. If the angle between the particle track and the direction of the field is less than about 30°, the conducting path may follow the track quite closely.

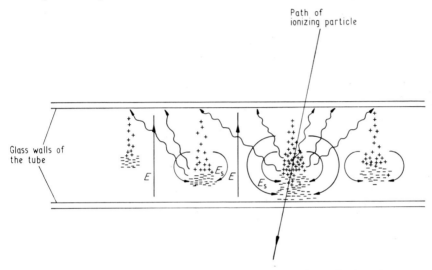

Figure 6. Schematic diagram of build up of the discharge with the production of streamers. E is the applied field and E_s is the field due to the streamers. In the space between the streamers E and E_s oppose each other and the resultant field is very low.

Breakdown in the 600 Torr tubes is known to occur in fields much less than the 5·5 kV cm^{-1} predicted for streamer formation†. It is not certain that streamers are being formed at the smallest fields and the Townsend type of breakdown described for the high pressure tubes is probably more evident. However, as shown in figure 5, streamers do occur for fields much less than 5·5 kV cm^{-1} and apart from the reasons already discussed, Penning ionization may also contribute to the lowering of the field required for breakdown. By this phenomena neon atoms can be ionized by collision with excited helium atoms. This constitutes a second ionization process which will enhance the rate of avalanche build up.

An indication of the formative time of a spark is given in figure 7 which is taken from the extensive results of Fischer and Zorn (1961). It is clear that the time for a discharge to build up depends not only on the gas, but also on the electrode configuration.

After the first streamer has formed, the discharge spreads along the tube in a manner similar to that described for the high pressure tubes. Photons from the streamer

† See figure 12.

release photoelectrons at the tube walls and secondary streamers are produced. These however do not entirely fill the volume of the tube as in the case of the high pressure discharge. They are well spaced out and distinct from each other. The reason for this is that the field distortion caused by the preceding streamers lowers the field in the surrounding volume and thus inhibits streamer build up close by. Ayre *et al* (1972) also measured the speed with which the discharge spreads along tubes of internal diameter 1·6 cm filled with Ne–He at 600 Torr. They found a velocity of $3·6 \times 10^8$ cm s^{-1}, being less than observed for the higher pressure, smaller diameter tubes.

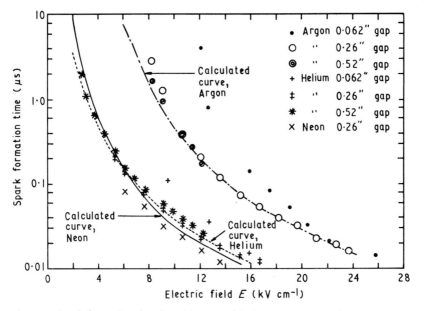

Figure 7. Spark formation time in noble gases (Fischer and Zorn 1961).

It is doubtful if too much emphasis should be placed on a basic difference between tubes in which streamers occur and tubes in which a Townsend mechanism is most significant. Very probably the latter is important at low fields and then more and more streamers will be produced when the field is increased. Figure 5(*b*) shows an interesting situation where the path of the particle is defined by the tubes seen end on but no very bright streamer is observed at this position in the side view of the tube. It is concluded here that there were few electrons available in the tube when the HT pulse was applied and these were not favourably placed to produce a streamer—probably they were less than the spark formative distance from the wall and hence did not multiply up to 10^8. Nevertheless photons were emitted in sufficient numbers to release secondary electrons from several positions on the other side of the tube. These electrons were able to produce streamers.

2.4. The termination of the discharge

Information on the subsequent fate of charges deposited on the inside glass wall is now becoming available. Holroyd and Breare (1972b) state that the charge collected on the tube's wall from the streamer will cause a reverse field opposing the applied field. They showed that the light emission from a tube lasts for a time of approximately 1 μs even though the applied HT pulse may exist for much longer (see figure 8).

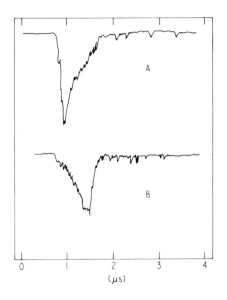

Figure 8. Profiles of photomultiplier pulses of light emitted from the front end of a flash tube. (A) particle passing through front of the tube; (B) particle passing through rear of the tube. HT pulse amplitude 4 kV cm^{-1}, $\tau = 4$ μs (Holroyd and Breare 1972b).

This implies that an avalanche quenches itself after it reaches the wall and the entire discharge is extinguished soon after it reaches the end of the tube. Hampson *et al* (1971) considered that this wall charge also affected the spacing of the streamers along the length of a tube.

2.5. The amount of charge involved in the discharge

The number of charges in the discharge can be calculated assuming the capacitance of a flash-tube is approximately 5 pF. In order to back off an applied voltage of 10 kV and thereby quench the discharge, 4×10^{11} charges must be deposited on the wall. This approximate calculation should be compared with the estimate from photographic plates by Coxell *et al* (1961) of the number of photons emitted in a flash. They estimate 10^{12} photons are produced and since, according to Corrigan and von Engel (1958) the number of photons will exceed the number of ion pairs, there is good agreement between the two estimates.

o

3. Basic properties of neon flash-tubes

3.1. Efficiency of detection in relation to the applied high voltage pulse

3.1.1. Definition of terms. Undoubtedly, the most important characteristic of the flash-tube is the probability that it will flash after an ionizing particle has passed through it. In this respect two terms have been defined. The internal efficiency, η, of a flash-tube is taken to be the probability that it will flash if a particle passes through the gas inside the tube. Experimentally it is more helpful to measure the layer efficiency, η_L, which is defined as the ratio of the number of single flashes observed in a layer to the number of particles which have passed through that layer. If it is assumed that no flash can occur when a particle passes through the glass walls and avoids the gas, the two efficiencies are related by a simple geometrical factor R. When the tubes in a single layer are close packed, R is the ratio of the external to the internal diameter of the tube such that $\eta = R\eta_L$. The efficiency will be seen to depend on the parameters of the high voltage pulse, in particular on the time delay between the passage of the particle and the application of the pulse. This time is defined as t_D and the actual rise-time of the pulse (10% to 90%) is defined as t_R. The length of the pulse is τ—this will refer to the time constant, in the case of exponentially decaying pulses.

The time after the passage of the particle when the internal efficiency of detecting the particle has fallen from 100% to 50% is referred to as the sensitive time, t_S. After a tube has flashed, charges remain in the tube and would cause a second flash if the HT pulse were reapplied. The recovery time t_{REC} is defined as the time at which the tube has a 50% probability of re-flashing on the application of the second pulse.

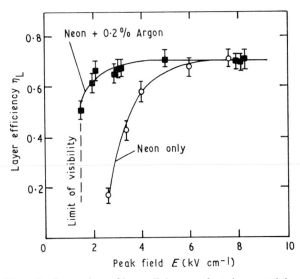

Figure 9. Comparison of layer efficiency η_L for tubes containing neon at 350 Torr and tubes containing neon plus 0·2% argon. Tube internal diameter 0·65 cm; HT pulse parameter: $t_D = 0·9$ μs, $\tau = 0·6$–2·2 μs (Barsanti *et al* 1956).

3.1.2. Effect of high voltage pulse magnitude. Several authors have studied the effect of varying the pulse magnitude. As expected the efficiency is low for small fields but reaches a plateau having almost 100% internal efficiency for higher fields. Figures 9 and 10 represent typical results. Although there is some merit to be gained from working with small voltages (see the discussion later on built-in clearing fields), the light emission is usually poor. The normal working conditions are thus well into the plateau region since there are no technical problems involved in the production of fields of this magnitude. The addition of 0·2% argon to neon (figure 9) is a good illustration of Penning ionization aiding the discharge. However light emission is particularly poor in this case and practical advantage cannot be taken of the effect.

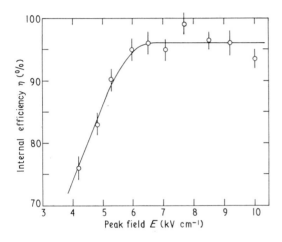

Figure 10. Variation of internal efficiency with field for tubes at 2·3 atm of 98% neon, 2% helium. Tube internal diameter 0·55 cm; HT pulse parameters $t_D = 3·4$ μs; $t_R = 0·5$ μs; $\tau = 3·5$ μs (Rochester 1960).

For very high fields the tubes remain 100% efficient for particle detection but spurious flashing begins to occur. The spurious flashes become more numerous as the field is increased and probably result from discharges in which the initial electrons were not caused by the passage of ionizing particles. The onset of significant spurious flashing does not seem to be well defined and is not reproducible in all cases. In practice it restricts the working range of the tube to a few kV cm^{-1}, from the knee of a plateau region to say 10 kV cm^{-1}. The problem is discussed in more detail in §3.6.

3.1.3. Effect of high voltage pulse rise-time. A slowly rising pulse will sweep electrons out of the tube without imparting to them much energy and the discharge will extinguish itself as the electrons reach the tube wall without a significant number of electrons having been produced to initiate further avalanches. Coxell and Wolfendale (1960) measured the efficiency for pulse rise times up to 1·7 μs. They used 6 mm internal diameter tubes at 2·3 atmospheres of neon, and their results (figure 11) show a slowly decreasing efficiency as the pulse rise-time is increased. It should be noted that efficiencies greater than 60% were obtained even for the slowest rising pulse; however, it is expected that the efficiency will fall off faster for a pulse of smaller magnitude.

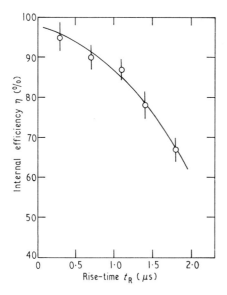

Figure 11. The variation of plateau efficiency with rise-time. Neon pressure 2·3 atm, $E_{max}=7·0$ kV cm^{-1}, $t_D=4·0$ μs and $τ=3·5$ μs (Coxell and Wolfendale 1960).

3.1.4. Effect of high voltage pulse length. The shape of the high voltage pulse depends on its mode of generation. A square pulse, derived from a delay line, or an exponentially decaying pulse, derived by discharging a capacitor through a resistor, are commonly used. Holroyd (1971) measured the efficiency as a function of pulse height for several pulse lengths using a *CR* decay pulse (figure 12). She observed that for

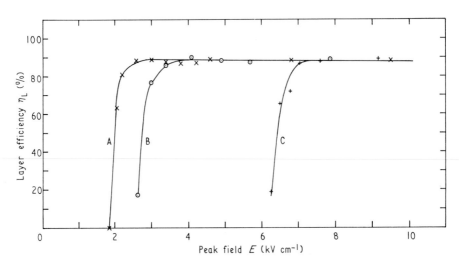

Figure 12. Variation of layer efficiency with field for different pulse lengths using a *CR* decay pulse. Tube internal diameter 1·6 cm, filled with 98% neon and 2% helium at 600 Torr. HT pulse parameters $t_R=70$ ns. (A) $τ=40·0$ μs. (B) $τ=4·0$ μs. (C) $τ=0·4$ μs (Holroyd 1971).

very short pulses ($\tau = CR = 0.4$ μs) the magnitude of the pulse had to exceed 7 kV cm^{-1} in order to obtain a discharge—even then it was very filamentary, resembling a faint spark and it did not fill the tube. For $\tau = 4.0$ μs the tubes performed correctly and for very much longer pulses ($\tau = 40$ μs) the performance was only slightly improved at the low voltages. The photomultiplier output traces, shown in figure 8, indicate that prolonging the HT pulse after the discharge has spread throughout the tube would not seem to serve any useful purpose since no further light emission is expected. In fact a long pulse has a definite disadvantage in that the slow moving positive ions, which remain in the gas after the light emission has finished, can be swept slowly to the walls of the tube and contribute to undesirable clearing fields. A long pulse increases the chance of spurious discharges also.

Although the variety of flash-tube types and the range of operating circumstances do not permit a simple rule to be made as to the pulse length, it would appear, according to the spark formative times given in figure 7, that pulses of a few microseconds duration are adequate for fields up to 10 kV cm^{-1}. A square pulse of this length is better than a CR decay pulse in that it does not sweep many positive ions to the tube wall. On the other hand, the CR decay pulse generator has the advantage of simplicity of construction and very little impedance matching is necessary.

3.2. Gas fillings

3.2.1. Composition. All successful gas fillings of flash-tubes have used the noble gases or mixtures of them. Their use is associated principally with their low breakdown voltage and the copious emission of ultraviolet and visible radiation. The ultraviolet is necessary for spreading the discharge along the tube and good emission in the visible is required since most arrays rely on optical read out.

The gas mixture in most common use is neon–helium in the ratio 98% to 2%. The large number of ion pairs produced in neon by the passage of a particle aids the easy formation of a discharge and gives a longer sensitive time than most other mixtures. Recently the author's group has found that cheaper gas mixtures of neon-helium are equally satisfactory, for example 70% neon with 30% helium is almost indistinguishable from 98%–2%. Similarly, a mixture in which helium is the major component (30% neon, 70% helium) is satisfactory (Conversi *et al* 1972). In the latter case the breakdown voltage is slightly lower. As far as light emission in the plateau region is concerned no differences in intensity were observed photographically and it is concluded that the ratio of neon to helium is not critical.

Other noble gas mixtures have been investigated; for example Barsanti *et al* (1956) found that 0.2% argon in neon reduced the minimum working voltage (see figure 9). Jesse and Sadauskis (1952) had shown that the total specific ionization for a mixture of neon and argon may be as much as 40% above that for pure neon, and there is thus a greater chance in this mixture of a discharge occurring when the HT pulse is applied. However, Gardener *et al* (1957) showed that satisfactory tubes were only produced by adding spectroscopic argon to the neon. Tubes with commercial argon had a very low efficiency, presumably caused by electron-attaching impurities in the argon.

3.2.2. Gas impurities. The effect of gas impurities, unavoidably present in the noble gas mixture, is an important consideration. Their effect is usually to increase the breakdown voltage of the gas and also to make it more difficult for the discharge to spread along the tube. The composition of commercial 98%–2% neon-helium is shown in table 1.

Table 1. Constituents of commercial neon (vpm = volumes per million)

Gas	Ne	He	O_2	N_2	A
Concentration	98%±0·2%	2%±0·2%	10 vpm	100–200 vpm	0·5 vpm

Coxell and Wolfendale (1960) found that increasing the nitrogen content to 1000 vpm had no effect on the efficiency. Table 2 gives their results.

Table 2. The variation of efficiency with pressure of nitrogen impurity

Nitrogen content (vpm)	250	500	750	1000
Internal efficiency η (%)	85–90	80–85	80–85	94–100

The neon in the tubes was of spectroscopic quality at a pressure of 600 Torr. The pulse characteristics were $E_{max} = 6\cdot5$ kV cm^{-1}, $t_R = 0\cdot6$ μs, $t_D = 4\cdot0$ μs and $\tau = 3\cdot5$ μs.

Oxygen is a similar molecular gas to nitrogen with the additional property of having a large cross section for electron attachment. It will readily absorb electrons during the discharge, thereby increasing the difficulty of producing a flash, and it will remove electrons in the time delay before the pulse is applied. Gardener *et al* (1957) showed that at long delays electrons were attached in air (presumably by the oxygen) but at short delays, even 1 Torr of air decreased the efficiency by only 20%. Rather similar results were observed by Holroyd and Breare (1972b) using tubes containing 70%–30% neon-helium with water vapour added. When the pressure of water vapour was near saturation (approximately 1% by volume at 20°C) it was difficult to operate the tubes even with large applied voltages. However, for a water vapour pressure of approximately 0·04 Torr, the efficiency at short delay was high but it decreased rapidly for delays greater than 2 μs. Moreover, water vapour and also oxygen cause a considerable decrease in the light emission from the tube.

Although commercial neon does contain a small amount of oxygen, Gardener *et al* (1957) showed that the characteristics of tubes with commercial neon were not appreciably different from tubes filled with spectroscopically pure neon. The additional cost of the pure gas is thus not justified. Coxell and Wolfendale (1960) made the important point that since the commercial neon may contain as much as 10 vpm of oxygen, there is little to be gained by evacuating the tubes below 10^{-3} Torr during manufacture. It has thus become the practice to evacuate only on a rotary oil pump, but with a liquid nitrogen trap in the system.

3.2.3. The gas pressure and tube diameter. Unlike spark chambers, which are almost always operated at atmospheric pressure, flash-tubes can be used without difficulty at various pressures; so far the pressures adopted have ranged from 200 Torr to 3 atm. For pressures below 350 Torr the maximum efficiency attainable was found by

Barsanti *et al* (1956) to fall. The reason for this is two-fold. At low pressures the number of ion pairs produced by the particle will on the average be small, thus the possibility of getting no suitably placed electron, even at zero delay, is now significant. Secondly, the rate of avalanche build up in the pulse will be slow, because the electron mean free path is increased, and hence the chance of the electrons being swept out without causing significant secondary ionization is increased. This later point is well illustrated in figure 13 where it is seen that at a pressure of 200 Torr the efficiency for a field of 3·6 kV cm^{-1} was 34%. When the field was increased to 8 kV cm^{-1} the rate of ionization increased with a consequent improvement in efficiency to 42%.

Investigation at high pressures up to 3 atm have been conducted by Coxell and Wolfendale (1960). The purpose of filling tubes at high pressure is to obtain a large

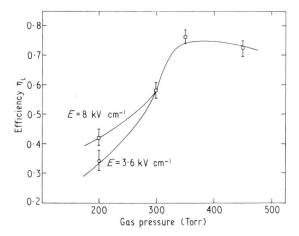

Figure 13. Efficiency as a function of the gas pressure for tubes containing neon plus 0·2% argon Tube internal diameter 0·65 cm. HT pulse delay $t_D = 0·7$ μs (Barsanti *et al* 1956).

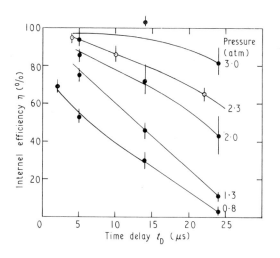

Figure 14. The efficiency–time delay characteristics of flash-tubes for several gas pressures. Tube internal diameter 0·55 cm; HT pulse characteristics: $E_{max} = 6·3$ kV cm^{-1}, $t_R = 0·5$ μs and $\tau = 3·0$ μs (Coxell and Wolfendale 1960).

number of initial ion pairs in a tube of small diameter. By this means the high probability of discharge formation at short delays is retained and also the electrons do not diffuse as rapidly to the walls of the tube—a long sensitive time is thus obtained even for small diameter tubes. The time delay characteristics for tubes of internal diameter 0·55 cm at various pressures are shown in figure 14.

For practical purposes, tube diameters from 0·4 cm up to 2·0 cm are used. Generally speaking, the smaller the diameter of the tube, the higher is the pressure within it in order to produce adequate ionization.

3.2.4. Temperature sensitivity. Since the flash-tube is a sealed unit in which the quantity of gas is constant, the ionization caused by the particle is not temperature dependent. Furthermore, breakdown conditions are not greatly affected by changes in the thermal energy of the gas molecules since it is the electrons which are responsible for avalanche build up in flash-tubes. The electrons are not in thermal equilibrium with the gas. It is not surprising therefore that temperature dependent effects have not been reported even though tubes have been used in temperature conditions ranging from 0° C to 40° C. Recently Breare *et al* (1972 unpublished) heated tubes to 100° C in order to vary the resistance of the glass. The effect is discussed in detail in the section dealing with clearing fields but it should be noted here that the tubes operated satisfactorily at all temperatures.

3.3. The sensitive time of flash-tubes

The relationship of the efficiency to the time delay between the passage of the particle and the start of the HT pulse has been investigated experimentally in great detail and by most groups interested in the flash-tube technique. The interest in this parameter stems from the fact that it can be derived theoretically and a good check on the performance of the system can thus be made. Furthermore, many experiments require the use of a long time delay in order either to permit decision making circuits to operate or to allow particle discrimination by means of ionization loss.

The early theories relating efficiency and time delay were developed by Conversi *et al* (1956) and by Gardener *et al* (1957). It was assumed that ion pairs were produced in the centre of the tube and diffused outwards. Only the electrons needed to be considered and the number remaining in the tube after a given time were calculated. Allowance was made for those electrons which, although they were still in the gas, were too close to the wall to produce a discharge.

A more accurate theory was later developed by Lloyd (1960) in which electrons produced by the ionizing particle were initially situated along a line at $x=$ constant, where x and y are the coordinates of the tube which are perpendicular to its axis.

If the probability of an electron being produced in an element of path length $\mathrm{d}y$ is $Q_1 \, \mathrm{d}y$, then the number of free electrons produced in the tube which survive at time t is calculated, assuming diffusion to be the only removal mechanism, to be:

$$\bar{n} = 2Q_1 \sum_{\beta} \exp \frac{(-\beta^2 Dt/a^2)}{\beta J_1(\beta)} \int J_0 \left(\frac{\beta r^1}{a} \right) \mathrm{d}y$$

where D is the diffusion coefficient of the electrons, a is the tube radius, t is the time delay t_D, r^1 is the initial position of the electron in polar coordinates and β has values in the series 2·4048, 5·5201, 8·6537. It also assumes the initial distribution of electrons was poissonian and Q_1 ion pairs per centimetre were produced initially.

In order to put this equation into a form for ready use, a factor f_1, defined as the probability that a discharge could be formed from one electron, was introduced. Hence the efficiency at time delay t_D is related to the probability that there are one or more electrons remaining by

$$\eta = \exp(-\bar{n}) \sum_{m=0}^{\infty} \{1 - (1-f_1)^m\} \frac{n^{-m}}{n!}$$

$$= 1 - \exp(-f_1\bar{n}).$$

Lloyd also showed that the theory could be extended easily to allow for other electron production processes, that is, from metastable atoms. Other loss processes, for example loss by electron attachment to impurities, can also be accounted for.

The relationships can be applied to any flash-tube system by the use of appropriate values of D, a, Q_1 and f_1. Lloyd found it convenient to plot η as a function of Dt/a^2 for a range of values of a, f_1 and Q_1. This is shown in figure 15.

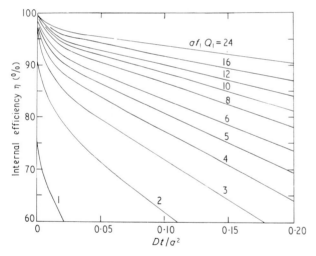

Figure 15. Variation of computed efficiency with time delay (for small time delays) as a function of f_1 the 'electron efficiency' (Lloyd 1960).

For time delays so long that Dt/a^2 exceeds 0·2 the first term of the β series may be used alone and the efficiency depends only on $af_1Q_1 \exp(-\beta_1^2 Dt/a^2)$. This is the theoretical foundation for the empirical rule found by Coxell and Wolfendale (1960) who showed that the efficiency is a unique function of t_D/P, where P is the gas pressure. This follows since a is a constant and f_1Q_1 is almost a constant. The relationship is shown in figure 16.

By comparison with experimental result, an appropriate value for D in neon plus 2% helium was estimated to be 1800 cm^2 s^{-1} at one atmosphere. The factor f_1 has the value approximately unity at 0·6 atm and approximately 0·4 at a pressure of 2·3 atm for the conditions of pulse rise time and magnitude normally adopted.

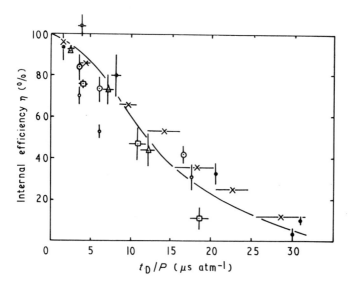

Figure 16. The variation of efficiency with the ratio of time delay to pressure. The curve is an approximate best fit to the experimental points (Coxell and Wolfendale 1960).

The nature of f_1 was not specified in detail by Lloyd, but clearly it should depend on the HT pulse parameters and may vary from one gas mixture to another. Although it is not fully defined it is significant that the need to use unrealistic values of $f_1 > 1$ have never been reported. Holroyd and Breare (1972a) have recently used a Monte Carlo method to study the random motion of electrons initially distributed in the same manner as described by Lloyd and have obtained very similar results. Here it was assumed that a spark formative distance of 0·8 cm existed and that electrons closer to the positive wall than this were unable to produce a discharge. The quantity f_1 used by Lloyd must have a similar significance. A theoretical curve of efficiency against time delay has been constructed by J M Breare *et al* (1972 unpublished)†.

3.4. Clearing fields

As mentioned earlier, the sensitive time of flash-tubes has been measured for most systems as an indication of the performance of the system. Under suitable conditions efficiency–time delay characteristics, as indicated by Lloyd, have been reproduced. However, on many occasions the efficiency falls below the predicted value. It is

† See figure 19.

generally found that the efficiency at short delays is 100% but for delays greater than 5 µs the efficiency may be as low as one half of Lloyd's predicted value. Furthermore, a reproducible result does not always occur. The cause of the discrepancy was first indicated by the Durham group as due to clearing fields built up by the discharges themselves and Stubbs and Breare (1973) observed similar effects in a sealed glass spark chamber. They calculated that fields of the order 1 V cm^{-1} existed for periods of some minutes after the discharge.

3.4.1. Nature of the clearing fields. As the electrons in a discharge strike the glass surface they become attached to it at that point and because the glass has a very high resistance the charges do not quickly disperse. The glass thus charges up and in such a manner as to reduce the net field and quench the discharge at that point.

When the applied HT pulse has decreased to a small value the electrons which remain on the surface constitute a clearing field. Any of the comparatively slow moving positive ions left in the gas will probably be attracted to these negative wall charges and recombine with them. Some of the positive ions will already have been swept out by the tail of the HT pulse and will adhere to the glass wall on the opposite side of the tube to the electrons. The strength of the clearing field will thus depend also on the number of positive ions which are attracted to the wall. Holroyd and Breare (1972b) found that the efficiency was highest when the HT pulse was short—in other words when the positive ions were able to drift back to the electrons instead of being pulled to the opposite wall. This is shown in figure 17.

It was found by Ashton *et al* (1971a) that the efficiency depended on the rate of events in the system, being smallest for the shortest time interval between events.

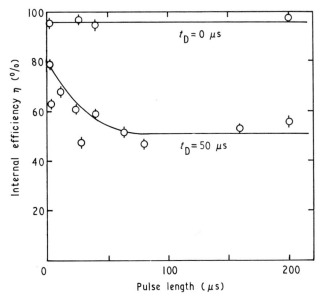

Figure 17. Variation of internal efficiency with HT pulse length at $t_D = 0$ and 50 µs. HT pulse parameters: peak field 4 kV cm^{-1}, $t_R = 50$ ns (Holroyd and Breare 1972b).

This is consistent with the idea of the fields being caused by charges from previous discharges.

3.4.2. Decay of the clearing fields. The dispersion of the charges is still not fully understood, particularly since the glass is a very poor conductor. Conduction which does occur is usually by motion of sodium ions rather than electrons, except in the cases of special glasses containing significant amounts of vanadium pentoxide (Sutton 1960). These glasses, however, are not used in flash-tube manufacture. Soda glass, type S95, which has been used for the manufacture of most commercially produced flash-tubes has a volume resistivity of $5 \times 10^{12}\ \Omega$ cm at 20 °C. This high value would account for charges remaining on the walls in significant quantities for periods of several minutes. The decay of charges is shown in figure 18.

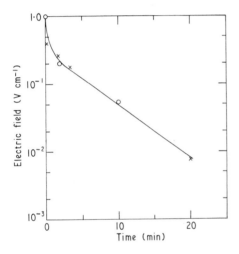

Figure 18. Clearing fields estimated from efficiency measurements as a function of mean interval between discharges (Holroyd and Breare 1972a).

Apart from the exponential decrease, a more rapid decay process at short times is indicated in figure 18. This implies that a second process must be considered which could be the phenomena of back sparks mentioned by Stubbs (1971). The charges initially deposited on the walls of the tube are sufficient to back off the applied-field to the extent of being able to extinguish the discharge at that point and to effect any neighbouring discharges. The magnitude of the field caused by these wall charges is therefore of the same magnitude as the applied field, namely several kilovolts per centimetre. When the applied field is removed, this clearing field remains and is of such a magnitude as to produce a second discharge, but in the reverse direction. Thus a back spark occurs as the HT pulse is removed. The time of occurrence of the back spark is not precise and faint diffuse flashes sometimes observed in flash-tubes minutes after an HT pulse could be of a similar nature to that just described.

The contribution of the back spark to the decay of the clearing field has not yet been calculated quantitatively but it would account for the rapid decrease in clearing field at short times after the event.

3.4.3. The resistance of the glass. The lack of success with flash-tubes constructed of 'pyrex' glass can be explained in terms of the even higher resistance of borosilicate glass than soda glass—a value of 5×10^{14} Ω cm is not uncommon for pyrex. Clearing fields would be expected to last for several hours in such tubes.

The resistance of glass is known to change rapidly with temperature. In general a decrease in resistivity of approximately one order of magnitude occurs for a 25 °C rise in temperature and is well represented by the equation discussed by Sutton (1960):

$$\log \rho = A + \frac{B}{T}$$

where $A = -1\cdot5$, and $B = 4\cdot24 \times 10^3$, for S95 soda glass and T is the temperature in degrees absolute.

An efficiency–time delay curve has been measured under controlled conditions (in particular repetition rate and pulse parameters) for a range of temperatures up to 100 °C by the author's group. An example of the measurements is given in figure 19 which illustrates well how the effect of clearing fields decreases as the temperature is raised. This is assumed to result from a lowering of the resistance of the glass. In the same series of tests it was shown that a clearing field built up in one tube affected the efficiency of several adjacent tubes, regardless of whether these had also recently flashed. Attempts to reduce the effective resistance of tubes to a suitable value by coating the inside surface with a thin metallic film have so far been unsuccessful.

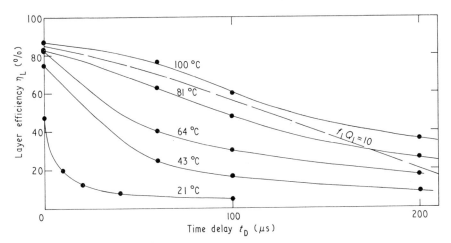

Figure 19. Layer efficiency against time delay at several temperatures. Internal tube diameter 1·6 cm filled with 98% neon and 2% helium. The broken line is the calculated efficiency following the method used by Lloyd (1960) with $f_1 Q_1 = 10$ (J M Breare *et al* 1972 unpublished).

3.4.4. A longer term clearing field. It should be noted that much more persistent clearing field effects have been noticed by Holroyd and Breare (1972b). These persist for several days and occur after an array of tubes has been pulsed regularly at high flashing rate for a period of several hours. These long term effects are equivalent to fields of a few volts per centimetre but whether they are of the same nature as the other clearing fields is not known.

3.4.5. Externally applied clearing fields. Early attempts to apply external DC clearing fields to flash-tubes, similar to those used in spark chambers had met with limited or no success. Coxell and Wolfendale (1960) showed that fields of 2 kV cm⁻¹ had no measureable effect on the efficiency–time delay characteristic. Chaney *et al* (1973) attributed this failure to charges being able to move round the glass surface and annul the effect of the DC field. They applied an AC clearing field at 50 Hz, which alternated faster than the charges could move in the glass to counteract it. It had a considerable effect on the efficiency, as is shown in figure 20. Efficiency–time delay characteristics

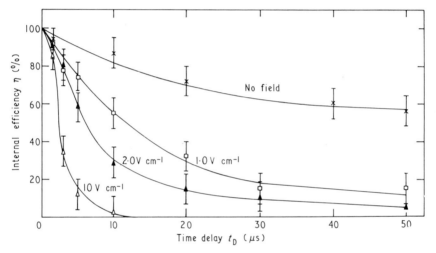

Figure 20. Internal efficiency plotted against time delay for several sinusoidal clearing fields. Fields are RMS values at 50 Hz. HT pulse parameters: peak field 4·2 kV cm⁻¹ and decay constant, $\tau = 36$ μs (Chaney *et al* 1973).

were obtained similar to Meyer's (1963) measurements with DC fields in spark chambers except that a long tail exists in Chaney's results. This tail is attributed to events occurring during the zero of the AC cycle and can be considerably reduced by the use of 'square', rather than sinusoidal fields.

3.5. The recovery time

3.5.1. Measured recovery times. This parameter has been measured for most types of tube and Gardener *et al* (1957) showed that it varied considerably with the gas composition, being approximately 3 s for pure neon, but decreasing considerably for impurity contents as small as 1 part in 50 000.

The number of electrons produced in a flash-tube discharge is greater than 10¹¹ and several of these would remain in the tube after a second if diffusion was the only removal mechanism. However, the large variation in recovery time for different gas mixtures which have similar diffusion coefficients is not explained. Furthermore, it is very likely that the long tail of the HT pulse or the built in clearing fields would remove all the electrons in a very short time. For example, a field as small as 1 volt cm^{-1} would remove all the electrons from a flash-tube in approximately 50 μs. The long recovery time requires a further explanation.

3.5.2. The nature of the long recovery time. Since conventional metal electrode spark chambers filled with neon–helium mixture are capable of being operated at rates in excess of 10^3 events per second, the long recovery time is probably associated, at least in part, with the glass. It is suggested here that metastable atoms or positive ions release secondary electrons, either by collisions with other gas atoms, or by collision with the walls of the tube. Metastables in particular, because they are unaffected by electric fields, can remain in the gas for more than a second.

3.5.3. Reduction of the recovery time. Metastables may be de-excited by a reaction such as the following:

$$A^* + B \rightarrow A + B^+ + e^-$$

where the added gas B has an ionization potential suitable for de-excitation of A. Several molecular gases such as O_2, CO_2, NH_3 and CH_4 should be suitable for de-excitation of neon–helium mixtures and so far experiments with mixtures of oxygen in 70% neon–30% helium have shown promising results. Figure 21 shows the re-ignition probability as a function of time delay for several types of tube as measured by Gardener, together with recent measurements by the author's group. Recently,

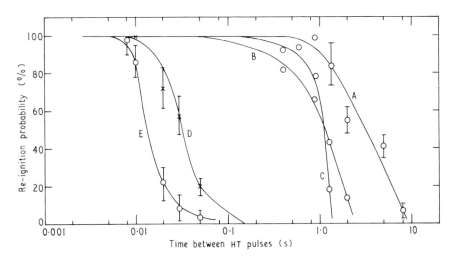

Figure 21. Re-ignition probability plotted against time between HT pulses for several types of tube (Gardener *et al* 1957). (A) Commercial neon at 665 Torr, (B) Commercial neon at 668 Torr plus argon at 1.2×10^{-2} Torr. (C) Commercial neon at 656 Torr plus air at 1.3×10^{-3} Torr. Also recent work by the author's group (D) 70% neon 30% helium at 600 Torr plus 0.4 Torr oxygen. (E) 70% neon 30% helium at 600 Torr plus 3.0 Torr oxygen.

CO_2 added to 70–30 neon–helium has also resulted in a much reduced recovery time. The possibility of impurities affecting the recovery time had previously been observed by Conversi *et al* (1972) who noted that tube cleanliness was a factor affecting both recovery and sensitive times. His group (Brosco *et al* 1973) has shown that very small quantities of SF_6 also reduce the recovery time.

It is clear that the nature of the long recovery time expounded above is by no means fully established, but it is included for lack of other explanations. Much work has still to be done on this problem.

3.6. Spurious flashing

Several authors have studied spurious flashing and it is probable that there are three main types of this unwelcome phenomenon. In the first place there are 'genuine' spurious flashes caused by the passage of a cosmic ray beforehand. The probability of this occurring can be calculated from the known sensitive time of the tube and the cosmic ray flux. Coxell and Wolfendale (1960) attributed a higher observed spurious rate than calculated from previous tracks to radio activity in the glass and surroundings. A spurious flashing rate of $1·12 \times 10^{-4}$ flashes per HT pulse per tube was measured. A third cause may well be dirt on the inside walls of the tube. This is often in the form of fine hairs, around which very intense and local fields would be generated. Breakdown from these points would be relatively easy and may be the explanation of tubes which repeatedly flash even when there is no apparent previous event. There is no known complete remedy for tubes which flash in this manner, but a general reduction in the spurious rate is obtained when HT pulses of minimum magnitude and length are used—the reason for this again follows the general argument that under these circumstances the minimum amount of charge is deposited on the walls of the tube.

4. Constructional techniques and the high voltage pulsing system

4.1. Manufacture of flash-tubes

The most frequently manufactured tubes are either 1·6 cm internal diameter, filled at 600 Torr or 0·6 cm internal diameter, filled at 2·3 atm. Soda glass of wall thickness approximately 1 mm is used, but careful selection of the glass is required in order to maintain a tolerance of 0·1 mm on the outside diameter. It is also necessary that the tubes are straight. This can be achieved by controlled heating of the tubes while they are rotating on rollers. The end window on the tube is formed from the tube by normal glass blowing techniques. For manufacture of tubes at 600 Torr, the glass tube is filled at the required pressure and the far end of the tube, which had previously been partly constricted, is heated until the excess outside pressure causes the tube to constrict completely and seal off. A pressure which is less than atmospheric is thus desirable, but following the technique introduced in Durham University, IRD Co Ltd, Newcastle upon Tyne, UK fill high pressure tubes by cooling the tube in a liquid nitrogen container. The gas pressure is adjusted to be just less than atmospheric pressure and then the tube is sealed off. When the tube regains room temperature the pressure reaches 2·3 atm. In order to stop light spreading to the rest of the array, tubes must either be placed in individual black sleeves or painted black for their entire length. Normally the tube is first of all painted white for approximately 20 cm of its length at the window end in order to increase light emission.

4.2. Framework for arrays

An advantage of flash-tubes is the ease of construction of an array. An electrode system can be made from readily available materials and accurate parallelism of electrodes is not very important. For example a plywood frame, suitably covered with aluminium foil as electrodes, will be equally efficient as a more sophisticated system, even though the accuracy of track location will have been sacrificed.

Figure 22. Examples of small arrays of flash-tubes used in Durham University.

In most systems, either one or two layers of tubes are placed between the electrodes (figure 22). To obtain optimum packing, alternate layers are stacked with their centres staggered. Also this procedure makes it impossible for a particle to pass through the system at any reasonable angle without going through the gas of at least one of the tubes, assuming that the tubes are of normal wall thickness, that is 1 mm.

For accurate location of a particle path, each tube should be carefully positioned and several techniques have been evolved for this. V slots have been machined in an aluminium channel to act as cradles for the tubes. The digitization method of Ayre and Thompson (1969), to be described later, requires electrostatic shielding and this has also been used to locate the tubes. It consists of an aluminium block into which accurately placed holes for the ends of the tubes have been machined. In either case locational accuracy to 0·1 mm can be achieved.

It is not necessary that the electrodes, which are normally sheets of aluminium, should lie close to the tubes. For purposes of tube alignment the electrodes may be

P

separated from the tubes by 1 cm or more. Such a situation alters the overall capacitance of the system and requires a larger voltage to maintain an adequate field in the tubes but has no detrimental effect on the tubes' performance. Such an electrode spacing will also affect the built-in clearing fields since the distribution of field lines will be altered when the conducting electrodes are moved away.

4.3. High voltage pulse generators

Flash-tubes will operate satisfactorily even when long pulses with poor rise-times are applied. One of the advantages of flash-tubes, therefore, is that sophisticated systems in which attempts to match high voltage pulsing circuits to the impedance of the array is not of over-riding importance. Most pulse generating systems consist of a unit placed remote from the array and coupled to the electrodes by earth wires and independent HT leads. These leads are not necessarily coaxali.

It is generally found convenient to make the output impedance of the pulse generator small compared with the impedance of the array. In this way the load on the pulse generator is not significantly altered by connection to the array.

The impedance of a flash-tube array is principally the capacitance of the electrode plates, assuming air dielectric, to which must be added a contribution due to the glass tubes. For 1·6 cm internal diameter tubes, this contribution is approximately 6 pF per metre of tube for systems where the electrodes are placed close to the tube. It is approximately 3 pF per metre if two layers of tubes are close packed between the electrodes. For 0·6 cm internal diameter tubes the approximate capacitances have

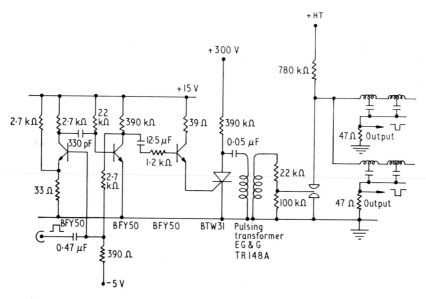

Figure 23. High voltage pulse generator using solid state devices and producing a 'square' pulse from lumped delay line, developed for the Durham University MARS spectrograph (Ayre 1971).

been measured to be approximately 10 pF and 5 pF respectively. Arrays with capacitances in excess of 10 000 pF can be operated from a single pulse generator without difficulty.

There are many published circuits for generating high voltage pulses with short delays and fast rise-times which are suitable for flash-tube arrays. Reference should be made, for example, to Cronin (1967) or Schmitt *et al* (1967). Most systems are triggered by logic level signals, which must be amplified considerably in order to finally operate a trigatron or thyratron. Figure 23 shows a method of achieving this

Figure 24. Photograph of high voltage pulse generator used on the Durham University MARS spectrograph. The lumped delay lines occupy most of the volume of the unit, the amplifier and trigatron switch are in the top section.

amplification using solid state devices. The input signal is magnified by a factor of three in order to switch the silicon-controlled rectifier. In so doing a capacitor of $0.05\ \mu F$ is discharged through the primary of the pulse transformer, the secondary of which produces a large voltage pulse capable of switching the spark gap. The spark gap discharges the delay line through its characteristic impedance. The voltage developed across this resistor is fed directly to the electrodes of the array. Figure 24 shows a complex unit using this circuit which was developed for the Durham University MARS spectrograph. Several delays lines are visible, all of which are operated from the one amplifier and spark gap.

The use of air trigatrons rather than thyratrons as the final high voltage switch has the advantage of cheapness and simplicity. Figure 25 shows a simple trigatron constructed from steel spheres mounted onto brass threads. The tungsten trigger electrode is mounted in the low voltage side of the switch using glass sleeving as

P§

insulation. This device operates satisfactorily up to 30 kV and is triggered by a negative 5 kV pulse, but much smaller trigger pulses can be used if a barium titanate collar
(obtained by machining the dielectric of a barium titanate capacitor) is inserted around
the end of the tungsten trigger electrode (Cronin 1967).

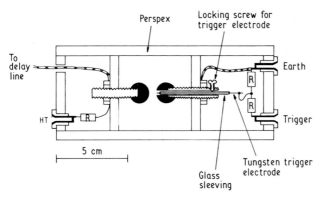

Figure 25. Diagram of simple air trigatron suitable for use in flash-tube pulse generators (Stubbs
1971).

5. Output of information from flash-tubes

Photographic or visual techniques were first used but several filmless techniques have
been developed during the last few years as bigger arrays with consequently higher
rates have been developed.

5.1. Nature and direction of the light output

The emission is predominantly in the yellow–red region of the spectrum corresponding
to the most intense lines in neon and helium. For photographic recording of events
most fast red-sensitive films have been successfully tried, for example Ilford Mark V
and HP 3, Kodak Tri X and the very fast Kodak 2475 and 2403.

The variation of light intensity has been studied by Coxell *et al* (1961). Observing
one tube, they found that the intensity varied from one flash to the next with a standard deviation of 5·1 % but could not ascribe all this variation to the flash-tube because
of changes in photomultiplier gain and other similar factors. A much greater variation
was noted in the average intensity of a group of tubes . The standard deviation of all
the tubes from the overall mean was calculated to be $\sigma = 17\%$.

A polar diagram, indicating the variation of light emitted at an angle to the axis
of a tube, is shown for short tubes in figure 26 and for longer tubes in figure 27. The
advantage, mentioned earlier, of painting the tubes white to aid reflection and diffusion of the light is very apparent for the short tubes. For long tubes the increase in
light at large angle is not so significant. This would indicate that a considerable
fraction of the light originates from the far end of the tube and because of multiple

reflection will be emitted at very small angles to the axis. This is consistent with the oscilloscope traces of light output shown earlier (figure 8) where a significant signal was received on the photomultiplier from the far end of the tube. A diffusing surface attached to the tube end has the desired effect of increasing the fraction of light emitted at large angles but at the expense of overall intensity, as is seen in figure 27.

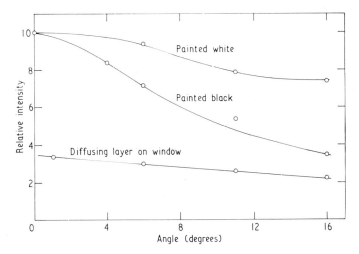

Figure 26. Polar diagram of light emission from a short flash-tube (Coxell *et al* 1961).

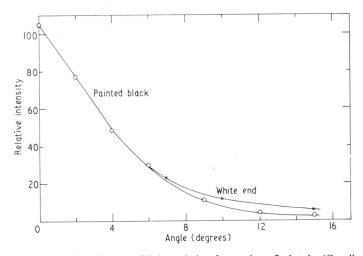

Figure 27. Polar diagram of light emission from a long flash-tube (Coxell *et al* 1961).

5.2. Variation of light output intensity with field strength

Coxell *et al* (1961) measured the light intensity for several tubes of different lengths and obtained similar results in all cases (see figure 28). The results follow the expected pattern in so far as the quantity ϵ/P, being the number of photons caused by an electron moving 1 cm, increases in a similar manner to the increase of α/P with field E/P—see for example Corrigan and von Engel (1958). The results in figure 28 were obtained for 98% neon and 2% helium. A similarly shaped curve of light intensity against electric field is to be expected for other gas mixtures.

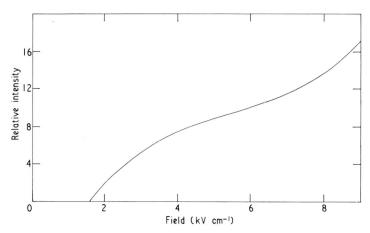

Figure 28. Variation of light intensity with peak field strength (Coxell *et al* 1961).

Photography along the axis of the flash-tube is not a problem as far as intensity is concerned, but the increased light at high field strengths may be useful when the edges of an array subtend large angles at the camera.

5.3. Mirror systems for array photography

Since the spatial accuracy of a tube is limited to its diameter it is possible to use long path lengths without loss of precision. By this means 5000 or more tubes can be

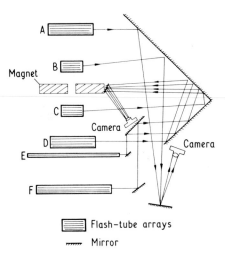

Figure 29. Arrangement of mirrors for photography of the flash-tube array in the Durham University nuclear-active particle spectrograph (Hooke 1973).

recorded on the same camera frame using path lengths in excess of 25 metres. Figure 29 shows an arrangement of mirrors for photography of an extensive air shower array. The mirrors are essential in order to reduce the angle subtended by the tubes at the camera and are arranged so that the optical path lengths from each group of tubes is roughly the same. This permits the use of a large diameter lens at f 1·8 without loss of definition and is to be compared with spark chambers, where the lens must be stopped down so as to give a depth of focus equal to the chamber depth.

5.4. Filmless read out systems

Several methods of obtaining information from neon flash-tubes without the use of film have been developed.

5.4.1. The photomultiplier method. The method described by Coxell *et al* (1961) uses a photomultiplier to record the light output from an array of flash-tubes. This output magnitude is related to the number of tubes in the array which had flashed. The authors suggest that this method has applications in density spectrum work on extensive air showers since the light output from the photomultiplier can be calibrated in terms of the number of flashed tubes in an array. They also suggest that the photomultiplier can be used as a preselector of events. The array can be pulsed in the normal way after the passage of an extensive air shower and if the light pulse height were greater than a predetermined value, indicating that a certain number of tubes have flashed, a camera shutter could be opened and the array re-pulsed.

5.4.2. The spark tube. Bacon and Nash (1965) reported the development of a flash-tube in which sealed electrodes are added. The electrodes were 1 mm wide copper strips on a thin paxolin card, separated by 1 mm and running nearly the whole length inside the tube. When the tube flashed, a voltage pulse was obtained from the strips owing to breakdown across the inside of the tube. They found that spurious discharges occasionally occurred between the strips but were eliminated by the addition of a quenching agent. In this case ethyl alcohol at a pressure of 30 Torr was added to the neon at 1 atm. They obtained detectable pulses with only an 85% efficiency and attributed the loss in efficiency to the internal electrodes not being parallel.

An advantage of the system is that it is still possible to photograph the tubes through the end window in the conventional way, but the increased cost of manufacturing a tube with a built-in electrode system would be a disadvantage.

5.4.3. The light sensing technique. Reines (1967) reported a technique which has been developed for use in the South African underground neutrino experiment. This large experiment uses about 60 000 neon flash-tubes of length two metres. Because of the large area covered by the tubes, photography is extremely difficult. A technique has been developed which electronically records the tubes which have flashed. The information is then displayed on a hodoscope which can be photographed more easily.

A cadmium selenide cell is placed in front of each flash-tube and is shielded from external light. The cell is then connected via a silicon-controlled rectifier and associated electronics to a light bulb on the hodoscope system. When the flash-tube fires, the light output from the tube is detected by the cadmium selenide cell as a change in resistance of the cell. This change is detected by the silicon-controlled rectifier, which consequently switches on a light bulb on the hodoscope board. This is photographed and scanned in the normal way.

Evans and Baker (1971) suggest that light-activated silicon-controlled rectifiers (LASCR) may be used directly as a sensor and memory store. The LASCR has two stable voltage states and may be triggered from its high to low state by light. This new state can be maintained until reset. It was found however that the poor light intensity received from flash-tubes required electrical pre-biassing of the LASCR, which thus became over sensitive to ambient temperature changes.

5.4.4. External probe method. Ayre and Thompson (1969) have developed a method of observing electronically whether or not a tube has flashed. Their technique, which is shown in figure 30, is now used on the Durham University MARS spectrograph. A

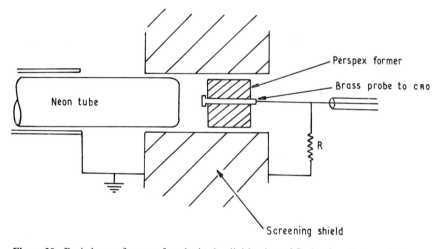

Figure 30. Basic layout for use of probe in the digitization of flash tubes (Ayre and Thompson 1969).

small probe, which for convenience is a brass screw, is placed close to the end window of each flash-tube and a pulse of several hundred volts can be obtained on the resistor R when the tube flashes. Care must be taken to correctly place the earth screening so as to avoid pick-up from the HT pulse voltage on the electrodes. By tapping off from R, a pulse of suitable voltage can be obtained and the noise when the tube does not flash is very small.

The pulse is caused by capacitative coupling from the discharge to the probe. During a discharge the gas is a conducting medium and acquires a potential between zero and that on the HT electrode. The pulse on the probe will have the same polarity as the HT pulse and its shape will be related to that of the HT pulse.

Since the discharge reaches the end of a tube at a time which is dependent on the distance of the original ionization from that end, Ayre *et al* (1972) show that the measurement of the delay in receiving the probe pulse can be used to obtain the coordinate of the particle along the tube. The variation of delay with distance was found to depend on the type of tube and measurements could not be made very precisely. The position of the particle can be located by the method to a precision of plus or minus 10 cm.

5.4.5. The vidicon system. Harrison and Rastin (1970) have developed a system in which a flash tube array is observed by a vidicon camera. A standard 405 line system is used, with the 25 frames per second producing a line scan period of 98 μs. The vidicon photocathode is scanned by the electron beam in a direction parallel to the image of the flash-tube layers. A pulse, which is registered when the scan of the electron beam moves across a fiducial bulb at the start of the flash-tube layer, is used to gate a 2 MHz timing signal. If a tube has flashed in a particular layer its coordinate is determined in terms of the signal frequency. The data from each layer of tubes are initially placed in temporary storage scalers and then transferred to a magnetic core store.

6. The application of flash-tubes

6.1. Track location by means of flash-tubes.

The most widely used application of flash-tubes is in the location of cosmic ray particle tracks and a vast number of experiments using the technique have been carried out. In particular, arrays of tubes have been used in magnetic spectrographs, as reported for example by Brooke *et al* (1962). Arrays have also been used to study the structure of extensive air showers (Earnshaw *et al* 1967) and Achar *et al* (1965) report the use of flash-tubes in neutrino interactions studies at great depths underground.

A primary consideration in most of these studies is the accuracy with which the particle path may be located. This problem has been extensively studied (Ashton *et al* 1958, Bull *et al* 1962b) and essentially it is a matter of deciding on the best line to draw through the tubes which have flashed in order to obtain the most likely trajectory of the particle. It has been shown that a tube may flash even if a particle passes through the glass wall of the tube and avoids the gas. This phenomenon results from energetic electrons knocked out of the glass by the particle. Another possible cause is a photon, which accompanies the particle, causing photo-electric emission or Compton scattering in the gas. Set against this is the possibility that an electron which passed through the gas did not result in the tube flashing. This may occur when the trajectory is near the wall of the tube and the path length through the gas is much less than the spark formation distance. Figure 31 shows experimental and theoretical results obtained by Bull *et al* (1962b) for the probability of flashing as a function of *r*, where *r* is the distance of the trajectory from the axis of the tube. It is seen that a significant probability of flashing occurs when the particle misses the gas altogether.

Before the introduction of computer techniques for analysis the most probable trajectory was found either by calculation, which was very laborious, or by laying a thread over a scale diagram of the array and adjusting it to get the most acceptable track as far as the eye is concerned. The trajectory chosen in this case could therefore depend on the skill of the scanner in deciding when a tube which failed to flash fell on the trajectory.

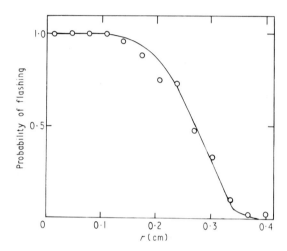

Figure 31. The probability distribution $P(r)$ of a tube flashing as a function of the distance r of the particle path from the centre of the tube. The continuous line is the effective $P(r)$ for tubes of 0·59 cm internal diameter corrected for errors in measurement of r only. The experimental points prior to correction are circled. (Bull *et al* 1962a)

The use of computers for the analysis of the track coordinates allows for much greater use of the probability distribution and also permits account to be taken of the many other errors, which may exist. These errors consist of variations in tube diameter and errors in actual location of a tube in an array. Thompson and Wells (1972) have computed track coordinates from a digitized array and estimate that the distance across an array of 8 layers of 0·6 cm inside diameter tubes through which a particle passed can be estimated to plus or minus 0·3 mm. Each layer of tubes was such that the axes of the tubes in a layer were staggered differently with respect to each of the other seven layers. In fact each layer was carefully placed so as to be staggered by an amount equal to multiples of one-eighth of the tube outside diameter. The design of such arrays has been discussed by Bull *et al* (1962a) who conclude that there is generally no significant difference between designed arrays and arrays in which the staggering is allowed to be random.

6.2. *Short term information storage by means of multiple pulsing*

The undesirable long recovery time of flash-tubes, which is usually a few tenths of a second, can be an advantage in some situations as has been indicated by Coxell and Wolfendale (1960). By repeatedly pulsing flash-tubes at short regular intervals after the passage of a particle, the tubes can be made to re-flash and thus retain their information. An example of the use of an array in this manner is described by Hughes *et al* (1964). If, during the subsequent 750 μs following the passage of a charged particle, a neutron was detected in BF_3 counters associated with the array, a record of the original track of the charged particle was required. It was obtained by pulsing the tubes immediately and then re-pulsing the array at 5 ms intervals and mechanically opening the shutter of a camera some 11 ms after the initial triggering particle. By only recording events involving neutrons, a considerable saving in film and analysis time was possible.

6.3. Ionization measurements with flash-tubes

Lloyd's theoretical considerations of flash-tube efficiency as a function of delay between the passage of the particle and the application of the high voltage pulse have been well supported by experiment. The theory implies that the efficiency for large values of t_D should depend on the amount of initial ionization. Several groups have utilized this fact in order to identify particles.

Ashton *et al* (1971b) using the large flash-tube array shown in figure 1, have searched for fractionally charged particles by operating with time delays of 20 μs or 40 μs. With such a large array the efficiency can be accurately determined from a single track since about 80 tubes are expected to flash when a singly charged particle passes through. A particle of charge $e/3$ is calculated to cause only about 40 tubes to flash.

Diggory *et al* (1971) demonstrated the ability of flash-tubes to detect differences in ionization rates caused by particles of different momenta. They measured the flash-tube efficiency for cosmic ray protons and mesons in the momentum range 0·1–10 GeV/c. Using time delays of 50 μs or 80 μs, variations in efficiency from 58% to 38% were observed and found to be in good agreement with theoretical estimates.

Andrews *et al* (1971) using various time delays observed heavy primary cosmic rays in a balloon-borne flash-tube array and obtained good correlation between the efficiency as predicted by Lloyd, allowing for the charge Z of the particle. Their array was digitized using the method of Ayre and Thompson (1969) and information on each event was transmitted to ground during the flight.

6.4. Application to accelerator experiments and some concluding remarks

The use of spark chambers instead of flash-tubes has up to now been preferred for accelerator experiments on account of the spark chamber having a shorter recovery time and also two dimensional spatial resolution. The resolution is also better than a flash-tube if a single flash-tube layer is compared to the spark chamber. Furthermore, the use of clearing fields in flash-tube arrays has only recently been established before which the sensitive time had not been easily controlled.

These facts have weighed heavily against the flash-tube even though it is a relatively inexpensive device and arrays are easy to set up and use. Also, arrays of almost any size and any geometry can be constructed and the system will operate for long periods of time. Unlike the spark chamber, the high voltage pulsing requirements are not very stringent. Pulse rise-times of 0·5 μs are often employed and the radiation and subsequent interference with neighbouring electronic circuits is thus considerably less than in spark chambers where rise times of 50 ns or better are desirable. Several methods of digitization of flash-tubes have already been developed and used in cosmic ray experiments.

Although the relatively large amount of dense material used in a flash-tube is a disadvantage as far as experiments with nuclear-active particles are concerned—and this is a difficult problem to solve—several of the earlier drawbacks have been overcome. Ways of controlling the sensitive and recovery times have been discussed and Conversi *et al* (1972) have already reported the use of flash-tubes in the experiments of the '$\mu\pi$ group' installed at the Frascati storage ring and have commented on the use of flash-tubes in accelerator experiments. The comments serve to illustrate the potential of flash-tubes in experiments involving leptons and the possibility in particular of their use in studies of neutrino interactions—their value here has already been demonstrated in cosmic ray neutrino experiments.

More work is still required on the current problems of the sensitive time and recovery time and this will take the form of investigations of both the gas mixture and the glass envelope. Research into the envelope may lead to the use of a glass of much lower resistivity than normal soda glass or to the use of another nonconducting material, in particular some form of plastic. Balloon-borne experiments and also experiments involving nuclear-active particles in general would benefit from the use of a flash-tube in which the envelope is a light weight material of consequently small stopping power.

References

Achar V C *et al* 1965 *Phys. Lett.* **18** 196–9
Andrews D, Corydon-Petersen O, Funch O and Rotenberg M 1971 *Proc. 12th Int. Conf. on Cosmic Rays* (Hobart: University of Tasmania) pp 1543–8
Ashton F *et al* 1971a *Nuovo Cim. Lett.* **2** 707–11
Ashton F *et al* 1971b *J. Phys.* A: *Gen. Phys.* **4** 895–907
Ashton F, Kisdnasamy S and Wolfendale A W 1958 *Nuovo Cim.* **8** 615–21
Ayre C A 1971 *PhD thesis* University of Durham
Ayre C A and Thompson M G 1969 *Nucl. Instrum. Meth.* **69** 106–8
Ayre C A, Thompson M G, Whalley M R and Young E C M 1972 *Nucl. Instrum. Meth.* **103** 49–52
Bacon D F and Nash W F 1965 *Nucl. Instrum Meth.* **37** 43–4
Barsanti G *et al* 1956 *Proc. of the CERN Symposium* **2** 56–60
Brooke G *et al* 1962 *Proc. Phys. Soc.* **80** 674–85
Brosco G, Conversi M and Giovannini M 1973 *Nucl. Instrum. Meth.* to be published
Bull R M, Coates D W, Nash W F and Rastin B C 1962a *Nuovo Cim.* suppl. **23** 28–38
—— 1962b *Nuovo Cim.* suppl. **23** 39–51
Chaney J E, El Disouki W and Breare J M 1972 *Nuovo Cim. Lett.* **6** 339–40
Conversi M *et al* 1956 *Nuovo Cim.* suppl. **4** 234–7
Conversi M, Giannoli G and Spillantini P 1972 *Nuovo Cim. Lett.* **3** 483–9
Conversi M and Gozzini A 1955 *Nuovo Cim.* **2** 189–91
Corrigan S J B and von Engel A 1958 *Proc. Phys. Soc* **72** 786–90
Coxell H, Meyer M A, Scull P S and Wolfendale A W 1961 *Nuovo Cim.* suppl. **21** 7–20
Coxell H and Wolfendale A W 1960 *Proc. Phys. Soc.* **75** 378–86
Cranshaw T E and de Beer J F 1957 *Nuovo Cim.* **5** 1107–17
Cronin J W 1967 *Bubble and Spark Chambers* vol 1 ed. R P Shutt (New York and London: Academic Press)

Diggory I S, Earnshaw J C, Hook J R and Turver K E 1971 *Proc. 12th Int. Conf. on Cosmic Rays* (Hobart: University of Tasmania) pp 1533–7
Earnshaw J C *et al* 1967 *Proc. Phys. Soc.* **90** 91–108
von Engel A 1965 *Ionized Gases* (Oxford: Clarendon)
Evans W M and Baker J C 1971 *Internal Rep. Rutherford High Energy Lab.* RHEL/M/H/4
Fischer J and Zorn G T 1961 *Rev. Sci. Instrum* **32** 499–511
Gardener M, Kisdnasamy S, Rossle E and Wolfendale A W 1957 *Proc. Phys. Soc.* **B70** 687–99
Glaser D A 1952 *Phys. Rev.* **87** 665
Hampson H F and Rastin B C 1971 *Nucl. Instrum. Meth.* **96** 197–203
Harries W L and von Engel A 1954 *Proc. R. Soc.* **A222** 490–508
Harrison D J and Rastin B C 1970 *Nucl. Instrum. Meth.* **77** 181–8
Holroyd F W 1971 *PhD thesis* University of Durham
Holroyd F W and Breare J M 1972a *Nucl. Instrum. Meth.* **100** 277–80
—— 1972b *Nucl. Instrum. Meth.* **100** 429–32
Hooke J R 1973 *PhD thesis* University of Durham
Hughes E B *et al* 1964 *Proc. Phys. Soc.* **83** 239–51
Jesse W P and Sadauskis J 1952 *Phys. Rev.* **88** 417–8
Lloyd J L 1960 *Proc. Phys. Soc.* **75** 387–94
Meek J M and Craggs J D 1953 *Electrical Breakdown of Gases* (Oxford: Clarendon)
Meyer M A 1963 *Nucl. Instrum. Meth.* **23** 277–86
Pack J L and Phelps A V 1961 *Phys. Rev.* **121** 798–806
Raether H 1964 *Electron Avalanches and Breakdown in Gases* (London: Butterworth)
Reines F 1967 *Proc. R. Soc.* **A301** 125–35
Rochester G D 1960 *Proc. 6th Int. Conf. on Cosmic Rays* (Moscow: USSR Acad. Sci) 312–15
Schmitt F *et al* 1967 *Nucl. Instrum. Meth.* **52** 331–37
Stubbs R J 1971 *PhD thesis* University of Durham
Stubbs R J and Breare J M 1973 *Nucl. Instrum. Meth.* **106** 381–7
Sutton P M 1960 *Prog. Dielectrics* **2** 112–164
Thompson M G and Wells S C 1972 *Nucl. Instrum. Meth.* **102** 35–44
Townsend J 1947 *Electrons in Gases* (London: Hutchinson)

Index

Addresses

Dr F Ashton — Department of Physics, University of Durham

Dr J M Breare — Department of Physics, University of Durham

Dr G Brooke — Department of Physics, University of Leeds

Dr J L Osborne — Department of Physics, University of Durham

Dr M G Thompson — Department of Physics, University of Durham

Dr K E Turver — Department of Physics, University of Durham

Dr hab J Wdowczyk — Institute of Nuclear Research, Lodz, Poland

Professor A W Wolfendale — Department of Physics, University of Durham

Dr E C M Young — Department of Physics, University of Hong Kong